The teaching of basic sciences

A survey
of the teaching of physics
at universities

Prepared under the auspices of the
International Union of Pure and Applied Physics

Unesco

Published in 1966 by the United Nations Educational, Scientific
and Cultural Organization, Place de Fontenoy, Paris-7^e
Printed by Koninklijke Drukkerij G. J. Thieme N.V.,
The Netherlands

Foreword

One of the activities conducted under Unesco's Natural Science programme concerns comparative studies, and, more specifically, surveys on the teaching of basic sciences (physics, chemistry, biology, mathematics, etc.) at university level.

The recommendations of the International Conference on Physics Education (Paris, 1960),[1] urging an international exchange of information about the teaching of physics, encouraged Unesco to start this project and to prepare this report and the survey which preceded it. This project report was carried out in close co-operation with the International Commission on Physics Education of the International Union of Pure and Applied Physics (IUPAP).

The IUPAP Commission on Physics Education was invited to propose a plan for the project, and to suggest the names of physicists who could conduct surveys and prepare reports on the teaching of university physics in the following countries: Czechoslovakia, the Federal Republic of Germany, France, the Union of Soviet Socialist Republics, the United Kingdom, and the United States of America. Unesco subsequently enlisted the services of the individuals named below as private consultants, and the project got under way early in 1962. During the course of the project, members of the science staff of Unesco and members of the IUPAP Commission on Physics Education conferred frequently with the co-ordinator for the project to maintain close liaison with the work.

1. S. C. Brown; N. Clarke, editors. *Proceedings of the International Conference on Physics Education.* New York, Technology Press and John Wiley and Sons, 1960.

Reports on the teaching of physics in their respective countries were prepared by Miloslav Valouch, Charles University, Czechoslovakia; W. Hanle, University of Giessen, Federal Republic of Germany; Michel Yves Bernard, Conservatoire National des Arts et Métiers, France; A. S. Akhmatov, Moscow Institute of Machines and Instruments, U.S.S.R.; Norman Clarke, Institute of Physics and the Physical Society, United Kingdom; and William C. Kelly, American Institute of Physics, U.S.A. Each national representative was asked (a) to make a survey of physics teaching in a number of universities of high reputation in his country, selected in such a way as to give a comprehensive picture of educational systems for educating professional physicists as well as for educating specialists in other fields, and (b) to submit a report summarizing his findings. Dr. Kelly served as the co-ordinator of the project.

The national authors had all completed their surveys and had submitted their reports by the spring of 1963. In the course of conducting these surveys, the authors consulted colleagues in their respective countries who could contribute to making the information presented here as complete and accurate as possible. A draft of the present international report, based upon these reports, was prepared by the co-ordinator and given to the authors for criticism and revision. At a meeting in Paris on 21–25 October 1963, the authors, the co-ordinator, and representatives of Unesco and the IUPAP commission considered all proposed revisions and prepared the final draft of this report. The information given was up-to-date at the end of 1963. It has not been possible to revise the text in order to incorporate the modifications and reforms that have been since introduced,

It has to be noted that opinions expressed are those of the authors themselves and do not represent official points of view of their countries or of Unesco.

Acknowledgements

The project that led to this report was made possible by the whole-hearted co-operation of many people. The national representatives wish here to record their sincere thanks for many kinds of assistance.

At Unesco, the survey was closely followed by the staff members of the Division of Science Teaching, Department of Natural Sciences.

The International Union of Pure and Applied Physics, through the office of its general secretary, Professor P. Fleury, and its Commission on Physics Education, not only devised a wise plan for the survey but provided an indispensable connexion with professional physics at the international level. Professor Sanborn C. Brown, the president of the Commission on Physics Education, worked closely with the Unesco staff and the national representatives in planning the project, solving problems that arose, and seeing the project to completion.

The American Institute of Physics furnished secretarial assistance in the preparation of the draft international report and also underwrote the cost of preparing copies of the draft report.

The Union of Czechoslovak Mathematicians and Physicists, through its Commission on Physics Education, provided the valuable aid of many professional physicists at the national level in the preparation of the Czechoslovak national report. The Physics Commission of the State Committee for Universities examined its design and its final wording.

In the Federal Republic of Germany information and advice were received from the Deutsche Physikalische Gesellschaft e. V. and especially from Professor K. Hecht and Professor W. Kroebel (University of Kiel) and Dr. G. v. Foerster (University of Giessen).

In France the author consulted L. Capdecomme, Directeur général de l'Enseignement Supérieur, J. J. Cessac, Inspecteur général de l'Instruction Publique, J. Chazel, Inspecteur général de l'Instruction Publique, A. Dognon, Professor at the Faculté de Médecine de Paris, P. Fleury, Professor at the Conservatoire National des Arts et Métiers, J. P. Mathieu, Professor at the Faculté des Sciences de Paris.

The report for U.S.S.R. was prepared with the approval of Mr. M. A. Prokofiev, Vice-Minister of the Ministry of Higher and Specialized Secondary Education, and Mr. S. K. Zinoviev, Vice-President, Department of Methodology of the same Ministry.

The author for the United Kingdom acknowledges help received from Professor M. H. L. Pryce and Dr. N. Thompson (University of Bristol), Professor Brian Pippard (University of Cambridge), Professor C. C. Butler (Imperial College, London), Professor B. H. Flowers and Dr. J. B. Birks (University of Manchester), and Miss Patricia N. Boston (Institute of Physics and the Physical Society, London).

In the United States of America, Professors Sanborn C. Brown, W. C. Elmore, A. C. Helmholz, P. Kusch and Allan M. Sachs were helpful in providing specific information for this report.

Contents

Appendixes

I. Introduction

The importance of the teaching of physics

The teaching of physics is of current concern to every nation. Aware of the fundamental role of physics in advancing the frontiers of scientific knowledge and in providing the groundwork for technological growth, both the scientifically proficient countries and the newly developing countries seek to provide greater opportunities for the study of physics by their citizens, and to make the teaching of physics more effective at every level of education. Statements by national leaders in almost every country could be adduced as evidence. Three will suffice to indicate the emphasis being placed on science and science education:

'The physical sciences occupy chief place among the natural sciences and on their successful advance depends the progress of associated sciences and of the national economy. The future prospects for technical progress are today determined primarily by achievements in the main directions of physics'.[1]

'My own belief is that science, and the scientific method, should be one of the pillars upon which education rests. It should be there from the first. It should never be disparaged. It should be an integral part of the whole'.[2]

'Thoughtful men now see another role for science and technology

1. 'The Development of Science', *The 1959-1964 Seven-Year Plan of the U.S.S.R.*
2. 'Scientific Education in a Scientific Age.' Address delivered by the Rt. Hon. Viscount Hailsham, Q.C., United Kingdom Minister for Science, at OEEC Seminar, 7 May 1960.

—a new and creative role that is still only dimly grasped. Science is the one common language understood the world over. It is dedicated to the discovery of truth and to scrutinizing every new finding and hypothesis without fear or prejudice. In science, new beliefs and principles win out over earlier ones because they have behind them the irresistible force of logic and consistency. By exchanging scientific viewpoints and working on common scientific problems—as exemplified so admirably in the International Geophysical Year and the two International Conferences on the Peaceful Use of the Atom—men of all nations may be drawn closer together'.[1]

The scope of the report

The present report contains the results of an international survey of the teaching of physics in universities. The report has two principal purposes: (a) to assist newly developing countries to launch programmes in university physics, and (b) to enable scientifically established countries to learn what other countries are doing and to compare educational practices in physics. Greater emphasis will be placed here upon the first of these purposes but it is hoped that both will be served. Although the teaching of physics will be discussed at each level at which physics is studied, the report will deal primarily with the teaching of physics at universities and other institutions of higher learning.

Contents of the report

Each of the following chapters is devoted to a particular aspect of the teaching of physics. The introduction to each chapter serves to define the problems to be discussed, and to orient the reader toward what follows. The main portion of the chapter is devoted to the various approaches to the teaching of physics in the countries participating in the survey, consisting in most instances of pertinent excerpts from the national reports. The reader will notice striking similarities and also striking differences among these approaches.

1. *Strengthening American Science*. A report of the President's Science Advisory Committee, Washington, D.C., 1958.

Each chapter concludes with a summary—stating the extent to which there seems to be agreement among the educational practices described.

Most of the detailed information in this report—syllabuses, lists of experiments, lists of books, and so on—appears in the appendixes. Since it was one of the chief objectives of this project to make available such detailed information, the national representatives offer the appended material without apology to the reader for its length. They believe that its availability may help to put discussion of the reform of physics teaching upon the firmer foundation of knowledge of specific national practices.

For the convenience of the reader, the appendixes are grouped by the chapter in which they are first cited and are numbered accordingly. Within each group the appendixes are in the alphabetical order of the names of the countries from whose reports the information was taken, with the following sequence: A—Czechoslovakia, B—the Federal Republic of Germany, C—France, D—the U.S.S.R., E—the United Kingdom, and F—the U.S.A. Thus Appendix III C1 contains material from the French report pertaining to the subject of Chapter III; other appendixes to Chapter III deriving from that report would be designated III C2, III C3, and so on.

As he reads this report, the reader will want especially to refer to the appendixes to the present chapter—summaries of the organization of education in the countries participating in this survey, including an organization diagram for each country and a brief explanatory text that defines the more important terms. In addition, the reports in the *World Survey of Education*, published by Unesco, will be helpful in making clear the way in which education is organized at each level. Volume II deals with primary education, Volume III with secondary, and Volume IV with higher education.

This report deals primarily with physics and with those parts of mathematics that are a part of the education of the physicist. In these days of rapid growth of physics and its pervasion into many other fields of science, it is difficult indeed to decide where the boundaries of physics lie. The following chapters will attempt to make clear the prevailing opinions about these boundaries in the countries reporting. The reader's attention is also directed, however, to reports on the teaching of the other basic disciplines, including mathematics, now being prepared under the auspices of Unesco.

The requirement that the length of this report be kept within reasonable limits has resulted in the omission of much material that appears in the national reports and that would conceivably be of interest to those concerned with certain parts of physics education, for example, lists of experiments, examinations, post-graduate courses, and so on. It is hoped that this additional material will eventually be published elsewhere. Plans to accomplish this are being considered by Unesco and the IUPAP Commission on Physics Education.

The spirit of the report

It was the intent of the organizations sponsoring this project, and of the national representatives, that this report should help to improve the teaching of physics. Few countries, indeed, can say that their optimum standards of physics teaching prevail universally within their borders. Accordingly, a choice had to be made at an early stage of this project between a merely statistical description of education in physics—good and bad—within the countries reporting, and a presentation that would stress optimum standards toward which all educational institutions within these countries strive and which the leading institutions have achieved. The second of these approaches was selected as being more in keeping with the spirit of the project. Wherever possible, therefore, this report stresses strong programmes in physics—those existing at leading universities—in full realization that not all universities can quickly reach these standards, but in confidence that these are the standards at which all should aim. To compensate for this bias, the report contains a final chapter dealing with some very real problems of physics teaching in the countries reporting, and with efforts being made to solve these problems.

This report contains no universal solution to the problems of physics teaching. The hopes of those who have contributed to it will be fully realized if the information and suggestions contained here lead to thoughtful re-examination of physics programmes, and to the development of many individual solutions of how best to teach this basic and powerful science.

II. Preparation for the study of physics in universities and related admission requirements of universities

Introduction

Most educators would agree that physics, a basic science, is properly a part of the early education of children. The ages at which different ideas of physics are presented, the mathematical levels at which these ideas are treated, the amount of time devoted to the subject, and the particular pedagogic approach adopted—all of these differ from country to country. That physics should be studied in some form during the pre-university years, however, seems undisputed.

A number of objectives of the early study of physics is commonly cited:

1. To give every child—not only those who will pursue higher studies—some basic knowledge of physics, an appreciation of the methods of the science, and an awareness of the contributions of physics to technology.
2. To stimulate interest in careers in physics and closely related fields, including engineering, among pupils capable of pursuing university studies.
3. To provide a basis of the important ideas of physics for later university studies.

The first of these objectives might be termed the 'general education' objective. It expresses the widely held conviction that all persons living in a technological age must possess a basic knowledge of physics. In terms of the number of pupils and teachers, the facilities required, and the concern felt for needed improvement of teaching, this objective, it seems fair to say, overshadows the other two. The other two objectives, however, are more directly related to the university teaching of physics—the subject of this report—and will be given greater emphasis here.

This chapter will attempt to answer the following questions:

1. What are the characteristics of pre-university physics teaching —educational objectives, content of the courses, kinds of laboratory or practical work, time devoted to physics, and preparation of the teacher—in the countries participating in the survey?
2. What is the relation of pre-university physics teaching to the teaching of mathematics?
3. What are the formal requirements in physics and mathematics for admission to institutions of higher learning, particularly for programmes of study that include physics?

Pre-university physics and mathematics in Czechoslovakia

One of the guiding principles of education in schools in Czechoslovakia is the endeavour to link school education closely with the practical demands of life. This principle also finds its expression in the polytechnical nature of education at all basic and general secondary schools. Therefore, great importance is attached to a sound grounding in the natural sciences, especially in mathematics and physics. The rapid development of modern technology, of mechanization and automation, demands the general raising of the level of education in these sciences, and an increasing number of mathematicians, physicists, engineers and other workers with an advanced knowledge of mathematics and physics.

Instruction in physics and mathematics by qualified teachers begins in the sixth form of the basic nine-year school. On the following page the number of weekly periods in these subjects at this type of school is indicated (one period equals forty-five-minutes).

Subject	Form			
	Sixth	Seventh	Eighth	Ninth
Mathematics	6	5	5	5
Physics	–	2	2	3
Practical exercises in physics (optional)	–	2	2	2

Secondary general school education lasts three years and is divided into three branches: the mathematico-physical (A), the chemico-biological (B), and the general branch (C).

The following scheme gives the number of periods devoted weekly to the teaching of mathematics and physics in the various forms of the three branches:

Subject	Form								
	First			Second			Third		
	A	B	C	A	B	C	A	B	C
Mathematics	5	4	4	5	4	4	5	4	4
Physics	4	2	3	4	3	3	5	3	4

In the mathematico-physical branch one period weekly is also devoted in each form to practical exercises in physics, and in the second and third forms two periods a week to descriptive geometry.

Appendix II A1 shows a brief outline of the contents of the subject matter for the individual forms of the mathematico-physical branch, as far as mathematics and physics are concerned.

In physics, the syllabus for all branches is, on the whole, identical. The greater number of periods for the mathematico-physical branch is mainly utilized to explain and practise more thoroughly the more complicated themes.

For the practical exercises in physics at the mathematico-physical branch, the children are divided into two groups, each of which has two periods of exercises per week with a total of about twelve experiments in one year. The other branches may hold non-compulsory practicals or groups of pupils may form a voluntary interest circle with the assistance of their teacher.

The syllabus of subject matter in mathematics for the chemico-biological and the general branches is less extensive. In particular, these branches do not teach the introduction to differential and integral calculus and to probability theory.

At the four-year vocational schools, ending with the school-leaving examination, the number of periods devoted to mathematics and physics varies greatly according to their special orientation, of which there are many. In general, less time is devoted to these subjects and less material has to be treated than at the general secondary schools.

The schools of the lower grades are faced with the most important task of stimulating their pupils' interest in mathematics and physics and in occupations in these fields. One of the most important means employed to foster interest in these subjects are annual competitions, so-called 'Mathematical and Physical Olympiades', organized for pupils of the secondary schools (Appendix II A2). The periodical *Rozhledy matematicko-fyzikální* (Mathematico-Physical Review), published under the auspices of the Jednota Československých Matematiků a Fyziků (Union of Czechoslovak Mathematicians and Physicists) for over forty years, also serves to stimulate the interest of the pupils in these sciences, especially with regard to pupils of secondary general educational schools. The journal also helps to organize both olympiades.

The specific prerequisite for admission to enrol in mathematics and physics courses at universities or in technical courses with a mathematico-physical base—in addition to presentation of school certificates and a school-leaving certificate—is a minimum knowledge in mathematics and physics, corresponding to the standard physics and mathematics instruction at the general branch of the secondary general educational school. (Applicants whose school-training in mathematics and physics is below this standard, for instance, those who attended secondary vocational schools, and who did not make up for this shortcoming in the meantime, are generally, even if they are otherwise considered to be very suitable for university study, obliged to attend supplementary courses before starting the first semester as well as during its courses. These supplementary courses are organized by the faculty.) During the admission interview conducted by the faculty of the university that the applicant wishes to attend, the applicant who wants to study physics is questioned in physics and mathematics. He will be judged, not so much on the merit of a satisfactory answer to this or that

22

question, but on the over-all picture received of his knowledge, intelligence and capability. In selecting applicants for admission, progress at school, the marks of the school certificate, and the result of the admission interview are taken into account. Outstanding performance in the Mathematical and Physical Olympiades also weighs heavily. At present, all suitable applicants for mathematics and physics studies are accepted at the universities, because of the great demand for graduates from these faculties.

Pre-university physics in the Federal Republic of Germany

The normal requirement for study at universities in the Federal Republic of Germany is the secondary school certificate (*Abitur*). The standard education consists of four years of primary school and nine years of secondary school. Physics instruction differs in the individual Federal States as well as in the types of school (secondary schools stressing classical languages, modern languages, or natural sciences). At present, most Federal States of Western Germany are in the process of changing their physics teaching policies on account of the Agreement of the Ministers of Education in Saarbrücken.

The present allocation of instruction periods devoted to physics and mathematics in the three different types of *Gymnasium* is given below in total numbers of periods from the eighth to the thirteenth form. In the two language types of the *Gymnasium* nowadays, the teaching of physics has become optional instead of compulsory in the last two classes. With this exception, physics is an obligatory subject. Since there are some differences in the programmes of the *Gymnasia* in the Federal States, only the total numbers of periods for the various types of school will be given below: in the (ancient and modern) language types of the gymnasium the total number of periods devoted to physics ranges from 320 to 560 periods, the last number including optional periods; in the mathematics and science type of the *Gymnasium*, the total number of periods is 560 to 720. (One period lasts forty-five minutes, and the school year has forty weeks.)

Far more periods are devoted to the teaching of mathematics. This is begun in the fifth form (i.e., in the first year at the *Gymnasium*,

23

at the age of 11) and ends in the thirteenth form in the majority of states. The total number of periods ranges between nearly 1,100 and 1,400 periods in case of the language types and 1,400 and 1,700 periods in case of the mathematics and science type of the *Gymnasium*.

No matter whether a pupil has opted for a physics course or not the *Abitur* (the school-leaving examination with which *Gymnasium* education ends) qualifies for enrolment at any German university or *Technische Hochschule*. However, statistics prove that even before physics had become an optional subject, students coming from a language type of school tended to enrol in arts rather than in science faculties, frequently on account of their feeling a lack of proficiency in mathematics and physics.

In rather rare but increasing cases, entrance to the university is obtained via the so-called second educational way. A pupil of an engineering school, who leaves with an assessment of 'very good' or 'good', can study a technical or scientific subject. Another way to get the *Abitur* is, for instance, visiting the 'evening Gymnasium'.

Pre-university physics and mathematics in France

The young student who is going to study physics at a university has followed the 'mathematics' option during his pre-university schooling. He studies mathematics for seven years, but one can discount the work of the *premier cycle*. Let us say that he has studied mathematics seriously for three years. He obtains around 500 hours of instruction (120 hours the first year, 120 the second, and 270 the third).

The table below indicates the importance of instruction in mathematics, if one compares the time allotted to mathematics with that for all the other subjects.

Age	Classes	Total schedule per week in literary and scientific subjects	Schedule in mathematics
18	Terminal class	33	9
17	Class 1	30	4
16	Class 2	28	4

The lessons last one hour, and the pupil should generally devote an equal amount of time at home to mastery of the course. He also must do a problem each week that is of the type that he should solve in the examination.

Let us not forget that besides mathematics and physics (which we will come back to), the young student is obliged to study chemistry and the natural sciences, as well as French and foreign languages, history and geography. The instruction is encyclopaedic in scope, and the student does not have a choice of subjects.

Appendix II C1 describes the main lines of the programme of mathematics instruction in the classes mentioned. The instruction endeavours to provide a solid foundation for the study of pure mathematics. The students are introduced to the use of symbols in set theory, such as $\ni$ and $\forall$. Physicists are following this development with some disquiet, hoping that this consolidation of the axiomatic basis of mathematics will not lead to a reduction in the knowledge of applied mathematics, which is indispensable for the physicist.

At the same time that he studies mathematics during the last three years of his pre-university education, the student takes a course in physics, comprising about two hundred and ten hours of instruction (sixty hours the first year, sixty the second, and ninety the last year). The lessons last one hour (sometimes an hour and a half), and are generally accompanied by demonstration experiments. Usually the same teacher teaches physics and chemistry. A close symbiosis thus exists between the two disciplines. The official programme in physics is outlined in Appendix II C2.

Besides this instruction in theory, the student obtains laboratory instruction. All of the schools possess a teaching laboratory, more or less richly equipped, where the students spend around seventy-five hours during the three years of their studies in the second cycle. The experiments last one hour, sometimes an hour and a half. An attempt is made to co-ordinate the laboratory sessions with those of the classroom. Thus, questions that are the subjects of laboratory experiments are not taken up in the rest of the course, but are studied first in the laboratory. When the student himself has observed the phenomenon, the teacher intervenes at the end of the laboratory session and summarizes briefly. The question is then considered to have been treated. The classroom discussion becomes, to a certain extent, a complement of the laboratory sessions, during which the teacher takes up points that would require experiments that would be too long or too delicate to be performed directly by the students. The list of experiments (Appendix II C3) depends upon the school, because it is determined in large measure by the equipment available. But, for several years now, the Government has made a strong effort to provide financial assistance in this area. The new schools possess teaching laboratories that are well designed and that are equipped by the efforts of the Centre National d'Equipment Scientifique which has developed, in collaboration with industry, well-designed pedagogic material. The interested reader can obtain further information from the Director of the Centre National d'Equipement Scientifique (29 Rue d'Ulm, Paris-5e).

Hitherto we have emphasized the most scientific option open to students, that which should be chosen by future mathematicians and physicists. But it is good to know that in all of the options, even those with a pronounced literary orientation, there exists a requirement for the study of mathematics and physics. To be more definite, the future linguist, or the future professor of French, by the time he has obtained his baccalaureat, has taken a mathematics course of about forty-five hours. He knows fairly well what a derivative is, an integral, a logarithmic or exponential function, and so on. In physics, he has taken a rapid tour of general physics, for eighty hours of instruction, and has spent twenty hours in the laboratory, performing some simple experiments. The young Frenchman who plans a career in law or economics has generally followed the most literary option in school (called 'philosophy and letters') because the option which has been specially designed for them (called 'economics') was created too recently to have a large clientele.

Let us leave the numerous students who are not destined for scientific careers and consider the kind of student who plans a scientific career, but not one in physics or mathematics. An option in secondary schools is open to them, called 'experimental science', which comprises a programme in physics and chemistry very much like that called *mathématiques élémentaires*. However, there is less mathematics in the third year of the second cycle of secondary school; the instruction is reduced by about one half (five hours weekly compared to nine) and deals mainly with algebra and analysis. Finally, considerable instruction in biology and other natural sciences (geology, zoology, botany, etc.) is given to the students. The future chemist has a choice between the option in experimental science and the mathematics option; experience shows that he is more successful in his career if he follows the mathematical option. The future biologist (that is, the agronomist, veterinary, physician, pharmacist) ought to follow the 'experimental science' option. In practice, since all of the options for the baccalaureat are equivalent, and since many people believe that it is not necessary to possess a scientific spirit to succeed in medicine, for example, a goodly number of students who present themselves for admission to medical studies have taken the literary option in their secondary schooling. This does not simplify the problems of their physics teachers later, who have to begin by providing some very elementary knowledge.

Pre-university physics in the U.S.S.R.

In the Soviet secondary schools all teaching subjects, including physics, are compulsory throughout the school, while the timetable and its content throughout the secondary school system are regulated by uniform curricula and syllabuses.

In the eight-year schools physics is taught in the sixth, seventh and eighth forms, and continued in the ninth, tenth and eleventh forms in the eleven-year schools.

Physics in the Soviet secondary school system might be described as a 'two-storey' process. In the eight-year schools an elementary physics course is provided in the sixth, seventh and eighth forms, covering, so far as the list of topics is concerned, all the main branches of physics, from mechanics and heat to the elements of atomic physics. This is the first 'storey'. On leaving the eight-year school the pupil has a complete, if only initial and rudimentary, picture of physics (and also of mathematics).

The physics syllabus for the ninth, tenth and eleventh forms of the eleven-year school is based on the eight-year syllabus and builds, so to say, a second 'storey' in each branch of the subject. This syllabus is substantially broader and more thorough than the elementary course, both in the classical and in the modern part, and leads straight to the physics course in the institutes of higher education. Moreover, the most advanced part of the physics course in the eleven-year school partly overlaps, in a number of branches, the first part of the course provided at the institutes of higher education.

The point of this structure is not difficult to see: millions of boys and girls finish their education in the eight- or in the eleven-year school and do not go on to higher education.

Under recent educational reforms and in connexion with the transition from the seven- and ten-year system to the eight- and eleven-year system, all the syllabuses, including the physics syllabus, were revised. The basic idea was twofold: to expand the teaching material illustrating the practical (technical) application of physics and its connexion with the life of the community, on the one hand, and to go deeper into all questions of theory and the phenomenology of physics as a science, on the other. Physics teaching in the secondary schools is thus now geared to the polytechnical approach in education and at the same time to the improvement of theoretical training.

The aims of physics teaching in the U.S.S.R. are as follows: to give the pupil a knowledge of the fundamentals of physics, ensuring that the polytechnical character thereof is made clear; to equip the pupil with the theory and practice of working with measuring instruments and laboratory apparatus and of the simplest calculations in physics, which are important for everyday life, and thus to contribute towards his industrial education and training in a trade; to promote the development of a materialist outlook and of scientific and atheistic convictions, to the development of patriotism, internationalism and respect for labour; lastly, most important of all, to help develop logical thinking, creative initiative, imagination, the capacity for self-teaching, and for independently solving theoretical and practical problems on the basis of a knowledge of physics and mathematics.

Class work is based on physical experiment in the form of demonstrations, direct laboratory work, and the practical physics work performed in each class at the end of the year in order to illustrate the theoretical material already learned. Forms of self-teaching include solving problems in calculation, drawing graphs, performing experiments and answering set questions, as well as long-term tasks in technical physics, such as making physical instruments or designing very simple technical apparatus in the school workshop.

By agreement with the mathematics teacher, problems with a physical content are solved during the mathematics lesson. This particularly applies to those branches of physics for which the mathematical training of the pupil is not yet adequate: for example, in discussing trigonometric functions or derivatives in the mathematics lessons, problems from the theory of vibrations or kinematics are solved.

Progress is checked by questions in class, by correcting tests done in class or at home and by examinations. A four-mark system is in use in Soviet secondary and higher schools (2, 3, 4 and 5); the mark 2 is regarded as unsatisfactory.

Preparation for school-leaving and matriculation. Admission to Soviet institutes of higher education is by competitive examination. The examination syllabus depends on the group of special subjects covered by the educational establishment concerned. In all institutes of higher technical education, for example, matriculation entails examinations in mathematics (oral and written), physics (oral), Russian (composition), and one foreign language (oral). The examinations in mathematics and physics are usually held first, since the marks in these two subjects are decisive in the competitive selection. The requirements in mathematics are very high. It is not uncommon for a large percentage of candidates to forfeit the right to take the other examinations because their marks in mathematics are unsatisfactory.

Preparation for the competitive examinations is either by self-study or by preparatory courses in the preparatory departments of the institutes of higher education.[1] This preparation is short, taking a few months to one year. The teachers are for the most part lecturers in the relevant departments of the institutes of higher

1. V. A. Kitaytsev, *Admission to Institutes of Higher Education in the U.S.S.R.*, to be published in 1965 in the series 'The International Study of University Admission, Access to Higher Education', Vol. II, Paris, Unesco.

education. The competitive examinations and the preparation for them follow special entrance examination syllabuses. In physics, for example, the syllabus (Appendix II D1) coincides roughly with the physics syllabus for the eleven-year schools. Very recently this syllabus was revised and slightly shortened, mainly in regard to the technical applications of physics and material duplicating the basic topics in the physics course of a higher technical school. At the same time, the requirements in regard to the fundamental principles of elementary physics were increased in the majority of institutes of higher education.

In the opinion of the overwhelming majority of physics teachers in higher education the basic requirements for the entrance examination in physics are as follows: the ability to formulate physical concepts, definitions, laws and units of measurement strictly and accurately; knowledge of the basic quantitative relationships in all branches of the subject; ability to solve simple problems in physics and reduce the answer to the correct numerical result.

In all this, preference is given to the ability to grasp and to think physically, rather than to the candidates' general store of textbook knowledge.

The examining body is a committee of two. Its mark is final; there is no appeal and in no circumstances can the mark be altered. In the interest of complete objectivity, the written examination papers are submitted under an assumed symbol, not the candidate's surname.

Before the examinations, which are usually held in August or September in each institute of higher education, a great deal of preparatory work is done under the direction of an Admissions Board appointed by the rector of the academic body concerned. The chairman of this board is the rector himself and its members are professors, lecturers and representatives of the students' and other social organizations.

Admission to higher education is based on State plans which lay down admission quotas and turn-out targets, obligatory on departments and rectors, for a number of years to come. Plans of this kind are drawn up strictly in accordance with the plans for the development of industry and the national economy.

Pre-university physics in the United Kingdom

As is pointed out in Appendix I E1, the children with whom we are primarily concerned in this survey are those who, in Britain, are selected at the age of 11 for grammar school education. They are about 22 per cent of the total number of children in the age range.

The grammar school course in Britain is normally five years and at the age of 16 children take the examination for the General Certificate of Education at the 'O' level. The examination may be taken in almost any school subject, and a reasonably intelligent child would probably take about eight subjects. Those children staying at school after this stage enter the sixth form for a two- (or three-) year course leading to the General Certificate of Education at 'A' level, which is virtually the examination for university entry. A child would normally take three or four subjects in this examination and his or her sixth form course would have been highly specialized. For a child specializing in science, for example, out of thirty-five or so periods a week, probably twenty-five would be devoted to physics, mathematics and chemistry, or with biology in place of one of the other three. The remaining time would be given to English, possibly a foreign language, religious instruction, and perhaps social studies. In addition to the 'A' level papers there is also a special paper (previously known as scholarship level) taken by those who wish to show clearly their capacity for university education in a subject (see Appendix II E1). Nevertheless, passes in the 'A' level papers are the basic entry requirements for universities and most universities demand three subjects at 'A' level. For the university departments of high reputation for which the competition is particularly severe, the actual marks obtained in these papers would be of extreme importance, and only students obtaining high marks would normally have much chance of acceptance. The independent schools—'public schools'—fit into this pattern in very broad terms as grammar schools, but they admit their children at 13 years of age instead of 11 years. Most of the children entering independent schools would previously have been educated in independent preparatory schools and not in the State primary schools.

The Scottish system has some important points of difference from

31

English practice. Furthermore, the whole Scottish system is at present undergoing considerable modification. For the purpose of this report English and Scottish standards of school education may perhaps be taken as broadly comparable except in so far as children, in general, leave school one year earlier in Scotland, and in Scottish universities follow a four-year course for a degree that would be comparable with that taken in England after three years.

A most important factor in the school examination system in England and Wales is that the General Certificate of Education, which, at 'A' level, is used as a university entrance examination, is not administered by the Ministry of Education, or by the universities, although both have considerable direct or indirect influence. There are nine examining boards, eight of which have their origin in university concern for assessment of the work of the schools. On those eight boards, individual universities are represented and a number of school headmasters or teachers of long experience also sit as individuals. In the detailed work of the subject panels that are responsible for the papers in individual subjects, responsibility would be carried by both university teachers and experienced schoolteachers. In individual subjects each of the boards publishes a syllabus on which its examinations will be set, and these syllabuses will similarly have been drawn up by panels of university teachers and schoolteachers. In the nature of things, all that an examining board can do is to issue an examination syllabus, but it is almost inevitable that this syllabus will largely determine what is taught in the schools which take that examination. Every school in the country has complete freedom to decide which examinations it will take, and indeed, it could happen that a school would take the examination of one examining board in, say, history, and of another examining board in, say, Latin or physics. There are many real advantages of the system. One potential advantage is that it should be easier to introduce changes in syllabuses than would be possible in a uniform system imposed and administered by the Ministry of Education. To some extent this virtue of flexibility does operate although there is some feeling that the boards tend to be conservative in their attitude to syllabuses. A problem which is not avoided in England any more successfully than elsewhere is that since schools are naturally anxious to obtain a good percentage of passes in the examinations, there is a pressure for courses to be heavily influenced by the examinations rather than to be devised on the best educational grounds.

For the past few years much intensive work has been done on the complete recasting of school physics courses, with the aim of giving all children—whatever their future careers may be—a broad but reliable understanding of physical principles and of the way in which the professional physicist approaches his task of increasing our knowledge of the material world. The proposed new syllabuses of the Science Masters' Association (whose name has now been changed to the Association for Science Education) are now being tried in various schools with the full co-operation of the Ministry of Education. A more ambitious reorganization of courses is being undertaken by the Nuffield Foundation, and it is highly probable that the next few years will see a complete transformation of school physics teaching in Britain.

From what has been said above about specialization and competition for university places it is easy to see that great emphasis has been placed in English grammar schools' sixth forms on giving children a high level of knowledge of a fairly narrow range of subjects, of which physics is one. This emphasis has been further intensified by the existence at Oxford and Cambridge of open scholarships offered by the colleges. The standard demanded for these awards is extremely high (see Appendix II E2) and the winning of an open scholarship carries very considerable prestige.

In practice, the English boy or girl leaving school to enter university will have studied the subjects of his university course for seven years at school and will have in these subjects a very high level of knowledge for his age.

Pre-university physics and mathematics in the U.S.A.

Elements of science and mathematics are studied by children in the first eight grades in the United States. The science studies may be merely one or two hours per week for a year of human physiology or 'health'. Often, however, it is a sequence of so-called 'units', each of which purports to give the child an understanding of some aspect of nature: the stars, magnetism, how we see, forms of energy, etc. These units are often parts of study cycles. The subject of 'magnetism', for example, comes up from one year to another. There is a tendency for vocabulary, rather than concepts, to be stressed; the mathematical basis of science is seldom referred to until the end of this period. Newer approaches to the study of science in the elementary grades are being developed by study groups of scientists working co-operatively with selected schools.[1] These newer approaches attempt to stress concept development more than traditional teaching does, and may lead to a strengthening of science education at this and all higher levels. The mathematics of the first eight grades is mostly arithmetic, dealing with the basic operations and stressing the application of these to everyday situations. Some simple algebra is taught toward the end of this period. The child also studies the simple geometrical forms, uses the mensuration formulas, confronts graphs for the first time, uses ratio and proportion, and performs exercises in the use of different units of measurement. The stronger schools, however, are introducing mathematics of a more formal sort that provides an introduction to mathematics as a deductive subject rather than a collection of rules.[2] The newer mathematics includes symbolic logic, probability, sets, etc. The reform is not yet widespread in the earlier grades.

For the last three or four years of secondary education, many of the stronger schools now provide several curricular paths, called 'tracks'. The track for the less able children provides general education, often including a course in 'physical science'. The track for the more able children contains studies of greater depth and greater sophistication, directed toward university studies. The work in this track also proceeds at a faster pace than that in the others, so that these children complete their secondary education with studies that are at least a year in advance of those of their classmates.

In the sciences, the children in the faster track typically study the

1. A. Calandra, *Symbols and Arithmetic Sentences*, St. Louis, Missouri, Washington University Bookstore, 1962.
   R. Karplus, 'Beginning a Study in Elementary School Science', *American Journal of Physics* Vol. 30, 1962.
2. The *'Strands' Report of the Advisory Committee on Mathematics to the State Curriculum Commission*, Sacramento, California State Department of Education, 1962.

biological sciences in the ninth or tenth grade, chemistry in the tenth, physics in the eleventh, and a second year of one of these in the twelfth. The sciences are studied in courses, each usually lasting two semesters in a school year of about 180 days. The weekly schedule of a typical science course includes six classroom periods of forty minutes each, two of which are consecutive and provide a two-period laboratory session. Demonstrations by the teacher and laboratory experiments by the student are both a part of the course.

The systematic study of physics in the schools occurs in a one-year course, followed infrequently by a more advanced course of one or two semesters. Note that the word 'systematic' is stressed. The children who study physics have encountered some of the ideas and vocabulary of physics before in the earlier grades. In content, the traditional high-school physics course—taken by about 70 per cent of those studying physics—anticipates the introductory physics course in colleges. It includes topics from mechanics, the properties of materials, wave motion, acoustics, electricity and magnetism, optics, and atomic and nuclear physics.[1] Applications of physics to technology are usually included. Simple algebra (up to quadratic equations and linear simultaneous equations), plane geometry, and a little trigonometry provide the mathematical base for the course. The physical interpretation of the slope of a curve and of the area under a curve may be introduced into the first course by teachers in the stronger schools, but calculus is typically not used. Problem-solving, ranging from simple exercises in substituting data into a formula to more demanding tasks, is a part of the course. Laboratory exercises are usually of the highly organized variety called 'cookbook' experiments.

The Advanced Placement Programme should be noted as a means of providing flexibility in educational programmes.[2] Schools taking part in this programme offer their more able pupils college-level courses in one or more of several subjects, using college text-books. These pupils are then given an Advanced Placement

1. *Physics Handbook*, Albany, Bureau of Secondary Curriculum Development, New York State Education Department, 1956.
2. *Advanced Placement Program: Course Descriptions*, New York, College Entrance Examination Board, 1962.
   Advanced Placement Program in Physics, Albany, Bureau of Secondary Curriculum Development, New York State Education Department, 1961.

examination in the subject studied before entering college. If they pass the examination, they are certified to have completed the equivalent of a college course in the subject. The colleges participating in the programme allow them to begin their college work in the subject at a more advanced level. The programme has many benefits for the schools in increasing the rigour of work done by the more able pupils. In physics, however, the number of Advanced Placement pupils has been small. The Advanced Placement Programme in Mathematics has been more successful. The acceleration produced by studying advanced mathematics in high school proves to be very advantageous to the college student.

The newer high-school physics courses—such as the course of the Physical Science Study Committee[1]—are considerably different from the traditional course or the Advanced Placement course. They stress understanding of the unifying concepts of physics and treat fewer topics in greater depth without attempting to cover as much ground as the traditional course. The PSSC materials include a new textbook and laboratory programme, simple laboratory apparatus, a comprehensive teachers' manual, films, and well-written monographs on special topics in physics. Science educators are hopeful that these courses—paralleled by similar ones in chemistry, the biological sciences, and mathematics—will instil new rigour and interest into the teaching of these subjects in the schools.[2]

The traditional sequence of mathematics courses in secondary schools has been algebra in the ninth grade, plane geometry in the tenth, and advanced algebra, trigonometry, and solid geometry during the eleventh and twelfth grades. Although this is still the pattern in many schools, changes are taking place. The newer approach, developed by such groups as the School Mathematics Study Group, stresses unifying themes or ideas in mathematics, such as: structure; operations and their inverses; measurement; graphical representation; systems of numeration; properties of numbers and development of the real number system; statistical inference and probability; sets—language and elementary theory; logical deductions; valid generalizations.

1. *Physical Science Study Committee*, 164 Main Street, Watertown, Massachusetts.
2. *Physics in Your High School*, New York, American Institute of Physics. 'Report on Broad Improvement in Science Education', *Science Education News*, American Association for the Advancement of Science, Washington, December 1961.

Textbooks and teachers' guides incorporating these ideas have been developed and are being tried.[1] Some schools are now offering their twelfth-grade pupils an introductory course in calculus.

The United States does not have a national system of required examinations for admission to institutions of higher learning. Universities and colleges base admission upon one or more of the following requirements: (a) graduation with satisfactory grades from a secondary school that has been accredited by a regional association; (b) a satisfactory rating in the Scholastic Aptitude Test (SAT) and in the Achievement Tests of the College Entrance Examination Board (CEEB), and (c) a satisfactory interview by the candidate with a representative of the institution. In addition, most institutions specify a number of desirable qualities of scholarship and character that they expect of their students. Requirement (a) is almost universal, the only exceptions being made for unusually able students who may be admitted after completing the eleventh grade or occasionally earlier. Pre-university studies are often specified in terms of Carnegie units, where a Carnegie unit is a full academic year's study in a secondary school subject. For example, one technological university requires for admission: English, 3 units; algebra, 2 units; plane geometry, 1 unit; physics, 1 unit; trigonometry, 0.5 unit; plus 7.5 additional units in secondary school subjects. Chemistry, modern foreign languages, and history are recommended by this institution but not required, and various allowances are made in interpreting the candidate's record to allow for changes introduced by recent curricular revision in some schools. It should be pointed out, however, that pre-university physics is not, at present, formally required for admission by all universities, even of students who will concentrate in the sciences or engineering. Approximately 350 colleges and universities also set requirement (b) for admission. The CEEB is a non-profit membership organization that provides tests and other educational services for schools and colleges, operating through the Educational Testing Service at Princeton, New Jersey. The Scholastic Aptitude Test is used to predict how well students are likely to perform in college.[2] It

1. *The Revolution in School Mathematics*, National Council of Teachers of Mathematics, Washington 6.
2. *A Description of the College Board Scholastic Aptitude Test*, College Entrance Examination Board, Princeton, New Jersey, 1961.

contains verbal sections (e.g., antonyms, analogies, reading comprehension, etc.) and mathematical sections, in each of which the student is tested by means of multiple-choice test items. Achievement tests are given in eleven disciplinary areas, including intermediate and advanced mathematics and physics.[1]

To inform pupils about career opportunities and about the educational requirements for various careers, most high schools have guidance officers who consult with pupils and their parents. The American Institute of Physics has prepared a series of booklets about careers in physics for the use of guidance officers, teachers, and pupils.[2] Such booklets are in demand in colleges as well as schools since many students do not decide upon a career until they have completed one or two years of higher education.

Summary

The foregoing reports have perhaps made it sufficiently clear to what extent and in what varied ways the educational practices in the six countries participating in this survey support the objectives listed in the introduction to the chapter. In each of these countries, children study the elements of physics in the lower schools. The number of pupils in physics decreases, to be sure, in the later years of schooling as the various attritional processes in education have their effect. Physics studies are extensive rather than intensive in the earlier years of schooling, but explore topics in greater depth and with greater reliance upon mathematical formulation as the child matures and his grasp of mathematics increases. There is agreement in these countries that practical or laboratory work by students and demonstrations by the teacher are an essential part of physics teaching; the ways in which these are provided differ considerably.

The secondary-school physics courses described here prepare the child—perhaps incidentally—for university studies in physics and

1. *A Description of the College Board Achievements Tests*, College Entrance Examination Board, Princeton, New Jersey, 1961.
2. *Physics as a Career. Why should you study physics in high school? Careers in college physics teaching. Careers in high school physics teaching. Rewarding careers for women in physics*, American Institute of Physics, New York.

related fields. In their content and organization they anticipate university work, as a comparison of this and the following chapter will make clear, even to the extent in some countries of being formally a part of a spiral educational process.

III. The education of professional physicists in universities to the first degree

Introduction

The students of physics in universities include those who are preparing to become professional physicists; those who wish to teach physics in the schools; future engineers, chemists, mathematicians, and geologists; students of the life sciences—the biological sciences, medicine, dentistry and pharmacy; and, in some countries, non-specialists seeking a liberal-arts education. This chapter is concerned with the first of these groups—the future physicists—and contains a review of their education up to the receipt of the first academic degree in the countries participating in the present survey. The advanced education of physicists, leading to higher degrees, will be discussed in a later chapter. The next chapter contains a description of the educational programmes for the other students of physics in universities, including physics teachers in schools.

The educational period that we are about to describe begins for the would-be physicist at the age of about 18 and continues to the age of 22 in some countries or 23 or 24 in others. He enters upon his higher education with a preparation in physics and mathematics such as was described in the last chapter. Just as we noticed differences in that preparation from country to country, we shall find differences in the scope and level of university physics—some of them a direct result of the extent of school preparation, others deriving from the expectation that the student will continue his education by pursuing advanced studies after receiving his first degree. As was true of school studies in physics and mathematics, there are also differences among countries in the philosophy, objectives, and practices of university education in physics.

Nevertheless, 'physics is physics' and the basic education required to carry on research that adds to the knowledge of mankind or to teach physics in a university is much the same from one country to another. The young student ordinarily begins his university studies with a course in general or introductory physics that lays the groundwork for the later, more specialized studies in the various sub-areas of physics. Laboratory or practical work begins during the general physics course and extends into the later years, progressively becoming less openly didactic and more research-like as the student's command of theoretical and experimental physics increases. Studies in mathematics, chemistry, and other fields related to physics carry forward his education in those areas.

This chapter contains reports from the participating countries pertaining to the following topics:

1. The objectives and programmes of higher education for physicists—the educational philosophy and aims, the courses of instruction and the length of time devoted to each, and the requirements for the first degree or certificate or licence in various specialities of physics—up to the first professional degree.
2. The content of physics courses.
3. Examinations.
4. Laboratory or practical work.
5. Studies in mathematics and chemistry pursued by the student physicist.
6. Independent study and work experience.

The all-important question of who teaches university physics and the important question of what material—apparatus, buildings, books, etc.—is required will be taken up in later chapters.

The education of professional physicists in Czechoslovakia to the first degree

Professional physicists are in most cases trained at the faculties of traditional universities in Czechoslovakia. At most universities these students are trained at so-called natural science faculties (Bratislava,

Brno, Olomouc). The only exception to date is Charles University in Prague with an independent faculty for this purpose, the Mathematico-Physical Faculty. In the not-too-distant future, the setting up of similar independent faculties at other universities is envisaged, in order to meet the growing demand for physicists and mathematicians. In addition, one faculty, the Faculty of Technical and Nuclear Physics of the Technical University in Prague, also trains so-called 'technical physicists' (or physics engineers) for various positions in industry and industrial research institutes.

Objectives. The objectives in training professional physicists at the university faculties are given by the so-called 'profile of the graduate'. The graduate is expected to possess the following qualities: a broad, general knowledge of contemporary physics, and a profounder knowledge in a narrower specialization. He must also be able to acquire new physical knowledge by independent study of scientific literature.

He must be capable of solving independently current problems of general and applied physics, utilizing his own accumulated knowledge and all he can gain from the study of literature. He must be able to co-operate in solving more complicated research and development problems under the guidance of experienced scientific workers. He must be able to apply in his work predominantly either methods of theoretical physics (narrower specialization of physics) or experimental methods (other narrower specializations of physics).

He must be aware of the role of science in a socialist society and, in particular, of the main topical and prospective problems of physics, whose solution may pave the road for further progress of modern technics and for the advance of culture. He must also know the specific laws governing the development of physics as a natural science, based on a scientific world view.

Graduates will work either at scientific institutions which are engaged mainly in basic research, or in physics departments of technical research institutes and laboratories, experimental and development laboratories and departments of production enterprises, where problems are solved, requiring the application of the latest physical methods and discoveries.

42

Curricula. The training lasts five years. For the first two years, the curriculum is identical in all four semesters for the professional branch of physics, for the professional branch of mathematics, and for the training of mathematics and physics teachers. During the fifth semester, the whole professional branch of physics still follows the same curriculum, and in the course of this term, the distribution of students for the various specializations is being prepared.

The specializations have their own curricula, with some basic courses of lectures common for all specializations—namely the introductory course in general and experimental physics, and the course in theoretical physics. The curricula are reproduced in Appendix III A1.

In addition to pursuing studies in physics and mathematics, discussed below, the future physicist receives additional 'general education' at the university, including physical culture and the study of philosophy, economics, and modern foreign languages.

Introductory course in general physics. The purpose of the course in general or experimental physics is: (a) to convey a systematic and all-round knowledge of physics; (b) on the basis of experimental facts, observations and judgement to explain and define precisely the fundamental concepts and quantities, and (c) to introduce mathematical formulation of the physical relations and dependences. Also the principles of the basic methods of measuring quantities, of the verification of physical laws and of the application of physical knowledge in practice, especially in technics, are taught in this course. Beginning with the first and lasting until the end of the sixth semester, this course consists of about 265 hours of demonstration lectures and, during the first four semesters, approximately 80 hours of lecture-connected exercises. The lectures are held for a large number of students at a time. In Prague, there are two parallel courses, each attended by about 150 students. The lecturers are professors or experienced docents. For their exercises, the students are divided into smaller groups. The exercises are usually performed under the guidance of senior assistants, whose work is supervised by the lecturing professor.

In this course, physics is taught in two consecutive sections. During the first to fourth semesters (first and second year), an elementary survey of physics is given, which, in the fifth semester, is supplemented by more profound study of some more complicated topics in electricity and magnetism and, in the sixth semester, in optics. This division of the subject matter was decided upon in order to make it possible for students of the professional branch of mathematics to gain some general knowledge in this branch of science; such students, starting with the fifth semester, study according to their own curriculum, in which no further physics lectures are included.

The content of the subject matter is defined in the official syllabus (Appendix III A2), valid for all university faculties. It gives an outline of the matter to be treated which, at the same time, is compulsory for the examinations. The syllabus indicates only the range of individual topics, leaving their arrangement to the various faculties, as well as the choice of instruction methods as far as the individual parts of the subject matter are concerned. Examination in the subject matter treated during one semester always takes place at its end, bringing the total up to six examinations for the whole course.

Basic laboratory work. The physical laboratory exercises are conducted with the usual objectives: to teach the student the fundamental techniques of experiments and to acquaint him in a practical way with the simpler methods of measuring for all branches of physics, including the evaluation of the precision of the results. The actual laboratory exercises are, in the first semester, preceded by introductory lectures, acquainting the students theoretically with the basic problems of practical physics, in particular with the main methods of measurement, the theory of errors, various methods of evaluating results, and with appropriate calculation methods and aids. On this occasion, some typical methods of measurement are analysed, the students acquaint themselves with the laboratory regulations and rules for safety at work; they also learn to keep a laboratory diary, to write a protocol on the results of their measurements, etc. Finally, they are instructed in the use of supplementary literature. The curriculum provides for two hours a week for these lectures, but they are discontinued later in the semester.

During the first semester, a course in laboratory and workshop techniques is held, where students may learn the elements of chemical laboratory work, photographic processes, elementary workshop skills and working with glass, unless they have already done so before. For this course, two hours a week are set aside. There is also a course in technical drawing which the students may attend (two hours a week).

The actual laboratory exercises are carried out by the students from the second to the fourth semester inclusive, three hours each week. In the fifth semester, the number of hours is increased to four weekly. The experiments to be executed by students are partly altered every year and new experiments are introduced, especially in the fifth semester, according to the directives of the professor who heads the Chair of general physics, and who is the chief supervisor of the course in general physics and of the basic course of practical exercises. The exercises are performed in laboratories, which are generally especially equipped for this purpose. The students of one study year are divided into smaller groups of twenty to twenty-five students who conduct their exercises simultaneously. For the individual experiments, these groups are split up again into pairs. The distribution of experiments among the individual couples for the whole semester is announced at its beginning. This enables the students to fulfil their duty of preparing themselves in advance for each experiment with the help of instruction sheets, issued by the faculty, and by studying the recommended manuals.

The necessary apparatus and equipment for the individual experiments are permanently installed in the laboratories for the duration of the semester. Some experiments are prepared in the laboratories several times. For the more intricate experiments, students set up their own measuring apparatus themselves from the instruments and devices at their disposal. Before the current is turned on, apparatus set up for electrical measuring by the students themselves must be checked by one of the assistants present in the laboratory, in order to prevent damage to the instruments. The usual laboratory instruments for the divers experiments are generally available.

All practical exercises are supervised by an experienced, senior assistant, permanently employed for this work. A senior assistant is in charge of the work of each of the simultaneously working groups.

He is supported in most cases by two junior assistants. At the beginning of the exercise, the assistants check whether each pair is prepared sufficiently to carry out the experiments. Where this is not the case, the assistant is entitled to order the postponing of the experiment until an additional date in the first week of the examination period, when students catch up on those experiments they were unable to perform at an earlier date through ill health or other valid reasons. Throughout the exercises, the assistants follow the work of the students, and help them with advice and instruction. After the exercise is completed, they examine the manner and quality of the performance and check on the condition of the apparatus.

The students enter their working methods and the values determined into a notebook. This is the diary which each of the two students who form a pair is obliged to keep. In simple experiments, all measurements are repeated by each of them. When working on more difficult experiments, they take turns in observing and registering the measured values. Before leaving the laboratory, their notebooks are signed by the assistant. At home, the students work out a protocol of this experiment. This again is done separately by each student. At the next exercise, the students hand their protocols to the senior assistant, who reads and marks them. Next time, the assistant informs the students of their classification, drawing their attention to any mistakes and shortcomings in their work. All protocols are returned to the students at the end of the semester. In each semester, the student's work as a whole is evaluated and given a marked validation. Connected with the validation is a talk between the senior assistant and the individual student. On this occasion, the student's achievements and shortcomings in his work are discussed.

Introductory course in theoretical physics. The course in theoretical physics is the third of the main courses which form the backbone of the whole course of study. It aims at furnishing a general survey of present theoretical physics—to teach the students the elementary methods for formulating the mutual relations between physical quantities and describing phenomena by use of mathematics, the forming of hypotheses and theories as well as the deduction from general laws of conclusions which can be compared with the experimental results, and the most important mathematical methods of solving theoretical problems. This course runs from the third to the seventh semester, during which period about 245 hours of lectures and about 110 hours of lecture-connected exercises have to be attended.

Theoretical physics as a subject is divided into the following sections: analytical mechanics (third semester), mechanics of continuum (fourth semester), theoretical electromagnetism (fifth semester, 4/2[1] hours weekly), special theory of relativity (also fifth semester, 2/0 hours weekly), quantum mechanics (sixth semester), thermodynamics and statistical mechanics (seventh semester). The topics of the course are determined by a syllabus (Appendix III A3) in the same manner as for the course in general physics. Examinations are held at the end of the fourth, fifth, sixth and seventh semesters, i.e., a total of four examinations. The course is the responsibility of the Chair of theoretical physics.

Optional lectures, experimental work, etc. Apart from attending the obligatory lectures and experimental work within the framework of their curriculum, students may put themselves voluntarily down for other, non-compulsory lectures. These are held by the different Chairs and announced in the faculty list of lectures for each school year. Some of these lectures are repeated year after year, others are given only occasionally. Lecturers are teachers of the faculty, but also experts not belonging to it. The students may choose any lecture, but must have the consent of the lecturer. Students of each specialization may also register voluntarily for attendance at some lectures, seminars and laboratory work which form part of the curricula of other specializations, subject to the consent of the teacher. Noncompulsory lectures and exercises are not followed by examinations; the lecturer merely certifies by 'validation' the student's participation. Appendix III A4 shows, as an example, the plan of noncompulsory lectures in physics of the mathematico-physical faculty of Charles University.

Mathematics courses. For all students of the professional branch of physics, a basic course in mathematics is part of the curriculum.

---

1. In reproducing the curricula, the following abbreviations are used: 4/2 = four weekly periods of lectures and two periods of connected exercises.

It is subdivided into several partial courses, details of which are given in Appendix III A5: (a) mathematical analysis (5/2 hours in the first semester, 4/2 hours in the second semester, 4/2 in the third semester and 3/2 in the fourth semester). The aim of this course is to give a survey of the foundations of differential and integral calculus to serve both as background for the simultaneous course of physics topics, and as a base for the further studies of prospective professional mathematicians and physicists, and teachers of mathematics and physics; (b) algebra and analytical geometry, including introduction to algebra and analytic geometry (4/2 hours in the first and second semester), analytic geometry (4/0 hours in the third semester) and algebra (2/0 hours in the third semester and 4/0 in the fourth semester); (c) mathematics for physicists (4/2 hours in the fifth and sixth semester). This course of mathematical analysis is held for specialists in physics only.

The topics of the basic mathematics and physics courses are co-ordinated to a considerable extent. The majority of the professors who teach physics are not satisfied with the contents of the basic mathematics course and with the methods adopted to teach it. The physicists would like to see two parallel courses in mathematics: one for prospective professional mathematicians, the other for future professional physicists, directed predominantly at their specific requirements. It appears that sooner or later such a solution will be adopted. Meanwhile, however, the main obstacle for its realization is a relative shortage of mathematics professors. Some aspects of mathematics and mathematical methods, needed in particular by theoretical physicists, are dealt with in the appropriate physics lectures.

The specializations. The differentiation of the training of professional physicists during the sixth to tenth semester in specializations with their own curricula aims at these two main objectives: (a) to enable the future physicist to gain in at least one main field of modern physics a substantially profounder knowledge than he could possibly accumulate through balanced instruction covering all regions of this science, and (b) to educate graduates who will be able to get the knack of things at their future place of employment with a minimum loss of time and soon be able to do useful work. When arranging for the student's employment—which is done while he is still at the university—the necessary preparations in this respect are made in agreement with the student and the institute or enterprise he will work for, taking into consideration the university specialization of the student. In case it should not be possible to place a student according to his specialization or if the student does not, from the outset, possess the specialized knowledge his employer requires, the fact that his training took place according to the principle expounded under (a) will help him to work in another field of physics proficiently within a comparatively short time.

At present, the following specializations are taught at the universities: (a) theoretical physics; (b) solid state physics; (c) electronics and vacuum physics; (d) nuclear physics; (e) optics and precision mechanics.

Apart from these purely physical specializations, the training of astronomers, geophysicists and meteorologists proceeds according to independent curricula based on the basic curriculum for the first five semesters.

Students studying the specializations attend, in addition to the courses which are common for all specializations, other compulsory lectures, prescribed by the curriculum. They also participate in professional praxis (four weeks at the beginning of the eighth semester), and during the eighth and tenth semesters also prepare their diploma thesis. The work of the students of the specializations is supervised by the appropriate Chair, for example, the Chair of theoretical physics, of solid state physics, etc.

Preparation of the diploma thesis is an important means of education from the point of view of the before-mentioned objectives. As early as the seventh semester, the diploma projects are prepared and preliminarily discussed with the students by members of the Chair in question. At the beginning of the eighth semester, the projects are allocated to the students. The diploma project is some smaller research task, which, as a rule, forms part of the programme of the Chair's scientific work. Apart from such 'internal' projects, some students are charged with projects suggested by research institutes and laboratories, not belonging to the school. In such cases the students work directly at these institutes, and it is usually taken for granted that they will be employed there after graduating from the university. The establishment at which the student undergoes his professional praxis, mentioned before, is also chosen with a view to his diploma project.

Every student works independently under the guidance of a teacher of his Chair (professor or docent) or of an external scientific worker. He elaborates his experimental project, using apparatus which is usually especially designed for this purpose only, and, in some cases, sets up the apparatus himself. He must adhere to all laboratory regulations applying to anyone working there. He has to keep a laboratory diary and submit progress reports. Finally, he writes a thesis which he will have to defend later on. A certain number of hours are reserved in the curriculum for the preparation of the diploma thesis, but this is actually a formality, as the student in reality devotes all his spare time to this task.

His written thesis is judged by the teacher or scientific worker who supervised his diploma project and also by another teacher or external scientific worker, the so-called opponent. Both the supervising teacher and the opponent state their judgement in writing. The supervising teacher also evaluates the student's general methods of work. The student is acquainted with both evaluations prior to defending his thesis. This thesis, as well as the two evaluations, are also at the disposal of the other teachers of the department.

The student defends his diploma thesis at a public forum held at the Chair in question. At least one member of the faculty's State Examination Board of Physics must be present on this occasion. The student briefly outlines his methods and results, after which the opponent and the scientist who supervised the student's diploma project give their judgement. In the ensuing debate the student has to reply to objections and criticism by the opponent, and then answer questions any of those present may pose. On this occasion, the student must prove his broader knowledge in the whole field of physics from which his diploma project was chosen. The defence does not usually last more than one hour. After the debate, the Chair holds a non-public council, at which the entire performance of the student is considered and the degree of validation for his diploma thesis determined. Some diploma theses have a very high level, and their results are published.

The oral part of the finals is held by an examination commission of three—professors and docents of the faculty—one of them is a member of the Chair in question. The chairman of the examination commission is a member of the faculty's state Examination Board for physics. All three members of the commission question the student and follow the course of the oral which lasts approximately one hour. The questions posed are of a more general character and do not go into greater detail. Their purpose is to establish the student's whole level of knowledge in physics and to find out how he approaches concrete tasks. The commission classifies the results of the oral examination by the corresponding degree of validation.

When all these examinations are over, the State Examination Board reviews the results and marks of the defence and of the oral examinations in order to co-ordinate the criteria of classification. The board endorses or, in exceptional cases, alters the given marks. It awards the student who received the highest degree of marks for his defence and his orals and who had studied with more than average success throughout the whole course of study a 'special mention' degree. A student who has failed to make the grade can repeat his oral finals or his defence (which occurs very rarely) after approximately six months have elapsed. He takes up his employment in the meantime, but receives somewhat lower pay than the holder of a diploma.

Training of technical physicists. The so-called technical physicists are trained at present at the Faculty of Technical and Nuclear Physics, established in 1955 at the Technical University in Prague, with the aim of educating specialists in nuclear physics and technology. The very expensive technical equipment for scientific work in these fields of science necessitated the concentration of the training of nuclear physicists at this school in Prague. Shortly after this decision was realized, other specializations had to be added: physical electronics and solid state physics, both mainly directed at the needs of nuclear technology. This is a provisional stage. The merging of the training of technical physicists with that of physicists, studying at the faculty of Charles University, is being prepared. For this reason, this report is confined to a brief characterization of the prevailing state of training. The merging will probably be accompanied also by certain alterations in the curricula for the training of physicists at the university faculties. The course of study at the faculty of technical and nuclear physics lasts five-and-a-half years. In the first year, all main branches of study follow the same curriculum. Just as at the university, the backbone of the study schedule for the physical main branch of the faculty are three basic courses: general physics, theoretical physics, and physical laboratory exercises. Their contents are similar to those of the university courses, but more attention and time are devoted at this faculty to experimental and theoretical nuclear physics. In the first study year, four hours a week are earmarked for chemistry lectures. The division into specializations takes place in the case of nuclear physics and physical electronics at the beginning of the second study year, while the specialization for solid state physics branches off from the first specialization at the beginning of the third study year. During the last two semesters, when the students prepare their diploma thesis, the training in the mentioned specializations is further divided into an experimental and a theoretical branch. This study course is completed with a final State examination, part of which is the defence of the diploma thesis. Methods of study are the same as for university training. Graduates from this faculty are awarded the degree 'engineer of physics'.

The education to the first degree of professional physicists in the universities and *Technischen Hochschulen* in the Federal Republic of Germany

Students of physics in the Federal Republic of Germany heading for careers in industry, at universities, or at engineering schools, pass, after four or five semesters, a preliminary diploma examination (*Vordiplom*), and after some six further semesters, in most cases, the main diploma examination (*Diplomhauptprüfung*), which is a final examination (see Fig. 2, Appendix I B1). A certain number of these physicists, generally after a further four terms, proceed to take the degree of Dr.rer.nat. (or Dr.phil.nat. at Frankfurt). At some universities the doctor degree may be obtained without the main diploma examination as a prerequisite. At some *Technischen Hochschulen* the physicist may also obtain the Diploma in Engineering (*Diplomingenieur*) (Dipl.-Ing.) and go on to take the doctorate in engineering (Dr.-Ing.).

For the time being there exists no universal examination agreement. However, most universities follow, in the main, a diploma graduation order issued in 1942, with up-to-date amendments incorporated. According to these regulations, the preliminary examination is mostly an oral one and includes the following subjects: experimental physics; mechanics (in exceptional cases a different topic in theoretical or applied physics); mathematics; chemistry.

In the main diploma examination, special value is attached to the *Diplomarbeit* (thesis). The oral part of the final examination (*Hauptprüfung*) consists of the following subjects: experimental physics; theoretical physics; applied physics (a topic dealing with the application of physics over a wider area); a selected subject in mathematics, the natural sciences, or engineering. The rating of the *Diplomarbeit* is included in the total rating.

At present, a specially appointed board of experts is tackling the problem of finding a universally applicable scheme based on the above model. This board is working on behalf of the Permanent Conference of Education Ministers of the Federal States and the Board of University Rectors (*Rektorenkonferenz*), whose recommendations will decide the future structure of the courses of study.

Curriculum for physicists studying for the graduation diploma. No unified scheme of study applicable to all the universities exists. Furthermore, the students enjoy considerable latitude in their choice of subjects. The following outline describes a course conforming approximately to that offered at the majority of the Federal German universities.

Up to the preliminary examination (*Vordiplom*), priority is given to basic instruction in experimental physics (both lectures and practicals), in mathematics and chemistry, and in theoretical mechanics.

After the preliminary examination, more specialized instruction, particularly in physics, is given. Emphasis is primarily laid upon theoretical physics. In general a cycle of lectures extending over four terms is held. These lectures cover electrodynamics, optics, thermodynamics and statistical mechanics, atomic physics and quantum mechanics. In addition, there are practicals for advanced students, in different areas of experimental and applied physics, lectures on different branches of experimental and applied physics, and study in the chosen special subject.

Having completed this course, the students start on their individual diploma research work (*Diplomarbeit*), either in the field of experimental or theoretical physics, work which takes them about three semesters. During this time, the candidate continues his studies in theoretical physics and also attends internal activities of the institutes, such as seminars and colloquia (reports followed by discussion). A typical detailed curriculum for diligent students might look as follows (curriculum at the University of Giessen):

Semester	Subject	Number of periods per week
First	Lectures in experimental physics	5–6
	Lectures in experimental chemistry	4
	Physics practical	6
	Lectures in mathematics, with exercises	10
Second	Lectures in experimental physics	5–6
	Lectures in experimental chemistry	4
	Physics practical	6
	Lectures in mathematics, with exercises	10
Third	Lectures in experimental physics (i.e., atomic structure I)	2
	Lectures in applied physics	2
	Lectures in mathematics, with exercises	6
	Lectures in theoretical physics, with exercises	5
Fourth	Lectures in experimental physics (i.e., atomic structure II)	2
	Lectures in applied physics	2
	Lectures in theoretical physics	5
	Chemistry practical	12

After the preliminary examination

Fifth	Physics practical for advanced students	6
	Lectures in theoretical physics, with exercises	5

54

Semester	Subject	Number of periods per week
Fifth	Lectures in experimental physics or special lecture	1
(Cont.)	Lectures in applied physics	2
	Lectures on optional subject	6
Sixth	Practical for advanced students	12
	Lectures in theoretical physics, with exercises	5
	Lectures in experimental physics	1
	Applied physics practical	4
	Lectures on optional subject	6
	Physicists' colloquium	2
Seventh	Lectures in theoretical physics	5
	Lectures in experimental physics	1
	Physicists' colloquium	2
	Issue of *Diplomarbeit* during term	
Eighth	Lectures in theoretical physics	5
	Diplomarbeit	whole time
	Physicists' colloquium	2
Ninth	*Diplomarbeit*	whole time
	Physicists' colloquium	2
Tenth	Completion of *Diplomarbeit*	whole time
	Physicists' colloquium	2
	Preparation for examination	

Mathematics requirements. Education in mathematics for physicists varies a great deal at the individual universities. While most professors of physics are of the opinion that at present the lectures on mathematics for students of physics contain far too much abstract mathematics, on the other hand the importance of theoretical physics is growing and simultaneously, therefore, the importance of mathematics for the physicist is increasing. For years a way out of this dilemma has been sought. At present, things are still in a state of flux.

The lecture on mathematics ought to contain fields of importance to the physicist, like theory of sets, series, differential and integral calculus of one and several variables, ordinary differential equations, elementary theory of a complex variable (analytical geometry), as well as elementary theory of groups, vector analysis (with theorems of Gauss, Green and Stokes), and numerical analysis.

Practical exercises. Special value is attached to practical work. In general, two students work together on the same problem. Prior to the *Vordiplom* there is a course of practical work for beginners which generally takes up three hours on two afternoons per week, and lasts two semesters. During this course a total number of approximately forty to fifty experiments are made. Prior to the *Hauptdiplom* there are practicals for advanced students and in special fields like HF physics, electronics, nuclear physics. Only by actually handling and working with instruments and apparatus can the students acquire a feel for physics. In addition it is for them an absolutely necessary preparation for their diploma and doctorate thesis. These practicals are, moreover, specially important for the future schoolmasters, of whose education more details are given in Chapter IV. Those interested in examples of practical work for beginners or advanced students may apply to the Deutsche Physikalische Gesellschaft, e.V. z. Hd. Hauptgeschäftsführer Herrn Dr. K. H. Riewe, im Haus W. C. Heraeus GmbH, 6450 Hanau, Postfach 369.

Moreover, reference is made to the books about practical work in physics listed in Appendix IX B2.

Lecture demonstrations. At the German universities all students of physics, whether taking physics as their major subject or as their subsidiary subject only (e.g., other students of natural sciences, students of medicine, engineering, veterinary medicine, agriculture, etc.), attend an introductory eight-hours experimental physics lecture course during their first and second semesters. In the course of this series of lectures, a great number of experiments are carried out at considerable expense in order to give the students a clear idea of physical phenomena and their conformity with natural laws. Frequently the course is divided in two, and the part for those studying physics as a major subject is held differently from the part for those taking it merely as a secondary subject.

Many universities stress the importance of enabling the student to see as many experiments as possible demonstrated, and, in other courses too, many experiments, some of them of a difficult nature, are undertaken. For example, a student may have the opportunity of observing some unique complex phenomena or having demonstrated to him the rather difficult task of measuring the speed of light. No generalizations can be made about these lectures, however.

Examples of experiments for basic lectures in physics are given in Appendix III B1.

The education of physicists in France

The 'propédeutique'. The young baccalaureat in science who desires to continue his studies has a choice between two separate educational paths: (a) the *propédeutique* organized by the universities, and (b) the *propédeutique* organized by the establishments of the secondary level (the *lycées*), some of which possess an extension into higher education in the form of the *propédeutique*.

All of the universities possess centres offering *propédeutique* instruction. There are nineteen universities in France, distributed over the whole country. Some possess annexes (called university colleges), however, so that altogether there are around thirty centres at which one can study at the level of the university *propédeutique*, which is open to every holder of the baccalaureat. There is no entrance examination. As a result, the classes in physics are generally quite large (250 students per instructor in the theoretical course, for example), and it is difficult to supervise the work of the students. The oral part of the course is given by the professor in the form of original lectures. It is quite unusual for the professor to follow a textbook. The students have to take notes and, at the end of the course, to understand them; their work is facilitated usually by multicopied course notes distributed by the professor. The exercises and the class discussions are conducted by assistants (students preparing their doctoral dissertations) or by monitors (students who are about to complete their work for the *licence*), who are supervised by the professor. The professor also has the task of evaluating the work of the students at the end of the year. Practical work is given in the laboratory by the assistant professors; the professor seldom intervenes in this.

Programmes of instruction in the university centres are uniform throughout France. The student chooses among three options, each of which lasts one year. The third of these options, called Physical, Chemical and Natural Sciences (SPCN), is for future naturalists and will be discussed in Chapter IV. Here we will consider the second option, intended for future physicists and chemists, and called Mathematics, Physics, Chemistry (MPC), and the first option, intended for future mathematicians and physicists, and called General Mathematics and Physics (MGP). The schedules are as follows:

Disciplines	Weekly schedule	
	MPC	MGP
Mathematics	6	12
Physics	5	3
Physics laboratory	3	3
Chemistry	3.5	—
Chemistry laboratory	3	—

The university year lasts about twenty-five weeks. The preceding schedules take account of course sessions and sessions for the correction of problems. Each week or each fortnight, the students have to complete an assignment, which is corrected. They also have an oral examination. All of the marks thus obtained, plus the examination at the end of the year, serve to determine the student's grade. The final examination consists of written tests (generally a problem to be solved in three or four hours), a practical part (measurements to be made in the laboratory), and an oral part (questions about the course). If he is successful, the student receives the *certificat de propédeutique*. The average grade obtained has to be above 10/20. If he fails, because his grades were unsatisfactory, the candidate can retake the corresponding test in the following October. He keeps the grades obtained in the other parts of the course.

There are also about seventy centres of the *propédeutique* run by the *lycées*. The class sizes are smaller (about sixty students) and are, in principle, open to every holder of the baccalaureat. The educational programmes of the *propédeutique* of the *lycées* are uniform throughout France. They last two years and consist of three options.

The third, called Option C, is devoted to the natural sciences. We shall come back to it, but now we shall discuss Option B, which is for future chemists and physicists, and Option A, which is for future mathematicians and physicists. (One sees in this the analogy with the three sections of the *propédeutique* of the universities). The weekly schedules (in hours) are the following:

Disciplines	Option A	Option B
Mathematics	16	10
Physics	4	6
Physics laboratory	1	2
Chemistry	3	5
Chemistry laboratory	1	2

At the end of his studies, the student can present himself for the examinations of the *propédeutique* of the university. The *lycée*, not being a part of the university system, cannot organize examinations or give degrees. But these students rarely take the examination of the *propédeutique* of the universities. Instead they nearly always take the competitive examinations for entrance to the *grandes écoles*.

There are thus four programmes of instruction in physics at the level of the *propédeutique* to be discussed in this report. Two of them are taught in the *propédeutique* of the *lycées*, and two in that of the universities. (All neglect modern physics.) Option B of the *propédeutique* of the *lycées* is the most interesting example of these and is described in Appendix III C1. One can form an idea of the level attained by the best students by examining a problem (Appendix III C2) which had to be solved in two hours by those who desired to enter L'Ecole Superieure d'Electricité in 1960. The whole test lasted four hours and consisted of two problems at this level of difficulty.

Laboratory instruction is well developed in the *propédeutique* of the universities; the classes of the *lycées* place less emphasis upon it. In the universities the students generally have twenty laboratory sessions of three hours each during the year of the *propédeutique* (Appendix III C3). Explanatory sheets are given to them before the session, and they are supposed to turn in a report of their work at the end. The organization of laboratory instruction is generally the following: an assistant professor, placed under the authority of the professor, is responsible for the laboratory rooms and for the apparatus; he handles the credits and supervises the carrying out of the experiments and the work of the students. The students work in groups of two (or sometimes three), under the effective direction of an assistant who is supposed to maintain the apparatus set-ups entrusted to him (a dozen) and to guide the efforts of the students. In order to accommodate 240 students, it is necessary to provide six sessions of three hours each during the week. Thus, at each session, forty students work in pairs on twenty set-ups. They move from one experiment to another, session by session, until they have completed all twenty. At each session, two assistants at least are required to supervise the students and correct their work.

In mathematics, the programme of the *propédeutique* of the universities contains (Appendix III C1) substantial treatment of algebra (matrix calculus), analysis (power series, Fourier series, classical differential equations, partial differential equation of a vibrating string, multiple integrals, vector analysis), and vector geometry (the study of curves and of some simple surfaces). Furthermore, the students are introduced into the techniques of numerical calculations (the solving of equations, primitives, etc.). There have occurred during the past several years efforts to reform the methods of teaching, as the detailed text of the mathematics programme taught in the MGP will show. The programme in the MPC is less crowded with topics and remains much more classical. It is essentially the professional mathematicians who determine the programme and arrange the instruction. The physicists are not consulted and are rather unhappy about the state of affairs, believing that the mathematical programmes of both the MPC and the MGP are too much oriented toward modern mathematics and less useful for applications in physics. A reasonable compromise should be found. The mathematical programmes of the *lycées* are not fundamentally different from those of the *propédeutique* of the universities.

The Universities. Certificats d'Etudes Supérieures (CES). Let us now consider the situation of the student who has just obtained the certificate of the *propédeutique* after a year of work. His next step is to prepare himself to qualify for a certain number of certificates of higher education by pursuing studies that are much more specialized than those of the *propédeutique*. Theoretically, he can choose the certificates that he desires. Actually, as we shall see, his choice is limited by his vocational aims as well as by the hierarchy of knowledge; he must understand mathematics before attempting to study electricity.

In large part, a certificate of higher education corresponds to theoretical and laboratory instruction provided by a professorial Chair of the university. Theoretically, each Chair ought to organize the courses, the exercises, and the laboratory experiments corresponding to a certificate. In fact, the situation is not quite that, although it approaches that ideal. All of the universities have instructional programmes corresponding to the basic certificates in the following list, which is limited to the CES for physics and to some in mathematics: Mathematical Techniques of Physics, General Mechanics, Mathematical Methods of Physics, Electricity, Electronics, Electrotechnics, Optics, Thermodynamics and Physical Mechanics, Experimental Physics, Physical Crystallography, and—a certificate soon to be added—Technology. All of the CES have the same programme throughout the country. Each university is obliged to arrange the instructional programmes and recruit competent professors.

The universities can also offer instruction corresponding to other certificates if they have professors who are specialists in those disciplines. Thus, one also finds CES in: Theoretical Physics, Electronic Computers, Particle Physics, Mechanics of Vibrations, Plasma Physics, Solid State Physics, Nuclear Reactor Physics, Energetics, and Electron Microscopy and Diffraction. The corresponding courses have a structure comparable to that of the certificates in the first list, but the programme has not been nationally codified.

The preparation of each CES lasts for one year (occasionally CES are prepared in a semester). The instruction consists of about three hours of course per week and, in general, one session of exercises for two hours each week. The programme thus lasts about 125 hours. It is, to be sure, a very 'dense' course, and the student has to spend a great deal of time outside of class to understand the course and absorb the knowledge.

Practical instruction is provided in a weekly laboratory session of three hours, which means that around seventy-five hours of laboratory work are involved in the preparation of a certificate. The examination consists of a written test (a problem), a laboratory exercise that duplicates an experiment performed during the year (with different constants, to test the laboratory know-how of the candidate), and an oral interrogation. Thus the preparation of one CES requires around two hundred hours of official work. It is theoretically possible to prepare three CES a year, but it is rarely done, and most students prepare only two.

The programme of the official CES of the first list, although organized by each university, is codified at the national level (Appendix III C4). In contrast with the official programme for the *propédeutique*, that for the CES is very brief and is stated only in broad outline (see also Appendix IX C1). This leaves a great deal of initiative to the holders of Chairs. The text of the official programme is there simply to facilitate the transfer of a student from one university to another and to fix an average national standard. Appendix III C5 indicates the level of the work by the text of a written test recently set for the CES in electronics at the University of Paris. The students had to solve the problem in four hours.

Laboratory instruction connected with a CES approaches research as closely as possible. Most often, apparatus that once served in the preparation of a thesis is used for practical work. By this means, one can have the students do interesting experiments without the expenditure of considerable funds for equipment. The organization of the instructional laboratory is comparable to that of the *propédeutique*. There is no official list of experiments, nor an official laboratory manual. Appendix III C6 contains, for the purpose of illustration, a list of experiments performed by the candidate for the CES in electronics at the University of Paris.

Thus the student who sets out from the *propédeutique* is essentially engaged in collecting CES. When he has five of them, he will be awarded the degree of *licencié*. This *licence* is called the *licence libre* and can be composed of any five of the CES. If he does not want to exert the effort to acquire the *licence libre*, he can obtain a Diploma of Higher Technique (DEST) with only two CES, but he has to choose a correct combination (for example, technology and electronics).

62

The grandes écoles. Pedagogically speaking, a *grande école* differs little from a university. They teach mathematics there, the various branches of physics, and also technical subjects (which are never, or hardly ever, taught by the universities, which confine themselves to pure science). The *grandes écoles* have courses, exercise sessions, and laboratory sessions. The programmes are analogous to those described above. The instructional laboratories are run like those of the universities, but, without exception, they are not connected with research laboratories. The 'oral' instruction is given by lecturers, who simply give courses and do their professional work elsewhere (most often in the large public or private research centres).

The student who has succeeded in competitive examinations in entering a *grande école* carries on studies comparable to those for the *licence* at a university. After three or four years, depending upon the *école*, he obtains, if his grades are satisfactory, the diploma of an engineer of '*Ecole de ...*'.

When does the student become a physicist? In France, the profession of 'physicist' does not exist officially. The scientific staffs are termed 'engineers' or 'researchers'. To enter that profession, one has to possess at least a *licence* or an engineering diploma of the *grandes écoles*. To compare this with the American system, these diplomas are situated at a level between that of Bachelor of Science and that of Master of Science. The recipients of the best *licences* and the engineering graduates of the best colleges can be compared to the Master of Engineering of the large American universities.

The education of physicists in the U.S.S.R.

The training of physicists in Soviet universities includes, but is not confined to, training at the first level; the actual level is considerably higher.

The training of specialists in physics in the U.S.S.R. takes place at the university faculties of physics. There are two qualifications for physicists: 'Physicist (teacher of physics)' (five-year course) and 'Physicist...', followed by the name of a particular branch of physics; for example, 'Physicist (specialist in molecular physics)' (course five-and-a-half years). The universities turn out physicists specializing in any of the following sixteen branches of physics: Theoretical physics; Low-temperature physics; Molecular physics; Optics and spectroscopy; X-rays and the physics of metals; Magnetism; Solid state physics; Physics of semi-conductors; Electricity; Nuclear physics; Radio physics; Electronics; High-polymer physics; Physics of the atmosphere; Geophysics; Biophysics.

The university physics course takes eleven semesters. In the first three years the first semester lasts eighteen weeks and the second sixteen weeks; in the fourth year, twenty-five and twenty weeks; in the fifth year, eighteen and fourteen weeks; in the sixth year there is one semester of thirteen weeks. The total number of obligatory academic hours (excluding practical work in the special subject, on the graduation thesis and on the State examinations) is 4,780.

As in all institutes of higher education there are three main types of studies at the university faculties of physics: lectures, laboratory work (practical) and seminars (applied), the main emphasis being on lectures. Examinations are held in all the disciplines and tests are set in a number of subdivisions of particular disciplines, in subdivisions of the laboratory practical work and for the seminar work.

The following disciplines, determining the graduates' specialization as physicists, are pursued.

Disciplines	No. of hours
Higher mathematics	
Mathematical analysis	480
Analytical geometry and higher algebra	150
Methods of mathematical physics	188
General physics	
Mechanics, molecular physics, electricity and optics	372
Atomic physics	108
Nuclear physics	64
Practical physics	526
Fundamentals of electrotechnology and radiotechnology	120
Theoretical physics	
Theoretical mechanics	120
Field theory and electronic physics	120
Thermodynamics and statistical physics	114
Quantum mechanics	125
Specialization: study	470

Disciplines	No. of hours
Specialization: laboratory work	450
Selected special papers	156
Mathematics of computation and electronic computers	42

The syllabuses of the general and theoretical physics courses are given in Appendixes III D1 and III D2. The disciplines determining the graduates' field of specialization are enumerated in Appendix III D3. The courses on general physics, theoretical physics and the special subject are staggered: the higher mathematics and general physics courses start in the first semester, the special subjects are studied in the sixth to tenth semesters.

The general physics course. General physics, as one of the basic academic disciplines taught in the faculties of physics and of physics-and-mathematics, must cover all divisions of this extensive field of natural science. Students in both faculties mentioned are required to complete the full course, irrespective of their professional aim or special subject.

For this reason the syllabuses (Appendix III D1) laid down under the academic curriculum for the general, atomic and nuclear physics courses are combined into a single syllabus for a course entitled 'General Physics', subdivided into the following parts: Part I (mechanics, molecular physics, electricity and magnetism, optics); Part II, Atomic physics; Part III, Nuclear physics.

The number of teaching periods allocated to each of these parts in the curriculum remains unchanged. The universities are entitled, at their own discretion, to call on various departments to cover the different parts of the single General Physics course.

The universities themselves are responsible for allocating the syllabus material to lectures, seminars and laboratory classes, except that the number of periods spent on the syllabus shall not exceed the total number allocated by the curriculum to Parts I, II and III of the course respectively.

The practical course accompanying the general physics course runs parallel with the corresponding division of the lecture part of the course. In the practical part as much independence as possible must be allowed in the student's work (work on theoretical material essential for completing the exercise set).

Practical work. Practical work for the first part of the general physics course is done in the first two years. In the fifth, sixth and seventh semesters the students do their practical work in the special subjects (atomic physics thirty-six hours, nuclear physics thirty-six hours, radio physics forty-eight hours). This practical work corresponds to the second and third parts of the general physics course. The level of practical work in the special subjects is much higher than in general physics, and calls for considerable theoretical knowledge and experimental skill. The practical course is preceded by work in the turnery, fitting shop, glass-blowing shop and radio repair shop.

The subjects covered by the practical syllabus for the general physics course are listed in general terms in Appendix III D3. Appendix III D4 gives the actual list of laboratory work performed at the University of Moscow. Students perform forty-eight exercises over the two years of the general physics course—twelve exercises in each semester. One exercise in each section of the syllabus is obligatory; the rest are at the tutor's discretion. A preliminary talk on practical work is given as an introduction (elements of error theory and processing measurement results). The student gradually masters the technique of computing with slide rule and arithmometer at the beginning of his practical work and submits test work to the tutor. The test on work with the slide rule is not included in the forty-eight exercises.

In the first semester, exercises are on mechanics (with the exception of the section on oscillations); in addition, the student completes very simple exercises on molecular physics. In the second semester, exercises are on the oscillations and wave section and on the molecular physics section. Practical photographic work is done during the first or second semester. The assignments indicated in the syllabus are completed in full, taking twelve periods and counting as two exercises. In the third semester students work on the electricity and magnetism sections, and in the fourth on the optics section.

The student knows which exercise he is to perform a week in advance. The assistant of the Chair first discovers whether the student is sufficiently familiar with the subject in question. If not, the student is not allowed to work with apparatus, but the assistant of the Chair suggests essential reading. After completing the measurements the student must calculate the required results and show this to the assistant while still in the laboratory. Measurements made only according to instructions, without understanding the approach to the solution of the experimental task set, do not count. Whenever possible, the final record also is made in the laboratory. In this case the record of the test and the mark is entered in the record book on the same day as the exercise is completed. If the final report requires further work (constructing curves, introducing numerical corrections and so forth), it need not be submitted until the next class.

Apart from the general and special practical work, obligatory on students of all specializations, the syllabus includes further practical work in the faculty of the chosen special subject from the fourth year onwards. In the fifth year, this work acquires the character of scientific research.

Theoretical physics. The syllabus for the course in theoretical physics (Appendix III D2) merely lists the main topics to be covered in the course; the sequence in which they are taught is left largely to the lecturer. The syllabus includes the most important theoretical questions of a general character and the most important concrete results and applications of general theory. It does not include matters of interest mainly to theoretical physicists. It is so designed as to permit consecutive exposition of all parts of theoretical physics starting with postulates of as general a nature as possible and avoiding parallelism.

Specialization. At the end of the third year the students are divided into two streams, one preparing for work in research institutes, factory laboratories, design offices and so forth, the other for school teaching. In the eighth and ninth semesters the students are directed to practical work in their special subject ('vocational practice'). Students in the first stream (those specializing in one branch of physics) take their 'vocational practice' in the laboratories of the university or of a scientific research body such as the Academy of Sciences, where they perform the duties of established staff members of the laboratory concerned.

The title and scope of the special courses for selection (Appendix III D3) and of the optional courses are established annually by the faculty committee. The syllabuses for these courses are discussed and approved by the same committee.

The students of high schools specializing in physics pass State examinations.

In universities, moreover, they defend a thesis whereupon they obtain a diploma which entitles them to teach physics in secondary schools or to conduct research work in the research institutes. Those of higher abilities are admitted to universities, pedagogic and other colleges as laboratory or teaching assistants.

Any graduate has the right to be admitted to post-graduate scholarship.

Faculties of physics. At the moment there are faculties of physics in forty universities in the U.S.S.R. The number of students in the faculties of physics and of physics-and-mathematics in the academic year 1960/61 was 30,560. In addition, there were 11,480 students in the faculties of engineering and mathematics. The best academic physicists and mathematicians in the country are concentrated in the university faculties of physics and of physics-and-mathematics, where many academicians, corresponding members of the Academies of Sciences and other eminent scientists, hold Chairs or lectureships. Since the intake of the physics faculties consists of talented young people, the universities are able to fulfil their aim of producing highly qualified physicists. Many of the country's leading scientists are university physics graduates.

Undergraduate education of professional physicists in the United Kingdom

Honours physics degree. The general level of attainment required for a degree in a British university is broadly the same throughout the country and the organization of courses in the universities follows with a few exceptions—notably Cambridge—a very similar pattern.[1] Typical details are given below and in Appendix III E for

1. *The Scientific Education of Physicists.* The Institute of Physics and the Physical Society (published annually).

the courses leading to the honours degrees of the universities of Bristol, Manchester and Imperial College, London; for Manchester the syllabuses of the second and third years of the course are given in full in Appendix III E1.

The basic academic qualification for a professional physicist in the United Kingdom is still the bachelor's degree of B.Sc. or B.A. and, although a large number of students now stay in the university to take post-graduate degrees, some of even the very best students still leave at the end of the course for the bachelor's degree. These students obtain such training in research that they may need in the early years of their first professional appointments. The universities, therefore, strive to contain within the bachelor's course an essential training that will permit a man to practise as a professional physicist.

The most important of the degrees of the universities of England, Wales and Northern Ireland is the honours degree in a single subject. In Scotland, the position is slightly different in that, in general, the universities offer not only a similar degree in a single subject but also a degree in a double subject that traditionally is as highly regarded. Thus a professional physicist in Scotland may have taken the honours B.Sc. in physics or the honours M.A. in mathematics and natural philosophy. For the present purpose, however, it is sufficient to concentrate upon the practice in England and Wales.

Most university physics departments would offer more than one kind of first degree. These might typically be as follows, all the courses requiring three years of study but being of different standards of difficulty in physics: (a) the honours degree in physics; (b) a general honours degree in physics and one other subject, usually mathematics; or (c) an ordinary/pass degree usually in two subjects of which physics would be one.

The overwhelmingly important degree for the future professional physicist is the first of these. In most universities students are accepted direct from school into a three-year course leading to the honours degree in physics. Similarly, students—perhaps, in general, the slightly less gifted—may be directly admitted to the course for the general honours degree, but a university may require all its students to start first in a general or pass course from which the more able will later be recruited into the honours degree course in physics. Although it is possible, in the same way, for a student to choose to enter, straight from school, the course leading to the ordinary or pass degree, many students find their way into this third course after entering one of the other two and finding the pace too difficult.

An honours degree course is a co-ordinated and planned course in physics and such subsidiary subjects as may be considered by the university to be necessary. The distribution of hours in such a course would be along the lines indicated in the following table which relates to the University of Bristol but which may be taken as broadly typical of most other universities.

Subjects	Year		
	First	Second	Third
Theoretical physics	100	170	160
Experimental physics	200	300	300
Pure mathematics	120	—	—
Applied mathematics	50	70	—
Theoretical chemistry	—	70	—
Practical chemistry	—	140	—

A student entering this course must take physics and two subsidiary subjects from the three mentioned above. Normally, the subsidiary subjects would be pure and applied mathematics but a small proportion of the students take chemistry instead of applied mathematics. The hours quoted are minimum hours and in experimental physics most students would devote more time than is quoted. At the Imperial College, London, a slightly different arrangement applies and it may be useful to give the subjects of the course in greater detail. All students at Imperial College take mathematics in their first year for a total of 195 hours (very similar to the 170 hours at Bristol). The physics of the course is as follows:

Subject	Hours
First year	
Classical mechanics	25
General physics	20
Vibrations and waves	25
Electricity and magnetism	35
Heat and thermodynamics	15
Atomic and nuclear physics	20

70

Subject	Hours
Second year	
Geometrical and optical physics	25
Electricity and magnetism (electromagnetic theory; electronics; magnetic and dielectric properties of matter)	55
Heat and thermodynamics (thermodynamics and statistical mechanics; kinetic theory)	35
Atomic physics (spectroscopy; discharge physics; electron physics)	35
Nuclear physics	20
Special relativity and quantum mechanics	20
Mathematics applied to physics	10
Third year	
Solid state physics (crystal lattice theory; electronic structure of metals; electron conduction and emission; transport and mechanical properties of solids)	54
Nuclear physics	25
Quantum mechanics	20
Electricity and magnetism	15
Mathematics applied to physics	15

In the third year students are also required to take either three or four of the following courses, the choice being made by themselves.

Subject	Hours
Optics	15
Photoelectronics	15
Spectroscopy	18
Electron diffraction	15
High energy nuclear physics	15
Cosmic ray physics	15
Acoustic and vibrational physics	15
Rock magnetism	15
Plasma physics	12
Physics of clouds	15

The practical work of the course is 200 hours in the first year, 250 hours in the second year and 240 hours in the third year.

The broad similarity of courses is shown by the corresponding details of the University of Manchester. Here the mathematics totals only 113 hours and is spread over two years. The physics course is as follows:

Subject	Hours
First year	
Classical mechanics	44
Vibrations and waves	25
Relativity	11
Electricity and magnetism	44
Properties of matter	40
Second year	
Quantum mechanics	26
Atomic physics	27
Optics	30
Electricity and magnetism	44
Thermodynamics	20
Electronics	22
Third year	
Quantum mechanics	35
Nuclear physics	35
Solid state physics	42
Experimental methods	36

In addition, in the third year, lectures are given on special topics but these are not examined. The practical work is of about 150 hours in the first year, in the second year 150 hours plus about 175 hours on electronics, and in the third year 300 hours.

Practical work. Practical work, i.e., experimental work done by students, has traditionally been a most important part of British courses, but in some quarters it is now being challenged as being of less inherent value in training than British tradition would suggest. The usual practice in the first two years of the course is for practical work to consist of fairly standardized experiments, the apparatus for which would generally remain set up in the laboratory through-out the term to be used by successive students who would commonly work in pairs. In the third year it is common for students to work individually and to do only four or five experiments in the year, these experiments being no longer of a standardized kind but more in the nature of minor research investigations.

Programmes at Cambridge. In Cambridge, as in Oxford, the selection of students for admission to the university is the responsibility of the colleges and not of individual departments. A student whose aim is to qualify as a physicist would take the Natural Sciences Tripos course and examinations, which are in two parts. Part I, on which a degree can be obtained, is a two-year course. The examination is taken at the end of the second year although the abler students compress the actual course into less than the full two years. In this course, at least three subjects must be taken. After Part I, a student may be accepted into Part II physics which is a specialized physics course. It is the Part II examination which is usually equated to the honours degrees of other British universities. The coverage of knowledge of physics achieved by a student who passes in Part II is roughly similar to that of the course described for Manchester, but it will be clear from the nature of the organization of the first two years that the Cambridge student has had a broader initial training than he would get in some other universities. On the other hand, it may be argued that this breadth must be gained at the cost of some loss of depth.

General honours and pass degrees. There is some difference of opinion about the place of the general honours degree in British universities. It is well recognized as a very useful degree for teachers of science in grammar schools, but it would be considered by most people to be a less suitable degree than the honours physics degree for a student who wished ultimately to have a career in research in physics. As a broad indication of the standard attained, one could assume that in the two subjects of, say, physics and mathematics, a student taking the three-year general honours course could reach a standard roughly similar in each subject to that obtained by honours graduates at the end of the second year.

The place of the ordinary or pass degree is different. For a good many years in many universities it has not been highly regarded and, indeed, thought of by many people as the degree granted to students who fail to reach the minimum standard for the award of an honours degree, or merely useful for students who have been diverted from an honours course at the end of the first or second year. In the past few years, however, several universities have made a thorough revision of their ordinary degree courses, and Manchester is one of them. There it is considered to be a good degree

73

for certain types of student, less taxing in some respects than the honours course but an appropriate and well-planned preparation for a scientific career, not usually in original research. As an indication of the standard that is reached, the syllabuses for the third year of the Manchester pass degree are given as Appendix III E2.

The Colleges of Advanced Technology, already referred to in Appendix I E1 have for some years been providing courses of degree standard in physics, leading to the Diploma in Technology. These institutions are now to become universities and their awards will in future be degrees. A feature of the courses of most of these colleges has been that they are of the 'sandwich type', a student spending six months in each year in the college and the other six months in carefully selected and supervised work in industry. A typical scheme for a course of this kind is the course for Diploma in Technology in Applied Physics of Northampton College of Advanced Technology, London, given below.

The curriculum consists of twenty-one teaching weeks per session for the first, second and third years, and twenty-seven teaching weeks per session for the fourth year.

Subjects	Hours per week (average)		
	Lectures	Tutorials	Laboratory
First year			
Physics	5	2	5
Mathematics	4	1	—
Chemistry	$1\frac{1}{2}$	—	$1\frac{1}{2}$
Engineering drawing	$\frac{1}{2}$	—	$1\frac{1}{2}$
Social studies	3	—	—
	14	3	8
Second year			
Physics ⎱	6	$2\frac{1}{2}$	$5\frac{1}{2}$
Applied physics ⎰			
Mathematics	4	1	—
Organic chemistry	$\frac{1}{2}$	—	—
Metallurgy	$\frac{1}{2}$	—	—
Electrotechnology	$1\frac{1}{2}$	—	$\frac{1}{2}$
Social studies	2	—	—
History and philosophy of science	1	—	—
	$15\frac{1}{2}$	$3\frac{1}{2}$	6

Subjects	Hours per week (average)		
	Lectures	Tutorials	Laboratory
Third year			
Physics ⎫	8	2	7
Applied physics ⎭			
Mathematics	3	1	—
Industrial economics and organization	1	—	—
Social studies	2	—	—
	14	3	7
Fourth year			
Physics	4	2 ⎫	3
Applied physics	4	— ⎭	
Project	—	—	7
Mathematics	1	—	—
Industrial economics and organization	1	—	—
Social studies	2	—	—
	12	2	10

Undergraduate education of professional physicists in the U.S.A.

Objectives of higher education. The objectives of higher education in the United States at the undergraduate level are (a) to provide each student with opportunities for liberal studies that will enable him to become a broadly educated person, and (b) to give him an educational preparation for a career at the bachelor's level or for advanced study toward a higher degree. It is important to note that both of these objectives influence the pattern of undergraduate education in the United States, although in varying degrees from one institution to another. Unlike the situation in some other countries, where formal liberal education is essentially completed before entrance to the university and where university education is limited to professional studies, the undergraduate programmes of even the technological universities in the United States lay considerable stress upon liberal education. Required studies in the humanities and social sciences take up roughly 20 per cent of the four undergraduate years of the science student, and elected studies in these areas or requirements for the study of foreign languages may raise the percentage to 30 per cent or more. Correspondingly, students of the humanities and social sciences are required to study the sciences and mathematics.

The student usually enters the college or university at the age of 17 or 18. To graduate with a degree of Bachelor of Arts or Bachelor of Science, he must ordinarily complete four academic years of study. (Unusually talented students can enter college at an earlier age and can qualify for graduation in a shorter time by independent study and by demonstrating their command of required subjects by passing 'advanced standing' examinations. Brilliant physics students have been known to complete their undergraduate sojourn in about two academic years.) The four academic years, including eight semesters, extend over a little less than four calendar years in most institutions, but can occupy as little as two and two-thirds calendar years in institutions that follow a more concentrated trimester schedule in which three academic semesters are included in one calendar year.

Requirements for the bachelor's degree. The semester-hour is usually the unit of credit in which academic courses are measured. A course of one semester-hour is one that meets for lectures or discussion once a week for about fifty minutes during a semester of roughly fifteen weeks. Most science and mathematics courses are three or four semester-hour courses. (Laboratory work is often depreciated in the granting of credit: a weekly three-hour laboratory session, meeting for a semester, is often given one semester-hour of credit.) The work load of the science student is a minimum of about forty-eight hours per week during the undergraduate years: roughly sixteen hours of lectures and class discussion, six to ten hours of laboratory work, and the remainder spent in study.

For graduation, most institutions require the student to obtain around 120–130 semester-hours of credit, or the local equivalent of this number, with satisfactory academic standing—usually at least a 'C' average on a scale of grades on which 'A' is the highest mark and 'D' the lowest passing mark. Although a few institutions, before awarding degrees, examine their students in all subjects studied, a comprehensive examination of this kind at the end of the undergraduate years is not typical in the United States. The course and its examinations are usually the milestones of academic progress in undergraduate education.

Four survey institutions. The physics departments of four institutions of higher learning in the United States have kindly provided for this report detailed information about their physics programmes to supplement more general information taken from other sources. These institutions are the University of California at Berkeley (Berkeley, California), Columbia University (New York, New York), Massachusetts Institute of Technology (Cambridge, Massachusetts) and Swarthmore College (Swarthmore, Pennsylvania). The first three are universities, offering work leading to bachelor's, master's, and doctor's degrees in physics. Swarthmore is a liberal-arts college, offering a bachelor's degree programme in physics. California is a state university; the other three are private institutions. Many other colleges and universities in the United States could have provided equally valid information about their strong programmes in physics. The four named above are representative of high-quality education in physics, however. They also differ among themselves in interesting ways—reflecting the diversity of higher education in the United States.

Minimal requirements for a bachelor's degree in physics. The minimal four-year undergraduate programme of instruction for a physics major at the four institutions surveyed contains an average of forty-three semester-hours of physics, nineteen semester-hours of mathematics, and nine semester-hours of chemistry. (Nationally, the undergraduate preparation for graduate work in physics requires around thirty-six semester-hours of physics and eighteen semester-hours of mathematics. The programme of preparation for high-school physics teaching and other less intensive undergraduate programmes in physics—offered by many liberal-arts colleges—require around twenty-six semester-hours of physics and eighteen semester-hours of mathematics.) In addition, the student may elect additional courses in these subjects, and usually does so to the extent of spending about 75 per cent of the four years in work in these subjects. He must also satisfy the requirements in the humanities and social sciences, and may elect additional courses in those areas. The table below indicates roughly the minimal requirements in physics, mathematics, and chemistry in semester-hours for a bachelor's degree with a major in physics. Appendix III F1 contains the detailed minimal course requirements at these institutions.

Subject	California[1]	Columbia	MIT	Swarthmore[2]
Physics (total)	34	41	56	40
General physics, including laboratory[3]	12	13	20	8
Mechanics	5	6	4	8
Electricity and magnetism	6	6	—	4
Electromagnetic radiation including physical optics	3	3	4	4
Thermodynamics and statistical mechanics	—	—	4	—
Experimental physics[3]	2	4	12	—[4]
Quantum mechanics and atomic physics	6	6	8	4
Other physics	—	3	4	12
Mathematics (total)	16	18	18	24
Calculus, analytical geometry	16	12	9	16
Differential equations	—	3	3	—
Other mathematics	—	3	6	8
Chemistry (total)	10	6	13	8
General chemistry	10	6	10	8
Other chemistry	—	—	3	—
Other subjects in science, electrical engineering, or mathematics (electronic networks, etc.)	—	—	10	—

1. Note that in addition to the required courses listed here, other courses (three semester-hours of thermodynamics, two additional hours of experimental physics, two of other physics, three of differential equations, and three of other mathematics) are recommended to physics students at the University of California and are usually elected by them.
2. The honours programme for physics majors.
3. One semester-hour of laboratory represents two or three clock hours.
4. All of the Swarthmore physics courses have laboratory work associated with them.

The general physics course (*introductory course*). The objectives of the general physics course, which introduces the student to the study of physics at the university, are usually assumed to be these: (a) to impart knowledge of the underlying, unifying principles of physics that can be rigorously expressed in mathematical terms, and that are powerful and widely applicable tools in the expression and solution of problems in nature; (b) to convey to the student some of the curiosity of the physicist concerning the physical world; (c) to enable him to learn the limitations and scope of the descriptions and interpretations of physics; (d) to give him an understanding of the historical development of physics; (e) to introduce him to the phenomena of physics and to the precise methods of measurement in physics; and (f) to develop in him certain skills —verbal, mathematical and manipulative.

At the Conference on Improving the Quality and Effectiveness of Introductory Physics Courses, held at Carleton College in September 1957, under the sponsorship of the American Association of Physics Teachers with the support of the General Electric Company, teachers of introductory courses were urged to reduce the number of topics in the course so that greater depth and rigour could be achieved:

'Physics, as a body of knowledge, is now far too extensive to receive adequate general coverage in an introductory course. The instructor must not sacrifice depth and understanding by attempting to cover too many topics in encyclopaedic fashion. As one of our colleagues has well said, "Let us uncover physics, not cover it".

'It was the opinion of the conference that a satisfactory introductory physics course could be constructed around the following seven basic principles and concepts and the material leading up to them:

'1. Conservation of momentum.

'2. Conservation of mass and energy.

'3. Conservation of charge.

'4. Waves.

'5. Fields.

'6. The molecular structure of matter.

'7. The structure of the atom.

'Lest this list appear too brief, we point out that the discussions of such topics as Newton's laws of motion would ordinarily be included in the development of the principles of conservation of energy and of momentum at an introductory level'.[1]

Additional topics named by the conference for enrichment of the course included the electromagnetic theory of radiation, the second principle of thermodynamics, the special theory of relativity, and quantum theory.

The general physics course for physics majors[2] varies in duration

1. 'Improving the Quality and Effectiveness of Introductory Physics Courses', *American Journal of Physics*, Vol. 25, 1957. See also the articles by Holton, Michels and Whaley in that issue of the *Journal*.
2. G. Holton, 'On the Teaching of Physics as one of the Basic Sciences at University Level', *Contemporary Physics*, Vol. 4, No. 6 and Vol. 5, No. 1, 1963.

from one institution to another from two to four semesters during the first two undergraduate years. The trend is toward four-semester courses. The course is accompanied by the study of calculus and differential equations, and increasing use is made of these in formulating the principles of physics and in solving problems as the course progresses. The elements of the course are: (a) lectures, usually accompanied by physics demonstrations; (b) recitation or quiz sessions; (c) laboratory work; (d) examinations.

The lectures are given two or three times per week to classes that, in the universities, range in size from 100 to 300 students. There is a tendency to increase the size of lecture classes these days as enrolments increase. The limit is set by the size of existing lecture rooms and by the ability of the students to hear and see. The order of topics generally follows that in a textbook. To illustrate the organization and the pace of the lectures, Appendix III F2 contains the schedule for the courses Physics C1006, C1007, C1008, at Columbia University in the autumn of 1961/62. The lecturer seldom follows the textbook closely, but rather carries out the discussion as he thinks best, occasionally introducing topics that are not in the textbook and often omitting topics that are. Mimeographed notes and problems are rather routinely distributed to the students to supplement the textbook. Occasionally, if the lecturer is writing a new textbook, the whole course may be taught from mimeographed notes, which are sold, as textbooks and laboratory manuals are, by the college or university bookstore. Demonstrations by the lecturer are given during the lecture period, but the emphasis on these varies considerably from one lecturer to another. Some place heavy emphasis on demonstrations in their teaching; the lecture bench is covered with demonstration apparatus during their lectures. Others, of a more theoretical bent, seldom perform demonstrations. Most lecturers give at least one or two demonstrations each week.[1]

The use of television is being tried in lecture rooms. At a few universities, closed-circuit television is used to give demonstrations by a single lecturer to students in several different classrooms at

1. R. M. Sutton, *Demonstration Experiments in Physics*, New York, McGraw-Hill Book Company, 1938.
V. E. Eaton, *Proceedings of the Wesleyan Conference on Lecture Demonstrations*, 1959. (Copies may be obtained from the editor at Wesleyan University, Middletown, Connecticut.)

the same time, as a means of handling large classes in introductory physics. More commonly, closed-circuit television—requiring a portable television camera and several television receivers in the room—is used as an 'electronic magnifier' so that large classes can see the demonstration of small objects such as meter scales, etc. Optical projection is also being increasingly resorted to, usually by means of large stage overhead projectors.[1]

Recitation or quiz sections contain smaller numbers of students (twenty to thirty) and meet once or twice a week to discuss problem solutions, to review the principles discussed during the lectures, to clear up difficulties and answer the students' questions, and to conduct short examinations. The problem solutions are often submitted to the teacher, graded, and returned to the student. It should be noted that a serious didactic purpose exists in most undergraduate teaching: the teacher is there to teach the student. Both student and teacher take this purpose seriously—occasionally to the detriment of the student's later adjustment to more independent work, in the opinion of some observers. Conferences between student and teacher are a not uncommon supplement to the meetings of the recitation section as an informal means of clearing up difficulties for the student. It is appropriate here to remark that, with rare exceptions, physics professors can be approached by students without fear of rebuff. The professor expects his students to have a proper regard for his time, but he does not look upon the difficulties of students as unworthy of his attention.

Laboratory work in the introductory physics course varies from one institution to another between two extremes: the 'free' laboratory, and the highly organized and directed laboratory. The free laboratory is one in which the student either chooses subjects for experiments himself or selects them from a list of possibilities supplied by the instructor. The student then works out a plan of attack on the problem, assembles or builds the apparatus, and carries out an experimental investigation, keeping a laboratory notebook and conferring with the instructor when serious difficulties arise. A minimum of direction is given by the instructor, and the student

1. W. Eppenstein, *The Overhead Projector in the Physics Lecture*. Troy, Bookstore, Rensselaer Polytechnic Institute, 1961.

laboratory resembles as nearly as possible a research laboratory. There is no set schedule, the experiments sometimes requiring a month or more of laboratory sessions.

The advantage of the free laboratory, of course, is that it represents more nearly what physicists do in their laboratories and allows the student to explore an experimental problem in depth. It does this at the cost of a lessened range of experiments and with increased expenditure of supervisory time of competent experimentalists. Novice instructors require a great deal of supervision to run this kind of a laboratory. Provision of shop facilities, storage of apparatus between sessions, maintenance of a special stockroom, etc., also create problems.

The other extreme is the highly organized laboratory in which the students are told which experiment they will perform in each laboratory session, are given complete instructions for carrying out each experiment, and find the apparatus for the experiment more or less completely assembled and ready for data-taking when they enter the laboratory. The highly organized laboratory has the advantage of being able to serve large numbers of students efficiently. Universities that must offer laboratory work to some fifty to one hundred groups of twenty students each have little choice but to arrange things so that the introductory laboratory runs as smoothly as possible. Since real physics laboratories seldom run smoothly, the artificiality of this approach is at once apparent. In fairness to laboratories of this kind, however, it should be said that the contrived nature of the laboratory work is more apparent to the informed onlooker than to the students, to whom most—if not all—of the experiments are new experiences.

Most universities and colleges take the middle of the road. The free laboratory is an ideal which they strive toward even in their multi-section planning. Optional experiments or parts of experiments are provided so that the better students can have opportunities for freer experimentation than the regular experiments provide. If the group of beginning physics majors is large enough, they may be given laboratory work of the free variety in their own separate laboratory room. Printed notes and directions for experiments generally are tending to be more brief, and the experimental apparatus to be less in the nature of a 'set piece' than formerly; there is a decreasing use of 'device for coefficient of linear expansion', 'device for Young's modulus', etc.

Space will not permit more than a brief description of the standard introductory laboratory.[1] The laboratory section typically meets once a week for two or three hours for three or four semesters of a four-semester course. In the largest universities, the laboratory instructors are graduate student assistants who are supervised by a member of the professorial staff. In institutions with smaller enrolments, members of the professorial staff are directly in charge of the laboratory sessions. The students usually work in pairs; each pair has a set of apparatus. There are between twenty and thirty students in a laboratory class. Occasionally classes of forty are arranged; two instructors are provided in such instances. Generally, there is a different experiment performed at each of the twelve to fifteen laboratory sessions per semester, but some institutions —for example, MIT—arrange their laboratory work so that the student performs only four or five experiments each semester for four semesters.

The subjects of the experiments range across the topics discussed in the introductory course. Appendix III F3 contains a list of the laboratory experiments in introductory physics at the four institutions surveyed. Inspection of the list shows the greatest stress on mechanics and on electricity and magnetism. The average number of experiments per institution in each (arbitrarily set) division of physics is as follows: mechanics (including acoustics), nine; heat, two; electricity and magnetism, nine; electromagnetic radiation (including optics), four; and atomic and nuclear physics, three.

The student is supplied with a laboratory manual or set of notes that is often written and printed locally. He is expected to prepare himself for the experiment by reading the relevant notes and reviewing the theory before coming into the laboratory. Usually two experiments are set up in the laboratory at one time. This means that there are five to seven sets of apparatus for each of two experiments

1. S. C. Brown, 'A Survey of Elementary Physics Laboratories', *American Journal of Physics*, Vol. 21, 1953; and 'Do College Students benefit from High School Laboratory Courses?' *American Journal of Physics*, Vol. 26, 1958.
   H. Knauss, ed. *Proceedings of the Storrs Conference on Laboratory Instruction in General Physics*, Storrs, University of Connecticut, 1957.
   C. J. Overbeck, *Proceedings of the Northwestern University Conference on the Training of College Physics Laboratory Assistants*, Evanston, Northwestern University 1953.

to accommodate the twenty to thirty students. Each pair of laboratory partners works with the apparatus and takes data, following the plan for the experiment in the laboratory manual. The laboratory instructor moves around the room, asking questions and contending with the various logistical and administrative problems of the laboratory. If time permits, the students write their laboratory reports during the laboratory session, following general instructions given them for preparing reports. If time is not available, the report is completed at home. It is usually submitted to the instructor, graded by him or an assistant, and returned with many marginal comments and criticisms as well as a grade.

Examinations in the introductory physics course include (a) short examinations (quizzes) that may be given six or seven times each semester in the recitation periods; (b) hour examinations that are usually given two or three times each semester to the larger lecture classes, and (c) final examinations at the end of each semester. The quizzes test the student's understanding of the weekly assignments and stimulate him to keep up with the class; they usually last ten minutes and contain one or two questions. The hour examinations cover larger parts of the course. The final examination, which requires two or three hours for its completion, tests the student on his comprehension of the entire semester's work. Typically, the examinations are drawn up by the physics staff in charge of the course at each institution. Appendix III F4 contains a typical examination. The examination sheets are reproduced as given to the students. (Here and in later parts of this report, the citing of examination questions will be resorted to as a means of indicating the content and level of physics courses.) The semester average grade in the course for each student is usually compounded from his examination grades, a laboratory grade, and a grade for his problem solutions. The greatest weight is given, of course, to the examination grades. A typical distribution of semester average grades in one of these courses might be: A (highest grade), 10 per cent of the class; B, 10 per cent; C 40 per cent; D, 25 per cent; and F (failure), 15 per cent.

Upper-division courses for physics majors. The objective of the courses in the third and fourth years is to give the undergraduate physics major a preparation in some depth for his graduate studies or for employment at the bachelor's level.[1] The first two years of undergraduate studies have given him an introduction to many of the branches of physics that he will study in depth later, preparation in mathematics including calculus and an introduction to differential equations, and introductory chemistry. The various areas of physics are now taken up in separate courses, and treated with greater physical and mathematical sophistication. Differential equations and advanced calculus are used more and more routinely as the work progresses. The aim of most strong undergraduate programmes is to take the student through a serious course in quantum mechanics—one in quantum mechanics, not about quantum mechanics—before the end of his fourth year. The student is expected also to acquire a familiarity with the experimental techniques—high vacuum, electronic, particle-physics—of modern physics, and to repeat many of the important experiments that form the basis of contemporary physics. (This requirement is relaxed occasionally for students who show unusual promise as theorists, but even they are urged to be experimentalists during their undergraduate years.)

The minimal schedules of upper-division courses for physics majors in the four institutions surveyed (Appendix III F1) and enrolments in them have already been referred to. It should be noted, however, that most students go beyond the minimal requirements and elect additional physics courses. Good students may even take some of the beginning graduate courses in physics.

Some notion of the content and level of these upper-division courses can be obtained from the textbooks listed in Appendix IX F1 under the corresponding course numbers. It should be noted that these courses are in constant evolution. However, these textbooks indicate the general character of upper-division undergraduate work in physics in this country.

The laboratory work in the third and fourth undergraduate years may be either attached to particular courses or organized as a separate course or courses in experimental physics. At the University of California, laboratory work in optics is attached to the optics course, but all other undergraduate upper-division experimental

1. H. R. Crane, ed. *Reports of the First and Second Ann Arbor Conferences on Curricula for Undergraduate Majors in Physics*, Ann Arbor, University of Michigan, 1962.

work is provided in the courses Physics 110C, D. At Columbia, the undergraduate physics major works in the Ernest Kempton Adams Precision Laboratory, following a schedule that is prepared for him according to his interests and experience. Some seventy experiments can be performed of which about twenty are regarded as basic and are strongly recommended to the undergraduate student. MIT also offers a separately organized atomic physics laboratory for third-year undergraduates, following this in the fourth year by arrangements for the student to work on a project of his own or to serve as a laboratory assistant in a research laboratory. Swarthmore puts a steady emphasis on the laboratory throughout the four years; each of its physics courses has a laboratory attached to it.

The laboratory work is unlike that in the introductory course, not only in level and degree of sophistication, but in organization. The apparatus used is usually research-grade equipment. Indeed, many of the pieces were originally constructed in research projects and were 'inherited' by the undergraduate laboratory. The laboratory notes are voluminous with many pages devoted to the theory of the experiment, to the experimental techniques and to the use of equipment, but with rather brief instructions about the procedures. Instead of multiple set-ups for each experiment, there is usually only one. The students 'rotate' from one experiment to another. The usual practice is to leave most of the equipment permanently set up, unless there is a severe shortage of space. The students may work individually, but usually work in pairs. They are expected to keep laboratory notebooks. The reports on the experiments are either written up in the notebooks or are submitted separately. The reports are graded and returned with the instructor's comments.

A minimum of three or four hours is devoted to each laboratory session. Some experiments require a whole day for data-taking, and some require several sessions. The reports require for their preparation at least as much time as is spent in the laboratory, usually more. The students are instructed how to write a good report, including analysis of experimental errors, etc.

Appendix III F5 contains a list of many of the upper-division experiments performed by undergraduate physics majors at the four institutions surveyed. The list is not complete and can never be complete in a report of this kind because the experiments are being constantly replaced or revised. However, it does indicate the great range of experiments and the increasing sophistication of many of the experiments now performed by undergraduates.

Policies vary as to whether the undergraduate is expected to carry out a project of his own in the fourth year and write a thesis based upon it. The University of California and Columbia University do not require this, but do provide opportunities for physics majors to serve as assistants in the research laboratories. The Columbia Physics Department has a committee to arrange such opportunities. Swarthmore does not require a thesis, but has an honours programme, as described below, and also provides jobs for student assistants. MIT requires a thesis based on an experimental project in the fourth year. The extent to which the student at MIT is directed by his faculty adviser depends upon the student's abilities. Some students work quite independently in MIT research laboratories; others are more closely supervised in instructional laboratories. A few of the titles of recent undergraduate theses in one research area at MIT are: 'Experimental verification of the magnetic pressure law' (in plasmas), 'Probe measurements in high-speed gas discharges', and 'Microwave and probe measurements in a cesium plasma'.

Honours courses in physics have been referred to several times in this report. They are special courses, or separate sections of standard courses, reserved for students who wish to be honours candidates and who have been doing superior academic work. An honours degree is granted to students who take the required honours courses, maintain high academic standing, and receive a favourable recommendation from the faculty. Honours courses maintain a higher level of discussion and a more rapid pace than parallel courses for the other physics majors. The University of California offers one honours course in the fourth year—a seminar which includes study of a standard (graduate-level) book on theoretical physics, and reports on current theoretical and experimental problems. Columbia and MIT do not designate courses as honours courses. At Swarthmore, the honours programme is highly developed. During their last two years, honours students take Physics 102, 112, 113, and Mathematics 101, 102 (Appendix III F1). A course in mathematics following Mathematics 101, 102 is recommended, but not required. Each honours course or seminar at Swarthmore is limited to six to eight students; one staff man is responsible for two courses, i.e., twelve students. The honours work is thus practically a tutorial programme. Visiting examiners—physicists at leading universities—are called in each year to set written examinations, conduct oral examinations, and inspect the laboratory notebooks of the honours students.

A copy of a typical examination in upper-division courses in physics is included in Appendix III F6. The reader is referred to Appendix III F1 for information about the place of the corresponding courses in the course sequence at each of the four institutions.

Mathematics courses. The minimal mathematics requirements for the bachelor's degree in physics at the four institutions surveyed have already been stated in Appendix III F1. The student can, and usually does, go on from the basic courses to more advanced and more specialized courses available in a wide variety in both pure and applied mathematics.

During the past five years, physicists have felt an increasing concern about the content of the mathematics courses being offered to their students. At some institutions, the basic mathematics courses have acquired what physicists believe is an excessively formal character. Greater stress is placed upon topics of interest to pure mathematicians, and less upon applications of mathematics to the sciences. The order of topics, too, is not such as to allow the student's increasing grasp of mathematics to keep pace with the increasing mathematical requirements of his work in physics. Dissatisfaction with these courses has led some physics departments to consider giving mathematics courses suited to the needs of their students. At other institutions—MIT is one—close and effective co-operation between the mathematicians and physicists has led to mathematics courses that please both groups.

Courses in chemistry and other sciences. The teaching of chemistry, like the teaching of physics and mathematics, is undergoing a rapid evolution. A description of present courses in chemistry taken by physics majors is not indicative of what these courses are likely to be in the future. At present, the usual requirement is for a one-year introductory course in chemistry. Additional upper-division chemistry courses are optional. As an example, the content of the introductory chemistry course at MIT is described in the 1961/62 MIT catalogue as follows: 'General Chemistry 5.01: Fundamental principles of chemistry; gas laws; mass and energy relationships in chemical changes; writing and the use of chemical equations for quantitative calculations; factors affecting the rate and equilibrium of a chemical reaction; correlation of equilibrium conditions through the mass-action law and the electromotive force of voltaic cells; atomic structure, chemical reactivity of elements, and the Periodic Table; chemistry of certain of the elements of groups 1, 2 and 3 of the Periodic Table. Laboratory work largely quantitative in nature and integrated with lectures and recitations. General Chemistry 5.02: Application of chemical principles to the correlation of the chemical behaviour states; chemistry of the ionic species; quantitative application of the principles of equilibrium to chemical reactions; structural chemistry of crystals and of molecules; acid-base systems; introduction to the chemistry of carbon; nuclear reactions. Laboratory work emphasizing chemical properties of the elements in aqueous solution. Use of facts and principles to develop a scheme for the qualitative separation of the elements. Analysis of unknown mixtures'. Similar descriptions would hold for the introductory courses at other leading institutions.

Additional work in chemistry may be elected by the student, but —with some exceptions, of which MIT is one—physics departments usually do not require their students to take more chemistry. Undoubtedly, the reason is that as physics and chemistry draw closer together, the subjects of many chemistry courses are covered in physics courses and vice versa. Thermodynamics, for example, is usually taught in both the physics department and the chemistry department with significant differences of approach, but with emphasis upon the same basic principles. The merging of physics and chemistry in various research areas—the study of the solid state, for example—will probably lead to a new alignment of instruction in the two fields during this decade. Educational experiments are already being conducted—successfully, according to some observers—in merging the introductory physics and chemistry courses into one physics-chemistry course of three or four semesters.[1]

Work in other scientific and engineering subjects is usually optional and is elected by the physics major according to his personal interests. Some of the subjects suggested by the four institutions in the survey to their physics majors as worthy of consideration include spherical astronomy (quantitative development of basic techniques involved in astronomical observations and interpretations), engineering drawing and descriptive geometry, logic and natural science, the philosophy of science, engineering sciences (e.g., fluid mechanics, linear systems), and biological sciences.

After graduation. Where does the graduate of one of these programmes go? Of the roughly 5,000 persons who receive bachelor's degrees in physics each year, it is estimated that about 3,000 go on to advanced study in physics in a graduate school. (In the four institutions of the survey group and in comparable institutions, a much higher percentage—90 to 95 per cent—of physics majors enter graduate schools.) Some of the others enter graduate work in related fields, engineering and mathematics, for example; a few enter professional schools, notably schools of medicine; and a few become high-school teachers. Perhaps half of the 2,000 who do not continue their studies in physics as full-time graduate students of physics take jobs in industrial or governmental laboratories at the bachelor's level. (Some of them carry on graduate studies at nearby universities in evening classes.) In these positions, they serve as assistants to the senior physicists, doing highly useful, but usually not independent work. Some industrial laboratories prefer to obtain their technical assistants from among bachelor's-degree physicists.

To assist undergraduates in physics to develop a professional interest in physics, to provide them with information about opportunities for graduate study and for employment, and to encourage them to become members of scientific societies in physics, the American Institute of Physics conducts a Student Section Programme. There are AIP Student Sections in about 200 colleges

1. E. C. Fuller, R. R. Palmer, eds. *Report on the Beloit Conference on Teaching Physics and Chemistry in a Combined Course*, 1961. Copies may be obtained from the editors at Beloit College, Beloit, Wisconsin.

and universities throughout the country, enrolling about 5,000 under-graduate physics students.[1]

Summary

The preceding national reports indicate a degree of consensus concerning the educational preparation of the young physicist. The formal programmes last from three to six years of university studies. Where the requirement for the first degree is for three or four years, it is expected either that the student will begin his university work with an unusually intensive preparation in mathematics and physics, or that he will carry on post-graduate studies for several years before beginning professional work of an independent kind. The primary objective of these university studies is to provide a knowledge of the diversified phenomena of physics, unified by a firm understanding of the fundamental concepts and great organizing generalizations of physics.

The first course in physics taken by the university student is almost invariably a course in general or introductory physics, covering the various sub-fields of physics and lasting one or two years. In several countries, this course is paralleled by a separate course in theoretical physics, which takes a more mathematical approach to physics, emphasizing the mathematical description of nature, but, like the general physics course, also emphasizing the unifying principles of physics. Indispensable knowledge of the phenomena of physics and its experimental procedures is imparted to the student by lecture demonstrations connected with these courses and, in first-hand fashion, by practical or laboratory exercises. The practical work of the laboratory provides the most 'physicist-like' activity possible at this stage of the student's education and is heavily stressed in all of the countries surveyed.

The groundwork having been prepared during the first one or two years, more specialized studies follow, occupying the remainder of the student's sojourn at the university. These specialized courses in some countries are merely a device for subdividing physics for reasons of pedagogic convenience. The total preparation of the student is the objective, and these studies are simply steps toward

1. *AIP Student Sections Information Booklet,* American Institute of Physics, New York.

that objective. In other countries, the specialized courses are related to occupational goals of the student—he may want to be a nuclear physicist, for example—and his specialized studies are related to those goals and, often, to work experience also. The issue of broad preparation versus professionalization is handled differently in different countries, some providing differentiation into specialities in the third year, and others preserving a broad approach until the post-graduate years. Practical work universally becomes more like research in these years of specialization, preparing the student for independent work as a physicist.

Mathematics is the chief tool of the physicist, and his mathematical education is scarcely less important than his education in physics. What is particularly notable about the preceding national reports is the indication that in more than one country the teaching of mathematics to physicists is in danger of becoming excessively formal and unrelated to physics. This is a cause of concern to physicists, and has led to efforts among physicists and mathematicians to develop a style of mathematics teaching and a content of mathematics courses for physicists that are in harmony with both modern mathematics and modern physics.

In all except one of the participating countries, the accomplishments of the student are evaluated by a comprehensive examination of a formal kind, success in which is necessary before he receives his first degree. The examination may be accompanied by the preparation and defence of a thesis, but it is invariably aimed at exploring the strengths and weaknesses of the student's command of physics and mathematics. Several of the countries stressed that the examination was to find out whether the student could 'think like a physicist' rather than to determine how much factual information he had acquired. The United States provides an exception in that its universities do not ordinarily require the passing of a comprehensive examination for the first degree, reserving this requirement for the higher degrees.

IV. The role of physics in the education of school teachers, engineers and others

Introduction

Teachers of physics in the secondary schools require a preparation in physics that in its early stages is essentially indistinguishable from that of the physicist who will carry on research in physics, or become a professor of physics in a university. The successful secondary school teacher of physics and the university physicist have many qualities in common—intellectual vitality, competence in physics and mathematics, ability to present their subject well, enthusiasm, and so on. Indeed, the able secondary school teacher of physics is a 'professional physicist', and it is a matter of literary convenience that we discuss his education here rather than in the long preceding chapter. To be sure, there are differences between the education of the physics teacher and that of the research physicist —notably the length of the educational process and the final level attained.

Physics has an important role to play also in the education of engineers and technologists, chemists and other physical scientists, students of the life sciences, mathematicians, and even, in some countries, the non-technical student. As the body of knowledge in physics grows and diffuses into other areas of pure and applied science, the demand for instruction in physics increases. Many of the spectacular advances in related sciences can be traced to prior advances in physics. It is not surprising, therefore, to find that the education of students of related scientific fields and engineering

is regarded as incomplete without substantial physics content.
This chapter reviews among the countries participating in the
present survey the role of physics in the education of those preparing to be physics teachers in schools and in that of students in
related fields—up to the first university degree. Many courses are
common to the programmes of instruction for these students and
to those of the professional physicists. The reader will have occasion
frequently to refer to the preceding chapter for details. This chapter
will stress particularly the following: (a) the characteristics of physics courses for these students; (b) the ways in which these programmes differ from those for professional physicists.

Programmes in Czechoslovakia

The education of teachers. Future physics teachers for secondary
schools study at university faculties, together with the professional
physicists. Physics teachers for the sixth to ninth forms of the basic-
nine-year schools (the approximate equivalent of the former junior
secondary schools) receive their training at pedagogical institutes.

Every secondary school teacher must also have the necessary
qualification for teaching a second subject which, together with
physics, forms a so-called 'teaching-combination'. Physics, as a
subject at secondary schools, appears mainly in the two traditional
teaching combinations: mathematics-physics and chemistry-physics.
Teachers for these combinations are trained at all four universities.
Recently a new course was introduced at the Natural Science
Faculty of Brno University, offering training in the physics-geology
teaching combination. Every teaching combination has its own independent curriculum, approved by the Ministry of Education and
Culture. As pointed out earlier in this report, the curricula for a
certain combination are also almost identical at all faculties, differing merely in details. The course of study lasts five years for all
combinations.

Appendix IV A1 shows the relevant curriculum for the mathematics-physics combination at the Faculty for Mathematics and
Physics of Charles University. Beginning with the third study year,
the curriculum of the mathematics-physics branch for future teachers
links up with the basic physics curriculum which was described

in Chapter III. The teaching and the professional branches have the first two subjects of the curriculum in common (selected parts of experimental physics, and theoretical physics). As far as the other physics subjects are concerned, a general survey of knowledge in the principal contemporary branches of this science is given, supplemented by a survey of astronomy, geophysics and meteorology, and by exercises in topography. Experience in performing demonstration experiments is gained in practical exercises, held two hours a week throughout the seventh to ninth semesters. With the fifth semester, the elementary course in mathematics comes to an end. The remaining mathematics lectures and exercises are mainly used for dealing with the subject matter taught at secondary schools from the mathematician's point of view.

A considerable amount of time is taken up by theoretical and practical instruction in pedagogical subjects—too much, in the opinion of most physicists, who consider twelve hours weekly for psychology and pedagogics more than enough. Another sixteen weekly hours are devoted to the methods of teaching mathematics and physics. The actual training in methods of teaching is practised by two different methods. The first is the so-called 'school-practice' during the seventh and eighth semesters when students, divided into small groups, spend regularly one to two hours per week at some selected general secondary schools. At first, they are present only as observers during mathematics or physics lessons, which they afterwards analyse with their teacher. Later on, they are allowed to do some teaching, having previously prepared themselves for a certain part of the subject matter to be dealt with. The second method of practical training forms part of the 'professional practice' consisting of spending a four-week period during the ninth semester at a selected general secondary school. Faculty teachers are present throughout. The students are allocated certain forms at which they teach mathematics and physics in several consecutive lessons. They also take part in the general life of the school. Then there is a second part of the professional praxis during the eighth semester, designed to acquaint the future teachers with work in research and development laboratories in a similar manner as in the case of students of the professional branch. Training in psychology and pedagogics is conducted by the appropriate Chairs of the Philosophical Faculty. Theoretical and practical instruction in teaching methods is provided by the Chairs for methods of teaching mathematics and physics at the Faculty for Mathematics and Physics.

The mathematics-physics combination is further subdivided, enabling the student to major either in physics or mathematics, taking the other discipline as a subsidiary subject. In both cases, the curriculum is the same; the diploma subject, however, must always treat of the main subject. The oral finals in the subsidiary subject are taken at the end of the ninth semester, while those in the main subject are generally held towards the end of the tenth semester, at the time of the defence of the diploma project. Diploma projects for the teaching branch are less exacting than for the professional branch. Some students of the pedagogical branch, however, prepare and present diploma projects satisfying the requirements of the professional branch where they also take their Final State Examination in the main subject. These graduates receive in addition to the 'promoted pedagogue' diploma, entitling them to teach mathematics and physics, the 'promoted physicist' degree, if their major subject has been physics.

Although the majority of physics teachers in secondary schools are graduates of the mathematics-physics combination, some teachers take the chemistry-physics combination. Students of this combination follow, during the first two study years, a common basic curriculum for training chemistry and physics teachers as well as professional chemists. In the curriculum of this combination the physics courses are substantially the same as for the mathematics-physics teaching combination. It differs, however, considerably in the extent of mathematics instruction, which totals only ten hours weekly.

Those who wish to teach in the basic nine-year schools must also be qualified to teach two subjects. The actual study at the newly established pedagogical institutes lasts three years and is followed by one year of praxis at a school. The curriculum totals approximately one hundred and eighty-five weekly hours for the entire study course or an average of thirty-one weekly hours for the semester. In the mathematics-physics combination, for example, forty-eight hours are devoted to physics instruction, fifty-three hours to mathematics, and the remaining fifty-four hours to theoretical and practical pedagogical preparation and general education. The physics part of the curriculum comprises 20/10[1] hours of general physics, 0/8 hours of laboratory exercises, 0/6 hours of exercises in demonstration experiments and four hours a week for methods of teaching physics. The mathematical part of the curriculum contains these subjects: mathematical analysis 4/4 hours, arithmetic and algebra 6/9 hours, geometry 9/8 hours, drawing 3/5 hours. The remaining five hours per week are set aside for methods of teaching mathematics.

Physics for students of related sciences. Professional chemists have, during the first two study years, the same physics as students of the mathematics-physics combination (Appendix IV A1). In the seventh semester, the professional chemists' curriculum contains, besides other subjects, 4/1 weekly hours of instruction in selected parts of theoretical physics. The lectures concentrate particularly on quantum mechanics and physical statistics in connexion with problems of theoretical chemistry. Some aspects of physics are, of course, dealt with also in physical chemistry courses—for example, thermodynamics—or in other lectures arranged by the Chair of physical chemistry (for example, the structure of molecules, etc.).

Physics courses for students of the biological sciences differ from faculty to faculty. Most faculties teach physics 3/0 hours during the second semester, preceded by three weekly hours of mathematics in the first semester. More hours are devoted to physics at the Natural Science Faculty in Prague, i.e., 2/0 weekly hours during the first semester and 2/3 hours in the second semester, with the three hours of practicals utilized for physical laboratory exercises; 2/3 weekly hours of mathematics instruction are scheduled for the first semester.

The curriculum in applied geology contains 2/1 hours of physics instruction in the second and 3/2 weekly hours of mathematics in the first semester. There are, of course, also some weekly hours of special lectures and exercises in geophysics during the later semesters. The curriculum for applied geophysics contains a substantially greater number of hours for mathematics (18/4) and physics (11/7) instruction (not including special instruction in geophysics). For

---

1. In reproducing the curricula, the following abbreviations are used: 4/2 = four weekly periods of lectures and two periods of connected exercises.

the general geology specialization the same number of physics and mathematics hours is prescribed as for the applied geology students.

Courses for the various engineering branches. Introductory physics courses at the technical universities and colleges vary in scope and extent, according to the objective of the study course. They differ even to a certain degree from school to school and from faculty to faculty of the same branch. At present, their curricula are not yet entirely stabilized, and the situation is further complicated by the circumstance that the organization of production activities and professional praxis, which is much more extensive at technical universities and colleges than at the other schools of higher education, also differs in content and extent at the various faculties and branches of study. In this report, however, at least the average hours of physics instruction generally prescribed in the curricula of the main branches of study will be indicated. Physics courses are, as a rule, run by the so-called Chairs of technical physics and generally start with the second or third semester, lasting until the end of the fourth or, in exceptional cases, fifth semester. Some branches also provide special physics lectures for the higher semesters.

The civil engineering students follow a basic curriculum that provides for about 100/40 hours of physics instruction; geodesy and cartography students study physics for about 115/70 hours. Two-thirds of the time reserved for practicals is spent at laboratory exercises. Mechanical engineering students attend an introductory course in physics, totalling about 100/70 to 100/90 hours, including fifty to seventy hours of laboratory work. The later semesters of some specializations in this branch of study provide additional special lectures, for example, nuclear physics, solid state physics, etc. (forty to sixty hours). Electrical engineering students 'lead', so to speak, in the number of hours of physics instruction. Their introductory course has 200/135 hours, and that for the high-frequency section even 230/110 hours. Two-thirds of the time for practicals is devoted to laboratory exercises. In the later semesters, the individual branches and specializations also offer lectures on other topics in the field of physics. The chemical engineering students' basic physics course totals about 130/130 hours. The 130 practical hours are given over to laboratory exercises, spread over two semesters. Students of agriculture have relatively the least extensive physics instruction. The course is one of about 35/45 hours. The practical part during the second semester is utilized for laboratory exercises.

Physics courses for students of medicine. The faculties of general medicine, which also offer courses in dentistry, demand their students' attendance at three weekly hours each of physics lectures and practical exercises during the first semester. The so-called Chair of medical physics is in charge of this course. As the curricula of the hygienics and pediatrics faculties branch off, after the first two study years, from that of the Faculty of General Medicine, the same physics courses are attended by the students of all these faculties.

Programmes in the Federal Republic of Germany

Curriculum of candidates for school teaching in the 'Gymnasium'. One has to distinguish between physics as a major subject for future teachers of the middle and upper classes, and physics as a secondary subject for future teachers of the middle classes of the *Gymnasium*. When physics is a major subject, mathematics is generally taken as the second major subject. Thus, approximately half the student's time is available for studying physics. The programme of studies is so arranged that a student may pass the *Staatsexamen* for the teaching profession at the *Gymnasium* level after eight semesters. In most cases, studies last slightly longer. An intermediate examination, corresponding to the preliminary examination, has so far been introduced at only a few universities but is proposed by the Deutsche Physikalische Gesellschaft. The curriculum is roughly as follows:

Basic lecture in experimental physics, ten hours per week; Basic lecture in experimental chemistry, eight; Practical for beginners, twelve; Practical for advanced students, including demonstration training, approximately twelve; Lectures of higher level, experimental physics, applied physics, and special lectures, approximately ten; Theoretical physics (mechanics, electro-dynamics, thermodynamics and statistical mechanics, atomic physics, quantum mechanics), approximately twenty-five.

When physics is studied as a secondary subject, the curriculum is: Basic lectures in experimental physics, ten periods per week; Practical for beginners, approximately twelve; Theoretical physics, approximately five; Basic lecture in experimental chemistry, approximately four to eight; Other lectures in physics, four.

The *Staatsexamen*, with physics as a major subject, like the *Hauptdiplom*, permits later acquisition of the doctor degree; however, little use is made of this possibility.

It should be noted that students wishing to take up the teaching profession have to follow a similar plan of studies as the student who intends to take the diploma in physics. However, for his future activity as a teacher in the various classes of the *Gymnasia*, the student must additionally learn what subject matter from the various fields of physics he has to treat there, and how this is best presented. These matters of presentation require special consideration by the professors of the physical institutes, seeing that the problems arising in the teaching of physics are quite different from those treated in the general teacher training course. They include the selection of subject matter, demonstration experiments to be done by the teacher, experiments by the students, use of films, and introduction of modern subjects dealing, for example, with atomic and nuclear physics.

These extensive tasks have been tackled in different manners at the various universities. Of late, practical demonstrations for students wishing to become school teachers have become very common. This can be explained by the example of the University of Kiel. There, the training is supervised by the director of an institute. He specifically instructs the teachers not to look upon a school physics course as an abridged and simplified form of university training, but to draw it up in a special manner considering the age of the pupils and the main task of a *Gymnasium*, which is to provide a general education. What this means is explained in a detailed practical demonstration course where examples from all fields of physics are treated.

The students are asked in pairs to treat such problems experimentally and to demonstrate them. For this, a large collection of physics apparatus and the help of assistants are available. The demonstration of the experiments prepared in this manner, and the oral explanations given, are then thoroughly discussed in class from the scientific and physical point of view as well as from the didactic and methodical.

At other universities, different methods are adopted to prepare the students for their teaching profession, but at almost all universities it is increasingly realized that the training of the physics teachers-to-be is an important task for the future, not only from the point of view of the science as such but for the future education of the children in the *Gymnasiums*.

A note about the continuing education of the teachers already practising their profession will be found in Chapter VII.

Physics requirements for non-physicists. Physics, as a subsidiary subject, is required when studying mathematics, chemistry, engineering, biology, geology, mineralogy, astronomy, pharmacy, medicine, veterinary medicine or agriculture.

In the course of their preliminary examination, mathematicians studying for the graduation diploma are examined in experimental physics and theoretical mechanics. Accordingly, up to the preliminary examination, there are required:
Basic lectures in experimental physics, ten periods per week; Practicals in physics for beginners, twelve; Theoretical mechanics, approximately six.
The final diploma examination (*Diplomhauptexamen*) includes theoretical physics. Therefore, four lectures in theoretical physics (for instance, electrodynamics, optics, thermodynamics and statistics, atomic physics, quantum mechanics—each subject about five hours per week, exercises included) are required for these studies.

Students of astronomy must have attended the basic lectures in experimental physics, the major lectures in theoretical physics (including exercises), and the physics practical for beginners and for advanced students. Attendance at special lectures is also desirable.

The requirements in physics for other sciences are as follows:

101

Branch	Lectures in experimental physics. Periods per week	Practical work. Approx. number of periods per week
Chemistry	10	12
Engineering	8[1]	4–8
Physical chemistry	10	12
Biology	10	6
Mineralogy	10	12
Geology	10	6
Pharmacy	8	3
Medicine	8	2
Veterinary medicine	8	2
Agriculture	8	2

1. Additional periods, according to the branch lectures in theoretical physics (mechanics, electricity).

Programmes in France

The preparation of teachers of physics in secondary schools. Teachers-to-be follow much the same educational route as the professional physicists, progressing through the *propédeutique* and taking certificates of higher education in various special areas of physics and mathematics. A licence of instruction may be granted to a candidate who has successfully completed work for six certificates of higher education, taken from the following precisely specified list: mathematical techniques of physics; general mechanics; physical mechanics and thermodynamics; optics; electricity; electronics.

This diploma can be obtained in two years (more generally in three years). It corresponds to about 700 hours of instruction and 300 hours spent in the laboratory. Candidates in the competitive examination of recruitment (the Certificate of Aptitude for Instruction in Secondary Schools) generally take a year to prepare for it after obtaining the *licence*, in the course of which they learn pedagogical techniques. The examination requires general scientific knowledge (a written examination and problems in physics) as well as practical knowledge. The candidate also has to teach a model lesson before a jury. Centres preparing students for these examinations are generally to be found in the universities.

Physics for engineers. The reader is referred to Chapter III, and he is reminded that the minimal qualification for an 'engineer' or 'researcher' in France is a *licence* for which five certificates of higher education (CES) are required. The programmes for the various CES based on physics were described in Chapter III.

Physics for biologists. The *propédeutique* for biologists is organized by the universities, where it is called SPCN (Physics, chemistry and biology).

The *propédeutique* year follows this weekly schedule: mathematics, 2 hours; physics, 1.5; physics laboratory, 3; chemistry, 2; chemistry laboratory 3; geological and biological sciences, 8.5; biology laboratory, 4.5. The physics programme is given in Appendix IV C1. The mathematics course is very succinct. It serves as a review of the essential ideas of pre-university mathematics. The students also acquire some notions about statistics.

The practical work is very analogous to that of the other *propédeutique* programmes. The material is often the same. The examination usually consists of a written test two hours long, with a question about the course and a numerical application. There are also, of course, a practical test and an oral interrogation.

The *lycées* also run classes of the *propédeutique* oriented toward the natural sciences and called *Classes C*. They are concerned especially with the preparation for the competitive entrance examination of the Grandes Ecoles Biologiques. If their programme is analogous to that of the university *propédeutique*, their methods are different. Most often the classes are specialized. There are classes which prepare one for the National Institute of Agricultural Sciences, others for the College of Veterinary Medicine, others for the Agricultural Colleges, and so on.

Physics for students of medicine and pharmacy. Instruction in physics is given during the first year and during the first half of the second year. There is a gradual transition from the instruction in 'general' physics given by physicists on the staff of the Faculty of Science to the instruction in 'medical' physics taught by physicians on the staff of the Faculty of Medicine. During the first half of the first year, the students have one session of course each week and one session of laboratory work, which is very analogous to the instruction in the biological *propédeutique* that we just mentioned. The instruction is merely very brief and consequently the programme is very condensed. But it is taught in the same spirit: a physicist of the Faculty of Sciences gives the course, and the laboratory work is generally performed with the equipment of the Faculty of Science. It represents a *propédeutique* in pure physics, limited to a half year. The physicians intervene only to set the programme.

Eventually the instruction is given by the staff of the Faculty of Medicine, by physicians. It follows the same schedule (a session of course and a session of laboratory per week), and extends through the end of the first year and half of the second. The professors endeavour to compensate for the lack of time by resorting to vigorous measures. The course is multicopied, and the students are supposed to master the subject of the lesson in advance. The session is devoted to exercises and to clarifying discussions suggested by questions from the class.

If one excepts the programme of general physics taught by physicists, the programme of medical physics consists of the study of thermodynamics, oriented toward the study of the heat engine which is the human body; the study of the structure of matter with emphasis upon such phenomena as osmosis, diffusion, and adsorption; the study of optics, in its relation to the eye, and acoustics, in its relation to the ear. Finally, the course contains substantial content dealing with nuclear physics and X-rays and gamma-rays. We should note that the programmes in the medical specialities contain some topics from general physics, preparatory to that speciality. Thus the instruction in radiobiology includes topics in nuclear physics; that in radiology, topics in electricity; and that in optometry, elements of optics. They represent, in fact, chapters of a fundamental course, studied at the beginning of medical studies.

The educational programme in pharmacy is being reorganized and will probably be endowed with a *propédeutique*, comparable to the SPCN. As to the present situation, after an 'apprenticeship' of one year, spent in a shop that sells pharmaceuticals, the pharmacy student pursues formal studies at a university for four years. He takes a physics course during the first two years. The instruction consists of around one hundred and fifty hours of course work and seventy-five hours of laboratory work. As in the Faculty of Medicine, this instruction is given by pharmacists, who have furthermore the degree of *doctorat ès sciences*. The programme is essentially a study of the structure of matter, with emphasis upon applications to chemistry and biology. The phenomena of surface tension, adsorption, osmosis, etc., are carefully studied. For several years now, the pharmacists have received instruction in nuclear physics (about ten hours of course work and a few laboratory sessions). The necessary mathematical background is taught in the first year in twenty-five hours (two hours per week during the first semester); it corresponds to that required for the SPCN and uses the same textbooks.

Programmes in the U.S.S.R.

The training of physics teachers. Teachers of physics in schools are trained in the universities and also in teacher training institutes. The university course takes five years, the teacher training institute course four years. The difference is that university graduates have a broader training in scientific theory, whereas teachers graduating from the training institutes have a more fundamental theoretical and practical training in pedagogics and teaching methods. Experience has shown that when working jointly in a school, the two types of teacher are mutually complementary.

At the universities, the qualification 'Physicist' (teacher of physics) is granted to graduates who have obtained a certificate in teaching practice, and have passed the examinations and tests in the special subjects and special seminars, including the disciplines of the teacher training course, in accordance with the syllabus. After the basic studies (Chapter III) for students preparing to be school teachers, the time set aside for special subjects is devoted to a teacher-training course in the seventh semester (eighty hours), a course in methods of teaching physics in the eighth semester (one hundred and twenty hours), and a course in astronomy in the ninth semester. They are also sent to secondary schools for teaching practice. The curriculum provides for a total of twenty-nine to thirty-eight weeks of vocational practice.

In addition to educating physics teachers, in order to ensure a supply of teachers to small schools, the teacher-training institutes provide, also, five-year courses for training teachers in physics combined with other special subjects. Specialist combinations such as 'mathematics and physics' or 'physics and astronomy', where the main emphasis is on mathematics, and physics takes second place, have become fairly common. Such a combination makes it possible to train the broadly educated teachers required for the mass general education schools.

It, is noteworthy, also, that in recent years, under the 'Law on strengthening the relationship of the schools with outside life and further developing the national education system in the U.S.S.R.', it has become common practice to train physics teachers with a fairly pronounced technological bias. This training is provided under the specialist courses in 'physics and electrotechnics' and 'physics and general technological disciplines'. In these special courses, physics provides the basic training in general technological disciplines. On finishing training the teacher has the qualification of 'teacher of physics and electrotechnics' or 'teacher of physics and general technological disciplines'. These specializations are merely supplementary to the basic specialization in 'physics' at the universities and teacher-training institutes, and are an indication of the efforts made by the institutes of higher education, not only to maintain a high level of theoretical science in the training of young people in physics but also to raise this level in accordance with modern achievements in physics. The newly created specialized qualifications, combining physics with general technological disciplines, are making it possible to extend the influence of physics as a science and to present the laws of modern physics to students as the firm foundation of scientific knowledge.

Apart from these specialized courses, certain teacher-training institutes offer a specialized course in 'physics taught in a foreign language'. Here the basis is the discipline of physics, but at the same time a good deal of time is spent on the fundamentals of a foreign language (primarily English or French) and on teacher training practice in secondary schools, with independent physics lessons in the foreign language.

The four-year physics course in the teacher-training institutes covers, apart from general scientific and pedagogical disciplines, the following disciplines in physics: general physics, 624 hours; methods of mathematical physics, 78 hours; theoretical physics,

314 hours; the history of physics, 40 hours. More than 300 hours of this total are devoted to laboratory work; in addition, up to 100 teaching hours are devoted to practical work in a specialized field of physics. At the same time a number of optional courses can be taken (nuclear physics, electronics, a specialized course in optics and so forth). A total of 570 hours is devoted to higher mathematics, 135 hours to theoretical mechanics, 154 hours to astronomy. In addition, provision is made for 150 hours' teaching of electro-technics and radio technics. All students following the 'physics' specialization course spend thirty weeks in teaching and vocational practice. At the end of the course the students take State examinations, the main subject being physics.

Physics teaching in the institutes of higher technical education. In 1960 there was an important move towards broadening and modernizing the physics course in institutes of higher technical education. A new, more thorough and modern curriculum, covering 310 to 380 hours (against 190 to 250 hours in the old physics course), is now provided at all institutes of higher technical education in the U.S.S.R. The compilation of this course was preceded by widespread discussion in the press and at meetings of physicists in Moscow, Leningrad and other cities. The recurrent theme in this discussion was the conviction that a successful engineering career nowadays depended on a sound training in physics and mathematics, and that the importance of such training would steadily and rapidly grow in the coming years. The main tasks facing physicists in this field were outlined in a report made at the 1960 International Conference on Physics Education, held in Paris on the initiative of the International Union of Pure and Applied Physics and Unesco.[1] We shall keep this section short, since those who are interested in the details can find them in the above-mentioned report to the Paris conference.

In the majority of institutes of higher technical education physics is taught in the second, third, fourth and fifth semesters. The students take three examinations during the course and four practical tests. The programme contains eight main divisions, in the follow-

1. S. C. Brown; N. Clarke, editors. *Proceedings of the International Conference on Physics Education.* New York, Technology Press and John Wiley and Sons, 1960.

ing order: the physical fundamentals of mechanics; molecular physics, thermodynamics and phase transitions; electricity and magnetism; vibrations and waves; optics; atomic and molecular physics; solid-state physics; physics of the atomic nucleus and elementary particles. This is the normal sequence in the system of physics teaching. The only exception is the location of solid-state physics, which appears at the very end of the syllabus, before nuclear physics. The idea is that solid-state theory in the main is taught here, namely, the theory of crystalline lattices, band theory, and the fundamentals of the quantum theory of solids. Every physicist knows that, however strictly this material is taught, it cannot be mastered without drawing on a considerable reserve of knowledge from the field of classical and modern atomic physics. (The phenomenology of states of aggregation, including the solid state, is taught in the second part of the syllabus.) The lecture course is accompanied in all four semesters by a practical course in physics. The main purpose of the practical course is to teach the students modern methods of measuring physical quantities. In the second and third semesters a small amount of time is devoted to practical exercises in solving physical problems. It has been found advisable, in view of the pressure of time, to shift the centre of gravity of this important form of exercise to work done at home and to tutorials.

The general principles underlying the teaching of physics in institutes of higher technical education are: (a) irrespective of the technical specialization of the institute concerned, it must provide a systematic course, following a definite sequence, in the fundamentals of theoretical and experimental physics; (b) this course must be regarded as an integral and indivisible foundation for the technical disciplines; (c) in teaching the course, there must be a proper balance between the amount of classical and modern physics taught, without detriment to either; (d) in the interest of strict economy of teaching time, the physics course must be precisely co-ordinated with the teaching of the principal branches of higher mathematics.

It is believed that in the institutes of higher technical education, physics and mathematics must be regarded as the most important, basic disciplines, forming the foundation for the theoretical training of engineers. The work of the physics department must be built on this principle. At the same time, it is believed that the physics departments, in their capacity of scientific research centres, must not constitute isolated systems within the technological atmosphere of the institutes of higher education. The scientific research work of the departments of physics must bear some definite relationship, sometimes more, sometimes less close, to the subjects of technological physics. In particular, subjects for theses must be selected with this in mind. It is regarded as most important that the scientific research work of physics departments should be connected with the scientific research work of the engineering departments or directly with industry. To this end, the physics departments take part in planning students' graduation theses and in the work of the State examinations Board.

Physics teaching in the rural agricultural, medical and other institutes of higher education. In a fairly large group of institutes of higher technical education, of various specializations, physics has until recently occupied only a modest place in the curricula. These include institutes of economics and agriculture, institutes of higher education under the Ministry of Health, those associated with the food industry, trade and so forth. The total time devoted to all aspects of physics in such institutions does not exceed 150–170 hours, often even fewer.

The following reservation must, however, be made: in the engineering departments of these establishments the scope of the physics course is the same as in technical institutes, for example, the departments of engineering, agricultural electrification, hydrotechnics and melioration, machine profiling, the automation of the food industry and so forth, in the agricultural institutes and academies.

On the other hand, one hundred and seventy hours are devoted to physics in the departments of agronomy, of which eighty hours are spent on lectures and ninety on laboratory work. Lectures occupy eighty-eight hours in the clinical departments of the medical institutes, practical work fifty hours, and applied studies ninety-eight hours. In the pharmaceutical departments the physics course takes up two hundred and two hours, of which eighty-four are devoted to lectures, ninety-four to practical, and twenty-four to applied. With such a time-table, the physics course is bound to be compressed. Nevertheless, the aim, as in the institutes of higher technical education, is to provide a course in classical and modern physics, in a definite sequence and of valuable content. The course is illustrated in terms of applied physics according to the specialization of the institute of higher education concerned. In the agricultural institutes these illustrations are drawn from atmospheric physics, meteorological physics, subsoil physics, and many aspects of molecular physics and thermodynamics. In the medical institutes the physics course is closely connected with many problems in biophysics and physiology, medical instruments, physiotherapy and balneology, radiology and so forth.

Programmes in the United Kingdom

Teachers of physics in schools. In the grammar schools of England and Wales and in the senior secondary schools in Scotland, physics has been a part of the normal curriculum for many years, and in these schools the teachers of all subjects are usually university graduates with appropriate honours degrees. Indeed, before the Second World War, when the opportunities for physics graduates in industry and elsewhere were comparatively few, school teaching was one of the most sought-after occupations for graduates with very good degrees. In the United Kingdom, therefore, grammar school teachers do not follow degree courses specially designed for them; the normal procedure would be for an intending teacher to take one of the degrees referred to in Chapter III. Usually, he would afterwards follow a one-year course for a Diploma in Education and this would be taken in the university Department of Education. This course would include some material common to all intending teachers, such as educational psychology, but would also prepare him in the techniques of teaching his special subject. On the staffs of these departments of education are physicists who have themselves had years of experience as grammar school teachers, and in some departments much good work has been done on the development of new equipment for school teaching. During the one-year course, the young physics graduates would spend a few weeks teaching in a school under supervision. Although this course of teacher training

110

is now followed by the majority of those who enter the teaching profession, it is not obligatory, and a graduate who enters school teaching immediately after taking his physics degree is regarded as a qualified teacher.

In the secondary modern schools, to which three-quarters of the children in the United Kingdom go, physics would be taught as a separate subject to only the minority of the children, although a general science course would be given to a good many more. With the present shortage of qualified teachers, it is difficult to attract physics graduates to these schools, and some courses are available for non-graduate teachers to enable them to teach some physics. Most of the teachers in primary schools and secondary modern schools have received their training, which is now of three-years duration, in special teacher-training colleges which award certificates but not degrees. A few of these colleges now run special courses in physics, but the number of teachers trained in this way is so far too small to be able to say how successful this development has been.

For teachers in technical schools and technical colleges there are four technical teacher-training colleges in the United Kingdom, and a few physics teachers come from these institutions. In general, they are men who have spent some years in industry before deciding to enter the teaching profession, and they usually hold either a degree or a technological qualification of roughly comparable standard.

Physics for non-physics specialists. All the university departments of physics in the United Kingdom have a substantial load of teaching courses other than those intended for physics specialists. There are large classes of chemists, engineers, mathematicians, medical students, etc. Such courses extend over one or two years but it is not possible to give details that would be representative of all such courses.

It was explained in Chapter II that in the University of Cambridge, students take first Part I of the Natural Sciences Tripos and then take Part II in a single subject. The Part I course would be taken by those who would later specialize in, say, chemistry or metallurgy as well as by those intending to be physicists. The physics course for Part I is given in Appendix IV E1. This, in fact, is a proposed course, somewhat different from the one hitherto offered and, as will be seen, it includes some alternatives.

Colleges of advanced technology. The colleges of advanced technology and the other major colleges of technology exist primarily to train engineers and technologists, although, as was explained in Chapter II, some of them also train substantial numbers of physics specialists. The physics departments in all these colleges have a heavy volume of work teaching physics to future engineers and technologists but, again, courses would vary significantly from college to college.

Programmes in the U.S.A.

The education of physics teachers. At a series of conferences in the United States from 1959 to 1961 under the auspices of the National Association of State Directors of Teacher Education and Certification and the American Association for the Advancement of Science, a large number of scientists, educators, and state and local education officials discussed the optimum preparation for the teaching of the sciences and mathematics in secondary schools. The result of these meetings was the publication of the *Guidelines for Preparation Programs of Teachers of Secondary School Science and Mathematics.*[1] The *Guidelines* are not compulsory for teacher-training institutions, but they have been so widely discussed and increasingly accepted that they constitute the best description of the strong educational programme for teachers of these subjects.

The reader is referred to the *Guidelines* report for a complete description. The education of physics teachers is expected gradually to reach these standards; at present there is much room for improvement in this area.

Physics courses for engineering and chemistry students. Typically, engineering students and chemistry majors are required to take the same introductory physics courses as the physics majors (Chapter III). In addition, these students elect or are required to take some

1. Published by the National Association of State Directors of Teacher Education and Certifica - tion and the American Association for the Advancement of Science, Washington, 1961.

upper-division courses given by the physics department. For example, at the University of California, engineering students who wish to study physical electronics (within the Department of Electrical Engineering) are advised first to take the physics courses in electricity and magnetism (Physics 110 B) and introductory atomic physics (Physics 121). Graduate students and, beginning in 1962/63, undergraduates in metallurgy take undergraduate solid state physics courses. At Columbia, students of nuclear engineering and electrical engineering usually take such courses as nuclear physics (Physics 4040), and electricity and magnetism (Physics 4007–4008). At MIT, electrical engineering students are required to take introductory quantum mechanics (Physics 8.051).

Considering the basic nature of physics, one finds fewer requirements for these students to take courses with physics content from physicists than one might expect. The migration of physics course content from physics departments into other areas requiring it is far advanced in most institutions. Departments such as those in engineering and chemistry often offer their own versions of, say, 'electromagnetic fields and waves' or 'introductory quantum mechanics' instead of sending their students to the physics department. The younger faculty members in these departments are usually more thoroughly imbued with the spirit of contemporary physics than their senior colleagues, and want to give within their own departments what were formerly 'physics' courses. The problem of the relation of physics to engineering and to physics-related sciences is an exceedingly complex one in these days of explosive expansion of both science and technology.[1]

Physics courses for students of the life sciences and agriculture. Students who wish later to enter professional schools of medicine or dentistry, and students of pharmacy are almost universally required as undergraduates to take a one-year course in introductory physics—a 'pre-medical' course. This is often a course with four-semester hours credit per semester, including laboratory work, for two semesters. The course is often separate from that for science majors and engineers, which it usually resembles in organization. (Exceptions

1. 'The Role of Physics in Engineering Education', *Physics Today*, American Institute of Physics, Committee Report, December 1955.

are numerous, however, and include MIT and Swarthmore where single introductory physics courses are given for science majors, engineers, and students of the life sciences.) The pre-medical course does not impose such great demands on the student mathematically or in depth of treatment as does the 'physics major' course. Usually, formal calculus is not a prerequisite nor a corequisite, although the ideas of a derivative and an integral are often introduced as part of the course.

Students of agriculture take the pre-medical course or, in some institutions, a separate course.

Students of the biological sciences divide, according to their academic ability, between the pre-medical course and the physics-major course. (As the biological sciences continue their expansion into molecular biology, one can anticipate that biology students will increasingly take the physics-major course and go beyond it into more advanced courses in physics.)

Some institutions also offer intermediate courses in physics for students of the life sciences. At the University of California, Physics 132 is a three semester-hour course in modern physics that may be elected by students who have taken the pre-medical introductory physics course; it covers the elements of atomic and nuclear physics. At MIT, a fairly large number of pre-medical students major in physics as undergraduates. This is rather rare, however. In most institutions, the pre-medical student usually majors in chemistry or the biological sciences. Students of optometry at California take Physics 108 A (geometrical optics).

Physics courses for students of the liberal arts. The general-education or credit-distribution requirements of most undergraduate colleges in the United States bring to the physics departments students whose basic interests are in the humanities or the social sciences. The educational philosophy behind this is that science is an increasingly important part of contemporary civilization, and every educated person should understand the objectives, procedures, and some of the content of modern science. Academic physicists believe that they share with their colleagues in the other natural sciences the responsibility for educating 'non-scientists' among the college population and attempt to meet it in various ways. Colleges offer

114

either physics courses designed for these students, often stressing an historical or cultural approach, or multi-discipline courses that contain some physics content, but that cut across traditional disciplinary boundaries.

One example of this kind of course is Physics C1001–C1002 at Columbia University: 'An introductory treatment of crucial experiments and theories of physics: particle mechanics; heat and kinetic theory of gases; electromagnetism; wave motion; atomic spectra and the Bohr theory of the hydrogen atom; nuclear reactions; elementary particles'. Laboratory work is not included. Another example is Physics 7, 8 at Swarthmore College: 'The first semester consists in an analysis of motion leading to the Newtonian synthesis, the conservation laws of physics, the development of an atomic theory of matter, the Periodic Table of Elements, and the kinetic theory of gases. The second semester considers the evolution of modern physics: physical properties of light, aspects of relativity, the wave versus the quantum theory of light, certain electrical phenomena, the atomicity of charge, Bohr's model of the atom, radioactivity, fundamental particles, the nuclear atom and nuclear energy, stellar energy.' Laboratory work is included. At the University of California, Physics 10—A Descriptive Introduction to Physics—is given each semester to large classes with total enrolments of around 1,000. The course consists of three lecture demonstrations per week, dealing with some of the more important phenomena of physics. A fourth example is Physics-Chemistry 11A–11B at the University of California. The teaching of this course has been shared by a member of the Physics Department and a member of the Chemistry Department. Four major 'blocks' of content are stressed: Newton's laws, kinetic theory of a gas, simple electrostatics, and the Bohr atom. Laboratory work is included: weighing assortments of marbles as an analogue experiment in stoichiometry, electrolysis of water, etc.

It should be noted that many academic physicists take very seriously their responsibility for introducing the non-scientist to physics. The courses are often taught for a year or two by the most distinguished members of the physics staff, and inventiveness and imagination are perhaps shown more frequently in the teaching of these courses than anywhere else in the undergraduate curriculum.

Summary

From what has been said, the reader will understand that physics faculties have a considerable responsibility, not only for reproducing their professional kind by educating the professional physicists of tomorrow, but also for educating competent and zealous teachers of physics in the lower schools and specialists in the science and engineering subjects over whose disciplinary frontiers the flood of developments in modern physics is now pouring. The responsibility to teachers is generally met by a programme that is closely related to the first degree programme for professional physicists, departing from the programme for the specialist to allow opportunity for the student teacher to practise the teaching arts—including that of the lecture demonstration in physics—and usually terminating at a lower level than that reached by the future researcher in physics. The realities of school size and demand for science teachers require that some of these programmes educate teachers with hybrid specialities—physics-mathematics teachers, physics-chemistry teachers, etc.—and such provisions have been made in the educational programmes of many of the countries reporting.

The education in physics of non-physicist specialists—future engineers, chemists, geologists, mathematicians, astronomers, biologists, physicians, dentists, pharmacists, agronomists, optometrists, et al.—is usually limited to an introductory physics course of one or two years with accompanying practical work. In some countries this course is the same for all and is the course taken by physics concentrators. Generally, however, the courses are differentiated according to the needs and abilities of the students concerned. One is impressed by the list of specialists who study physics in universities—evidence that physics is truly a basic study that is required for competence in a large number of professions.

V. Advanced study in physics toward higher degrees

Introduction

This chapter provides a brief introduction to the subject of advanced or post-graduate physics beyond the first degree and toward higher degrees, culminating for some in the doctorate. The report is brief because it is believed proper in this first survey to emphasize university programmes that lead up to the first degree in physics. On the other hand, to plan an educational programme effectively at first degree levels, one must know some of the characteristics and requirements of educational programmes for graduate students. Although not universally required for a career in physics, attainment of the doctorate is increasingly expected of one who desires a career as a member of the staff in a university or as a leader of research in a laboratory. Accordingly, the short national reports here are intended to provide a review of educational programmes, followed by the highly selected and motivated students in physics who continue their university studies after receiving the first degree.

Advanced study in physics in Czechoslovakia

Graduates of the professional branch of the faculty who are awarded the diploma, 'promoted physicist', qualify for employment as expert physicists. The diploma, however, does not mean that they already possess the qualifications for independent scientific work for which one of the so-called 'scientific degrees' is required. There are, at present, four degrees of this type: the C.Sc. (Candidate of Sciences) and the D.Sc. (Doctor of Sciences) degrees entitle the holder to engage in scientific work, while the remaining two degrees, those of 'professor' or 'docent', signify in addition that these scientific workers have the necessary qualifications to teach at universities or schools of that level. In order to be pronounced docent, one usually must hold a C.Sc. degree, while the title of Professor is mainly conferred upon holders of the D.Sc. degree.

The C.Sc. degree in physics may be obtained by a university graduate who has passed the so-called 'candidate's examinations' and successfully defended a 'candidate's dissertation', which must prove his creative approach to scientific work in his particular field and also establish some new scientific results. The examinations are to reveal the candidate's standard of learning, his general level of knowledge in his particular branch of science, maturity in the field of philosophy, and command of foreign languages.

The right to confer the C.Sc. degree in certain sciences is awarded by the State Commission for the Awarding of Scientific Degrees, consisting of prominent scientific workers. It is only granted to university faculties, schools of that level, or scientific institutes which employ a sufficient number of qualified scientific workers in the particular branch. The State Commission also decides for which branches of science a C.Sc. degree is to be given, stipulates in which branches the candidates are to be examined, and supervises the awarding of the degrees.

Physics forms part of the group of mathematico-physical sciences. A candidate presenting a dissertation in experimental physics must, on the one hand, pass a general examination in experimental physics and a more specialized one in the field of which his dissertation treats. He must also display adequate knowledge in mathematics and theoretical physics. If his dissertation deals with theoretical physics, he is examined in this discipline and expected to possess appropriate knowledge in mathematics and experimental physics as well. The examination board consists in these cases of at least four members; one of them must be a scientific worker from some other establishment. As a rule, the scientist who supervised the candidate's scientific work is also a member of the board. The commission also appoints two opponents who state their

118

opinion regarding the merits of the dissertation in writing. Prior to defending his dissertation, the candidate must have passed the prescribed examinations. The defence takes place at a session of the physical section of the faculty or of the scientific council of the research institute.

The Doctor of Science degree is awarded to outstanding scientific workers who have defended their doctoral dissertation. No further examinations are demanded of them. The right to confer this degree in certain branches of science is also granted by the aforesaid State Commission and confined to some universities and especially important scientific institutes of the Czechoslovak Academy of Sciences. The doctoral dissertation must bear on the solution of a significant problem and, at least in its essence, have appeared in a scientific journal or been published as a scientific monograph. The dissertation is judged by three assessors not under the rank of D.Sc. or professor. The dissertation is defended before a wider public forum than in the case of the C.Sc. dissertation.

In view of the great significance of science for the advancement of society, the State takes necessary measures to ensure the planned education of scientific workers. There are several ways of training promising young physicists and to help them obtain their C.Sc. degree as soon as possible. One is the granting of fellowships of a maximum of three years, and another the scientific preparation of young graduates. In most cases this education proceeds under the guidance of a qualified 'scientific instructor'. In addition to universities, there are also some big research institutes, adhering mainly to the Academy of Sciences, which are selected by the mentioned Awarding Commission as 'training institutions'. The 'scientific instructors' guiding the work of their 'aspirants' are also confirmed by this commission.

Advanced study in physics in the Federal Republic of Germany

There is no actual course prescribed for the interval between *Hauptdiplom* and doctorate *(Promotion)*. In addition to the preparation of the thesis *(Dissertation)*, the student attends lectures in theoretical physics, or in some specialized subject. He is largely at liberty to choose his subject, the main aim being to make him work independently, especially for his thesis. The subjects for these theses depend on the fields of work of the individual institutes and differ, therefore, from one university to another.

The doctorate *(promotion)* is not dealt with in a uniform manner by the various universities of the Federal Republic which follow individual examination procedures. At the majority of universities, graduation with the final diploma examination *(Diplomhauptprüfung)* or the examination of teaching physics in secondary schools *(Staatsexamen)* is required before the student may take up work on the doctoral thesis *(Dissertation)*. In most cases, the total number of semesters, including the doctorate examination *(Promotion)*, amounts to about fifteen.

When applying for the doctorate *(Promotion)*, the thesis must be submitted. The thesis *(Dissertation)* must give evidence of the applicant's ability to do independent research work and to record the results appropriately. The thesis *(Doktorarbeit, Dissertation)* is expected to be a continuation of the diploma special study *(Diplomarbeit)*, if this is feasible. The doctoral thesis must embody essentially original scientific results justifying its publication. At most universities, publication of the thesis as a whole, or at least in part, in a science journal is required. At some universities the doctorate examination *(Promotion)* consists of a regular examination. At others, and this is now the general trend, the examination consists of a so-called 'colloquium', provided the student has already passed the final diploma examination *(Diplomhauptprüfung)* or the examination for specialist science teachers in secondary schools *(Staatsexamen)*. This colloquium consists mainly in a discussion covering the subject of the doctoral thesis. The procedure differs at the individual universities. At least three professors participate in the colloquium, representing two different branches of physics (experimental, applied and theoretical physics), or another section of the faculty of natural sciences.

In the Federal Republic of Germany, at present approximately 40 per cent of physics students study for the doctorate; the remainder leave with the diploma.

120

Advanced study in physics in France

The *licence* for the doctorate requires seven Certificates of Higher Education (CES). One of them must be chosen from the very specialized CES of that faculty—a very wise measure, because it requires the future researcher to obtain the CES taught by the Chair in his chosen speciality. For example, if he wants to prepare a thesis on nuclear reactors, he should study in the CES programme of Physics of Nuclear Reactors (which exists at the universities of Paris and of Grenoble).

The student who desires a career in scientific research undertakes his thesis research at the university or in a public research laboratory (Atomic Energy Commission, National Office of Aeronautic Research, National Centre for Space studies, etc.) or a private one. When the work has yielded some results (after about eighteen months) he can prepare a treatise and present it before the faculty. If he passes this oral examination satisfactorily, he obtains the title of doctor in his research speciality (e.g. Doctor of Electronics, of Solid State Physics, of Nuclear Physics, etc.). He should, before the oral examination, possess six CES, including the specialized CES which was directly connected with his doctoral degree. Finally, when the research work has given original results, the student publishes his thesis and sustains it publicly. He thus obtains the degree of *docteur ès sciences*. He should previously have obtained the *licence* for the doctorate.

It is obviously difficult to specify the length of this preparation. Let us say that it is about five years from the beginning of research to the thesis of the *doctorat ès sciences*. The schedule for these studies would be the following: baccalaureat, 18 years of age; obtaining the *propédeutique*, 19; obtaining the *licence*, the beginning of research, 22; sustaining a thesis for the doctorate in the speciality, 24; sustaining the thesis of the *doctorat ès sciences* (often called *doctorat d'Etat*), 27. The universities deliver about 500 diplomas of the doctorate in the specialities each year and about 300 of the *doctorat ès sciences*. Of these, about a third are oriented toward physics. These laureates usually stay in the laboratory where they prepared their thesis, gradually ascending the ladder of the hierarchy. A certain number undertake careers in higher education.

The thesis for the *doctorat ès sciences* requires original research; it is not possible to make any general statement about it. The theses of the doctoral specialities are less substantial and generally do not contain new results. They have the objective of bringing together some measurements made by the candidate, who must show thereby that he knows how to write clearly and to express his ideas orally.

Advanced study in physics in the U.S.S.R.

The training of research workers in physics is mainly effected through post-graduate studentship in colleges and research institutes.

Admission to post-graduate scholarship is granted to graduated specialists in physics. Within three years they must pass three examinations and carry out research work as a basis for their Candidate of Science thesis. The choice of thesis subject and the precise formulation of its title are left to the discretion of the author and his director of studies. This, in view of the wide range of specialist fields open to post-graduates, gives sufficient freedom in the selection of a subject. The thesis must contain novel scientific data as well as practical conclusions and recommendations, and demonstrate the ability of the competitor to conduct independent research, his deep erudition and special knowledge in the domains of physics bearing on the subject of the thesis.

A thesis for the doctor's degree in physics must constitute an original research containing theoretical generalizations and a solution of an important scientific problem. Most of the doctors' theses are the outcome of many years' labour by the authors.

A thesis is published, whereupon it is defended at a meeting of a faculty, college or a research institute board which is addressed by two to three officials and any number of volunteer opponents present at the meeting. The awarding of the degree is decided by ballot. Then the thesis is examined by the Highest Qualifying Committee, Vyschaia Attestacionnaia Komissiia (VAK), of the Ministry of Higher and Intermediate Special Education of the U.S.S.R., with the object of ascertaining the scientific value of the thesis. The same committee delivers the diploma.

The aforesaid committee (VAK) consists of the most prominent scientists in various branches of science. One third of the staff committee is renewed every year.

The qualifying committee comprises special expert commissions which examine each thesis and make decisions as to the expediency of awarding the degree. In some cases the authors of the theses are invited to give additional explanations before the expert commission or the plenum of the qualifying committee. The final decision of the latter is based on the consideration of the minutes of the defence and the conclusion of the expert commission.

The procedure of awarding degrees outlined above ensures a very high scientific level of the theses.

Advanced study in physics in the United Kingdom

Before the Second World War the M.Sc. degree was fairly commonly taken by graduates of good ability who did not proceed to a Ph.D. It was usually taken by research which extended over about two years. Nowadays, although the practice does vary a good deal among different universities, there has been an unfortunate tendency to regard the M.Sc. rather as a 'failed Ph.D.', but some successful attempts have been made to re-establish this degree as one of value. Some candidates still take it on the basis of a research project but the most interesting development, which many physicists regard as an important one for the future, is the establishment of a number of advanced lecture courses, with associated practical work, which lead to the award of the M.Sc. One of these is in Birmingham where a most successful course in nuclear physics, well supported by people returning from industry, has been established. In the University of London several courses of this kind exist, the special subjects including crystallography and acoustics.

In the University of Manchester this development of organized advanced courses leads to the award not of a degree but of a Diploma in Advanced Studies. The diploma may be taken by students who enrol specially for it but it is also made a necessary course which all research students must follow. The course lasts one year, and the lectures cover two terms of it. A written examination and an oral examination are held, and students are required also to undertake an experimental or theoretical project on which a report must be written. Each student must follow at least three courses of lectures in each of two terms. Full details of the course are given in Appendix V E1.

Although the Doctor of Philosophy degree (Ph.D.) is not in Britain an essential professional qualification as it is in America and some Continental countries, a substantial proportion of the best graduates do now stay at the university to take this degree. Hitherto, in contrast to American practice, the degree has been awarded essentially on the thesis, which has resulted from a piece of supervised research, with comparatively little emphasis upon organized courses of advanced lectures. The universities have always considered that the degree of Ph.D. should represent in some fair measure a hallmark of capacity for original research. In recent years the necessity for giving research students organized courses of advanced lectures has been widely recognized and is now commonly adopted. The importance of displaying real ability is, however, still regarded as paramount. The attitude of industrial and other employers to the form of training for the Ph.D. is sometimes critical and was reported upon by the Institute of Physics and the Physical Society in 1960.[1]

In addition to post-graduate work in the universities, some is undertaken in the colleges of advanced technology and this will certainly increase in volume and scope. At present, a post-graduate award available to the colleges of technology is Membership of the College of Technologists and it is intended that this should be of Ph.D. standard. It is likely that the colleges of advanced technology will shortly be able to award their own post-graduate degrees.

Advanced study in physics in the U.S.A.

The graduate student of physics ordinarily begins his graduate work at the age of about 22 after completing the undergraduate studies described in Chapter III. In deciding whom to admit to graduate study in physics, graduate departments of physics rely upon one or more, sometimes all, of the following: (a) inspection of the under-

1. *The Postgraduate Training of Physicists in British Universities*, The Institute of Physics and the Physical Society, London.

graduate record of the student; (b) appraisal examinations given by the departments themselves, and (c) the results of such national examinations as the Graduate Record Examination of the Educational Testing Service, Inc. Various kinds of information about the requirements of different graduate schools are made available to prospective graduate students by the American Institute of Physics. Included are booklets on the research specialities of academic physics departments, scholarships and fellowships available, and the steps to take in choosing a graduate school.[1] Most graduate physics departments distribute to undergraduate colleges brochures that describe their graduate programmes and the requirements for entrance. Only students who have shown evidence of professional promise are encouraged to study for the doctor's degree.

The objective of graduate education leading to the doctorate in physics is to give the student preparation in depth for a career in industrial research or in academic research and teaching in a college or university. Graduate studies terminating at the master's degree in physics are undertaken by some physics teachers in secondary schools, by teachers in the smaller colleges and universities, and by some who hold physics staff positions in industry or government. (Discussion of the master's degree in physics will appear later in this report.) Graduate studies leading to the doctorate in physics include a combination of course work and research, and stress breadth of preparation as well as depth. To be sure, some compromise between breadth and depth must be found, but most graduate departments of physics give their students further advanced preparation in several branches of physics as well as command of one specialized branch. The continuing ability of the physicist to break new ground in research—in both academic and industrial laboratories—testifies to the success of this broad preparation. The 1962 MIT general catalogue has stated this point of view as follows: 'Graduate students are expected to gain real familiarity with several of the branches of physics, not merely with one speciality. They will be well prepared for either academic work or industrial research, since the training includes a broad and

1. *Graduate Physics Research Specialties in American Educational Institutions*, American Institute of Physics, New York.
Graduate Assistantships and Fellowships in Physics, American Institute of Physics, New York.
Planning for graduate study in physics, American Institute of Physics, New York.

thorough understanding of both the fundamentals of physics and its advanced applications'. The requirements for the doctorate in physics include the completion of work in courses, the writing of a satisfactory dissertation based on original research, and the passing of examinations at several stages in the graduate career.

A considerable amount of formal course work—attendance at lectures, course examinations, etc.—is one of the distinguishing characteristics of graduate education in the United States. Although research is the heart of graduate education and the student is expected to prove himself as an independent investigator before he obtains the doctorate, the provision of graduate courses is believed to give considerable strength to programmes of advanced study. One can argue that the taking of courses should come to an end upon attainment of the bachelor's degree. In fact, however, such is the pace of contemporary physics, that the graduate of even the strongest undergraduate college finds formal instruction profitable in his graduate years in order to carry his undergraduate studies to an appropriately advanced level and to learn about the latest developments in physics. Graduate courses also serve to instruct physicists who feel in need of 'refresher' work and other scientists and engineers who want to learn about what is going on in physics. There are benefits for the faculty also in this kind of advanced teaching. Examples of some graduate courses in physics either required or recommended at three institutions are listed in Appendix V F1. Many other courses are offered in special areas.

Candidates for the doctorate in physics enter upon thesis research at times that vary somewhat from one institution to another, but are usually about one year or a year and a half after admission. Experimentalists can begin their thesis research somewhat sooner than theorists, the latter usually finding it necessary to pursue their course work a little longer before beginning an investigation in theory. At the University of California, for example, students who want to write an experimental thesis begin their research right after taking the preliminary examination in the second semester of the first year of graduate work; theorists usually begin their investigation a semester or two later. Most graduate students finish their course work in three or four semesters, and then are engaged full time in research.

126

There are usually three graduate examinations that must be passed by the doctoral candidate: the preliminary (or appraisal, or qualifying) examination, taken during the first year of graduate studies; the general (or comprehensive, or final) examination, taken usually after two or three years; and the oral examination in defence of the dissertation. The preliminary examination is usually a written examination (at the University of California it also includes an oral examination), and covers the undergraduate preparation. The comprehensive examination (called 'the qualifying examination for advancement to candidacy' at the University of California) may be written or oral or both. The oral examination in defence of the dissertation need not be described in detail here. It is similar to that given in other countries, differing only in the respect that the examination is usually not a public one. The average age at which the doctorate is obtained is about 27, and about 600 doctoral degrees were awarded nationally in 1962 in physics.

A minimum of one calendar year of full-time study beyond the bachelor's degree is ordinarily needed to obtain a master's degree in physics at most universities. The average time is nearer two years. About thirty semester-hours of advanced course work are required. The student must pass a comprehensive examination. A thesis is sometimes, but not always, required. The master's degree is usually the terminal degree of those few secondary school teachers of physics who carry on graduate studies within physics departments. For the others who receive it, it has been called a 'consolation prize', awarded to recognize academic achievement that is beyond the bachelor's level, but falls short of that required for the doctorate.

Summary

By means of post-graduate education in physics, a comparatively few, highly qualified students receive the opportunity to carry on research at the frontiers of knowledge, thereby testing their ability to make original contributions to the growth of knowledge in physics. Those who succeed in this qualify, in the measure of their accomplishment, for one of several advanced degrees—the master's degree, the *licence*, or the degree of candidate at an intermediate level, or the doctor's degree at the highest level. The time required is about two years of advanced study and research for the intermediate degree, and from three to seven years for the doctoral degree. These estimates, however, are averages over large numbers of persons and cannot safely be assumed to apply to an individual. Advanced degrees are awarded for accomplishments in research, and research seldom follows a definite schedule.

Although the emphasis in post-graduate education is on research, several countries have found it useful to add to their programmes advanced courses in physics as a means of raising the competence of the student to the highest possible level and of imparting to him the latest knowledge in the field. Where such courses are required, they are usually scheduled for the earlier part of the post-graduate period.

Examinations for advanced degrees are generally oral examinations in defence of the thesis or dissertation before a board of experts in the field of specialization. However, some countries supplement this by comprehensive written examinations that test the student's competence in physics over a wider range of sub-fields than is usually involved in writing the dissertation. Emphasis in post-graduate education in physics, as in education at other levels, is on preparing physicists who show originality whether it be in pure physics or in a branch of applied physics.

VI. Academic research in physics

Introduction

Research is inseparably associated with the teaching of physics in universities. It is generally conceded that physicists in a university should carry on research in order to add to the world's knowledge. Research also has a role to play in the teaching process in physics. The professor or some other member of the staff who gathers graduate students around him to do research, following their progress, and carrying on his own research on a related problem, is teaching even though no class meetings may be involved. At the same time, it is proper to ask the question: 'At what point does the physicist at a university who devotes himself to research cease to be a professor?'

This chapter is concerned with the role of academic research in physics, considering it as a form of teaching as well as a means of personal fulfilment for the physicist and the source of new knowledge.

Academic research in Czechoslovakia

Accepting the principle that a university is only worthy of its name if its activities are not confined to training experts, but also include high grade scientific research work, the Czechoslovak universities and schools of this level are scientific institutions as well as teaching institutions. They are on a level with the scientific institutes of the

129

academies of sciences and other research institutes which, together with the university faculties, form the so-called State Research Basis. The basis consists of scientific and research establishments of all branches of science whose technical equipment and personnel enable them to solve important scientific problems.

A certain number of research projects and problems are incorporated into the State Plan for Scientific Research because they are of major importance for the planned development of the country's economy and culture. The central body for questions of scientific research is the Government's State Commission for the Development and Co-ordination of Sciences and Technics, headed by a Minister. This commission draws up the mentioned State plan and, among others, allocates the necessary financial means for its realization to establishments of the State basis. As a rule, several scientific and research institutes, and even industrial enterprises, co-operate in solving partial problems of State research projects pending the application of research results in practice. Thus, most of the Chairs of physics, institutes and laboratories at university faculties take an active part in realizing the State plan research projects.

Apart from the State plan, there are a number of so-called 'departmental research plans', forming the basis of scientific research work on important problems which are not directly part of the State plan and have been entrusted to the institute of either a ministry, the academies of sciences or the universities. This research is financed by the State departments concerned; in the case of the universities, by the Ministry of Education and Culture. The aforesaid State commission co-ordinates all departmental plans with the State plan.

Each university faculty has its own plan for scientific and research work which includes State and departmental problems as well as the 'faculty problems', which mostly constitute long-term problems of basic research, for which not even an approximate time-limit can be set, nor the definite result foreseen. Work on these problems is also financed by the Ministry of Education and Culture, which supervises the scientific work of the universities through the State Committee for Universities.

This description actually represents merely the scheme of the organization of research work. In reality, co-operation is far-

130

reaching also among related Chairs and institutes of one or several faculties, among the Chairs and institutes of the academies of sciences, among the Chairs and institutes of various branches of sciences when solving complex problems, etc. And it is not always 'planned' co-operation, laid down by the research plans, but often has its origin in the initiative of the scientific workers. Nor are all research problems planned by a uniform method. The planning of basic scientific research, for example, differs somewhat from that of applied research. Planned research, facilitating, on the one hand, the co-ordination and concentration of means and personnel, leaves, on the other hand, sufficient freedom for science to advance according to its own laws of development. State support is also given to various methods of international scientific co-operation which, especially in the field of physics, has been taking on constantly growing importance.

Academic research in the Federal Republic of Germany

Even during their work for the diploma, students are initiated into research. The scope of the *Diplomarbeit* is modest; the results must not be absolutely new. The student is primarily expected to learn how to handle an experimental or theoretical task independently. The ability shown by the student in carrying out the work, apart from the result of the main diploma examination *(Diplomhauptprüfung)*, determines whether or not he will be allowed to undertake a *Doktorarbeit* later. The doctoral thesis, however, is of a more scientific character and has to embody new results. In general, the work will be published in a science journal.

The students studying for the diploma or doctorate are members of their institute and as such participate in all activities of the institute regularly. This is the time when the student develops his capacities to the full. Being continually exposed to the company of professors, *Dozenten*, assistants, and older, more scientifically experienced doctorate and diploma candidates, his capabilities and scientific creative imagination are awakened.

Those staying at the university after their *Promotion* continue on scientific work, partly by themselves, partly in teams with *Dozenten*, assistants, doctorate or diploma candidates. Proving their worth in scientific work is what is expected in the career of scientists.

As to the organization of research, the universities are subject to the federal states concerned, just as, in accordance with the constitution of the Federal Republic of Germany, all matters of education are the concern of the individual states. The Federal Republic of Germany has no Federal Ministry of Education. Co-ordination is effected by the Permanent Conference of Educational Ministers of the Federal States. Apart from this, several federal ministries have special interest in physics education and research at universities. The Federal Ministry for Scientific Research, for example, supports those institutes concerned with nuclear physics and aerospace research.

In Germany, academic research is done not only at the universities but also and very much so at the Max Planck Institutes. These are wholly devoted to research and not to instruction, in contrast to the university institutes. There are eleven Max Planck Institutes for physics and neighbouring subjects. The academic research is widely supported by the Deutsche Forschungsgemeinschaft. This represents a self-administration organ of the body of German scientists. It is mainly financed by public means of the Federal Republic and the states (Länder). Considerable financial assistance to research and education is given by the Foundation Committee (Stifterverband) of German industry. Limited means are put at the disposal of universities by local promoting societies. In 1957, an administrative agreement between the Federal Government and the governments of the federal states was reached and the so-called Wissenschaftsrat (scientific advisory council) was formed, which makes recommendations for the extension of existing universities and the formation of additional universities.

Academic research in France

Those who are teaching physics in universities in France are physicists who are recruited to carry out scientific work. This criterion is not entirely satisfactory because it tends to populate the universities with 'disinterested physicists' who are passionately devoted to their speciality, devote all their efforts to it, and generally do not follow the vocation of a teacher. They agree to give courses in basic physics only at the beginning of their careers, and endeavour as soon as possible to teach only their specialities. It seems necessary to restore a more just balance between the role of the physicist and that of the professor in recruiting teaching personnel in the universities. The situation is developing favourably otherwise, and one finds today at the University of Paris some specialists of considerable reputation who devote an appreciable part of their activities to instruction in general physics.

Scientific research calls for considerable resources not normally available outside very large universities. The tendency of small universities to undertake research without adequate means leads to mediocre results of little interest and so to waste of their scant resources.

In order to avoid such dispersal of effort there is now a trend among French universities to 'pair' with the big private or public research laboratories. In several provincial towns, university teachers have facilities for worth-while research, which they perform in a laboratory subordinate to the Centre National de la Recherche Scientifique, (CNRS) or to the Centre de l'Energie Atomique, (CEA). This frees the universities to devote all their resources to teaching and at the same time enables university teachers to work as they should.

Academic research in the U.S.S.R.

The research work in the domain of physics embraces a wide scope of scientific problems in various branches of physics.

They comprise: the physics of solids (theory of solids, physical aspects of the strength of materials, crystal formation, physics of solids at high pressures, physics of magnetic phenomena, etc.); nuclear physics; physics of plasma; thermal phenomena at high temperatures; methods of direct conversion of heat into electric energy; structure and evolution of the Earth; radioastronomy; radiophysics and radio engineering; semi-conductor electronics; etc.

The college departments select the research subjects independently according to the scientific interest of their members. As a general rule, the research work of a college department is conducted with the participation of undergraduates organized in research circles and societies.

The scientific research work in physics is, moreover, carried out by scientific societies and organized groups of physicists in numerous cities of the country. They also lend assistance in the task of improving the erudition of the teachers of physics.

An important part in the propagation of physical knowledge among the population is played by the All-Union Society of Propagation of Scientific and Political Knowledge, particularly by its numerous branches in different cities.

Systematic improvement of the erudition of schoolteachers in physics is carried out by special institutes.

Academic research in the United Kingdom

There is no physics department of a United Kingdom university that does not regard research as one of its crucially important functions. In Chapter II, reference was made to the Government Committee under the chairmanship of Lord Robbins that has recently published its report, *Higher Education*. The Council of the Institute of Physics and the Physical Society submitted written evidence to that committee which includes the following comment on research.

'We must direct special attention to the place of research in any institution that is educating physicists. In some quarters the view is held that one can separate research from teaching and it is argued that the universities ought not to be deflected from their main purpose—undergraduate teaching—by excessive concern for research. This is completely false. To attempt to put it into practice would be fatal to undergraduate teaching in science and technology. In educating physicists of the highest level, research is an essential ingredient of the environment and this is the crucial justification for university research.

'The value to the nation of university research in science is generally recognized. In its tenth annual report (1956–57) the Advisory Council on Scientific Policy stated that "the universities occupy a position of supreme importance in research.... Not only are their post-graduate schools the source of the majority of trained senior research workers in industry and government establishments, but it is in them that much of the country's research in pure science is carried out, and it is from their research, directed to the pursuit of knowledge regardless of its applications, that stem most of the major discoveries which subsequently can be applied to industry." We believe that this statement is still true, although perhaps not to the same extent as formerly. We also believe it to be important that it should continue to be true and that our best students should be trained by men making important discoveries in their subject.'

The majority of university teachers are still actively engaged in research and research ability is an important factor in deciding appointments and promotions.

Funds for research come from various sources. The University Grants Committee includes in its allocation of government money to universities some funds for research. Another government department, the Department of Scientific and Industrial Research, also supports research extensively in universities, particularly through grants to research students. Other government departments and industrial concerns also provide money for research that would usually be in the broad field of their special interest. The expensive nature of physics research does, however, involve difficulties and reference should be made to a recent report on this subject.[1]

Academic research in the U.S.A.

Basic research in universities of the United States is regarded as a part of the teaching and learning that is their primary mission. The attitude of most university physicists toward research is that it is an indispensable part of the learning process—the search for greater understanding of the physical world—that continues in the productive physicist throughout his lifetime. The physicist learns from his research, extending the bounds of his knowledge and, by publication and teaching, increasing the knowledge of others. The way in which he teaches his advanced graduate students is to counsel them in their research and often to work beside them in the laboratory. The strongest institutions are those in which research and

1. *Problems facing University Physics Departments,* The Institute of Physics and The Physical Society, London, August 1963.

teaching are intermingled to a considerable degree and stimulate each other. To be sure, universities engage in many developmental projects that are not basic research. The extent to which this is justified is a subject of debate within academic circles. Basic research on the other hand, as a means of educating students, of providing intellectual stimulation of the faculty, and adding to human knowledge, is viewed as indispensable to the role of the university.

Physics research in universities is organized in a variety of ways. The members of the professorial staff may carry on their research within the administrative structure of the physics department and with the financial support of outside agencies or, less frequently, with the sole financial support of the university itself. Increasingly, there is a tendency within large universities to set up special divisions for research in certain areas, often on an interdisciplinary basis. These divisions or centres have their own administrative organization, sources of funds, and large staffs of professional and supporting personnel. Often the divisions are organized around large physical facilities—accelerators, reactors, and the like. Members of the physics staff carry on research within these divisions; occasionally, professorial appointments are made jointly by the physics department and the research division. For example, many members of the Physics Department at the University of California at Berkeley carry on research at the Lawrence Radiation Laboratory. About twenty-three members of the staff have such research connexions with the Radiation Laboratory; the others carry on their research at the Physics Department. About half of the graduate students in physics do their thesis work, experimental or theoretical, at the Radiation Laboratory. The organization of research at Columbia University is different: the research divisions in physics are organized within the Physics Department. These research divisions include the Nevis Cyclotron Laboratory, the Pegram Nuclear Physics Laboratories, and the Columbia Radiation Laboratory. At MIT, many of the research groups in physics are parts of interdepartmental laboratories. The Cosmic Ray and Space Physics Group, the ONR Van de Graaff Generator Group, the Theoretical Group, the Rockefeller Electrostatic Generator Group, the Radioactivity and Cyclotron Group, the Elementary Particle Research Group, and the Linear Accelerator Group are in the Laboratory

136

for Nuclear Science. The Microwave Spectroscopy Group, the Nuclear Magnetic Resonance and Hyperfine Structure Group, the Atomic Beam Group, the Low Temperature Group, the X-Ray Emission Group, the Physical Electronics Group, the Physical Acoustics Group, the Plasma Physics Group, and the Statistical Thermodynamics Group are in the Research Laboratory of Electronics. Similarly, there is a Centre of Materials Science and Engineering.

Some physicists in the smaller universities and the liberal arts colleges successfully carry on significant research, but such are the pace of contemporary research in physics and the relatively large amounts of equipment and time required, that the odds are very much against research in colleges.[1] College physicists find it possible occasionally to carry on research on their campuses or to engage in co-operative research at a nearby university. Otherwise, college physicists must devote their non-classroom professional activities to the supervision of projects by students, to the development of new experiments for the instructional laboratory, the writing of textbooks, and so on.

Summary

The role of the university in physics in the survey countries includes both teaching and research. The latter is sometimes problem-oriented and developmental in nature, but is usually basic, directed at acquiring new knowledge for its own sake. The teaching function is complemented, stimulated, and made more effective by the research activities of university physicists. Research students and their professors interact in ways that enhance the work of each.

In the smaller educational institutions, the benefits of even the most modest professorial research are noticeable in improved teaching and the establishment of a spirit of inquiry. In the absence of research or other scholarly activity, the physics professor is too often in the position of 'ladling knowledge from a stagnant pool'.

The problems of supporting academic research and organizing it

1. W. H. Kruschwitz, 'Some Aspects of Physics Research in non-Ph.D. Granting Institutions, *American Journal of Physics*, Vol. 30, 1962.
   G. E. Pake, Can Four-year Colleges prepare Physics Majors for Graduate Work in Physics? *American Journal of Physics*, Vol. 29, 1961.

137

for greatest effectiveness are many and go beyond the scope of this report. Suffice it to say that the cost of conducting research in physics has risen to the point where university research funds must be supplemented, and governments and industry are playing an increasingly large role in supporting physics research in universities.

VII. Special programmes in physics: continuing education, evening schools, extramural education

Introduction

The preceding chapters have been concerned with what might be called the 'main line' of university education in physics, dealing with the full-time studies of young people between the ages of 18 and 27 who are preparing for careers in physics, physics teaching, or one of the other professions requiring a knowledge of physics. But there are other educational needs in physics. First of these is the need of the professional physicist in mid-career to keep up to date in his knowledge of physics. Present in all scientifically oriented professions, this requirement is particularly strong in physics because of the extraordinarily rapid advances being made in research. For example, in just one country participating in this survey, about 29,000 pages of research reports are published in the professional journals in physics each year. The explosive growth of new knowledge in physics throughout the world is an educational problem of the first magnitude. Its implication is clear—the education of the physicist and of the engineer is never at an end. He must be a learner all his life, acquiring new knowledge by all means available to him—by scientific books and journals, the activities of professional societies, and even the processes of continuing formal education.

Another problem is that of assisting young people to acquire an education in physics who are not in a position to become full-time university students. Ability in physics and a determination to succeed in becoming a physicist are not limited to the students who, at any moment, are enrolled in universities. Opportunities for part-time study are needed by the young person who is employed elsewhere, so that his talents, too, will be developed until he can become a full-time student.

This chapter deals with the following special programmes in physics in the participating countries: (a) opportunities for the continuing education of the physicist, the engineer, and others whose knowledge of physics must be kept current; (b) programmes in evening schools and extramural programmes by which instruction in physics can be given to part-time students.

Special programmes in Czechoslovakia

Conferences and societies. Conferences and other kinds of meetings are an important means of furthering the advancement of scientific work. They constitute occasions when younger scientists meet experts in their field of science and have an opportunity to acquaint themselves with the latest achievements and knowledge.

In the fields of physics, these meetings of scientists, all-Czechoslovak or with international participation, are mostly organized by the physical institutes of the Czechoslovak Academy of Sciences, the university faculties and the Union of Czechoslovak Mathematicians and Physicists, all of which usually co-operate in arranging these events. All conferences are planned, discussed and approved for each calendar year in advance. The necessary financial means are set aside in the budget of the organization which acts as organizer. The majority of participants in these meetings are delegated by the individual scientific institutes, universities, etc., who also pay their fares and other expenses. If necessary, meetings on special problems may also be held on a smaller scale without previous planning. They are, as a rule, organized by the Union.

The Union of Czechoslovak Mathematicians and Physicists, founded in 1862, has been playing an important role in scientific life. It counts as its members nearly all Czechoslovak physicists employed at various establishments, as well as teachers of all types and levels. Apart from membership contributions, the union receives financial support from the Czechoslovak and Slovak Academies of Sciences and from the Ministry of Education and Culture. Its commissions of experts are frequently entrusted with the preparation of proposals concerning the solution of questions of science or instruction. The union publishes a review journal in physics, mathematics and astronomy which deals also with teaching problems. Further, two journals containing the results of original work in physics are edited by the Czechoslovak Academy of Science. To foster the education of young scientific workers, the union also holds prize-winning competitions for those under 30 years of age.

Extramural study. Professional physicists are comparatively seldom trained by extramural studies at the universities. The only form of part-time study practically used is the so-called external study. This means that an employed person studies almost entirely according to the curriculum of the full-time or internal student. He is expected to master his subject through independent reading of literature with only the help of consultations for which he may have to travel to the university. He must sit for all examinations including the final State examination, and his study course may not be prolonged more than two years beyond the duration of the normal curriculum. The greatest difficulty for external students is the laboratory training. For this reason, mostly employees of research institutes and laboratories (laboratory assistants and technicians) choose this method of study. They also prepare their diploma thesis at their places of employment.

The faculties also arrange special courses for employed students who live in the same town. These courses last one or more years and are specially organized in certain branches of physics: solid state physics, metal physics, etc. The courses are generally held in the evenings and mainly frequented by engineers, working on research or development projects and requiring for their work special knowledge in the specific branch of physics. They are later examined in the individual subjects and receive at the end of the course a certificate, confirming their attendance, but no degree is awarded.

Mention must be made at this juncture of the so-called extraordinary study method, enabling persons who live in the university town to put themselves down for certain lectures chosen from the curricula, sit for the appropriate examinations, and receive a certificate that they have passed them.

The extramural training of physics teachers. Physics teachers are also trained by so-called 'long-distance' study. This type of training has its own curricula, and special textbooks and manuals are issued for this purpose. A special department at the university faculties is in charge of these studies. Extramural students are usually expected to attend consultations once a month either at the faculty or at a 'consultation centre' elsewhere. These consultations generally last about eight hours on one day and deal, in the form of a seminar, with the more difficult parts of the subject matter, besides helping individual students with their particular study problems. The consultations are conducted by faculty teachers who are assisted by selected secondary school teachers. During the school vacations, usually two-week courses are organized for all students with the chief objective of practising the subject matter and conducting practical laboratory exercises. During the course of their studies, participants take the prescribed examinations in the individual subjects and, at the end of their course, sit for their Final State Examination like any full-time student of the pedagogical branch. The subject matter for students of this type of training is the same as that for full-time students. The former may, however, study, if they desire, just one of the two subjects of any teaching combination.

Those who avail themselves of this extramural method of pedagogical studies are mostly teachers already employed at some type of school, who feel they want to enlarge or supplement their knowledge and raise their qualifications. Extramural studies are also a useful means of helping to overcome the present shortage of qualified physics and mathematics teachers for secondary schools. Also members of other professions who want to exchange their present occupation for that of a teacher are studying by this method.

The methods of extramural studies are being constantly improved and perfected. Charles University has opened a special Institute for Extramural Pedagogical Studies for the supervision and direction of the training of teachers with special emphasis on teaching methods. Out of its analyses of practical experiences, the institute suggests improvements in the methods of extramural study.

At the pedagogical institutes, extramural study courses are being introduced to train basic school teachers. The organization is similar to that mentioned above.

142

Then, there are the so-called Institutes for the Further Education of Teachers to keep the teachers up to date with regard to their knowledge in the subjects they teach as well as to their methods of teaching. For this purpose, regular lectures are arranged by the institutes for the teachers in the course of the school year and one-to-two week courses at vacation time. The institutes closely co-operate with the Union of Czechoslovak Mathematicians and Physicists which organizes the lectures and provides expert lecturers from the ranks of its members. Teachers who have to travel some distance in order to attend the lectures or courses have their fares and other necessary expenses refunded from State funds.

Another useful means for improving the work of physics teachers is the teachers' journal *Fysika ve škole* (Physics at Schools) issued by the Ministry of Education and Culture.

Special programmes in the Federal Republic of Germany

After their doctorate examination *(Promotion)* young physicists can become assistants or receive grants from various organizations. In this manner they can continue their research work and increase their knowledge. Numerous such possibilities are also provided by the Max Planck Institutes. Many physicists make use of this chance to improve their training in science before they go into industry or join a research institute. It is a rule for those intending to become university teachers.

An important aspect in the scientific progress of every physicist is the regular study of scientific journals and the participation in the meetings of the Physikalische Gesellschaft. Here, what must especially be pointed out, special divisions (so-called *Fachausschüsse*) treat the progress of science continuously in meetings and publications. Details about these activities can be obtained from the Deutsche Physikalische Gesellschaft.

School teachers can join continuing education courses that are being held by some State institutions *(Landesstellen für den Physikunterricht)*. Some universities also offer an increasing measure of possibilities for the continuing science training of physics teachers. The German secondary school teachers have their own professional society (Verein zur Förderung des Mathematisch-Naturwissen-schaftlichen Unterrichts, Förderverein), which also promotes con-tinuing education with the aid of periodicals and science meetings.

Special programmes in France

The continuing education of physicists and engineers. Maintaining the scientific competence of engineers (including physicists in this official category) poses an important pedagogic problem that the universities and the *grandes écoles* are attempting to solve with more or less success. The young physicist who is hired by a research centre or an industrial company has received a considerable educa-tion in the course of his studies, but except in special cases he requires a further period of experience on the job before his know-ledge can be fully utilized. He will be put to work by his new em-ployer on some very specialized subject. Soon he is going to know a great many details about this very limited subject, but, in conse-quence, he will forget little by little the rest of his knowledge. In the limit, the perfect specialist knows 'everything about nothing' (and would be represented mathematically by Dirac's delta func-tion). This situation is perhaps excellent for conducting the study that was entrusted to him, but it leads to an intellectual 'hardening of the arteries', and produces specialists who are unusable outside of their narrow speciality. One day, the work is finished, and the engineer has to look for something else to do. This requires the solution of two problems: (a) some structure should be adopted for courses of educational 'recycling' which would inform engineers about new specialities and orient them toward new studies, and (b) a basic education should be given to future engineers, to enable them to be 'recycled' rapidly, abandoning one speciality to acquire another.

Recycling courses are being developed in France (see also Chap-ter X) and are generally organized by the large industrial companies or the large centres of research. A good formula consists in bringing together for a week the engineers who desire to learn about a new speciality and some specialists in that field in a 'seminar', structured by some lectures. It does not seem that there are any particular pedagogical problems in this; the only difficulty consists in creating the contact and sustaining the discussions.

144

The continuing education of teachers. Until recently, there was no organization providing means of maintaining the scientific competence of the teachers of the *lycées*, who were left to themselves and were often isolated in small provincial towns. Recently, some recycling courses lasting one week were organized by the universities. During the week, twenty-five teachers of the *lycées* were brought together in a large research centre. They heard some informational lectures (four or five), spent several afternoons in the laboratory carrying out experiments with modern apparatus, and visited some of the large research installations. The experience showed, in effect, that physics teachers in *lycées* soon lose any familiarity with physics research and with industrial physics that they may once have had. The goal of these courses is to plunge them back into this atmosphere. This recognizes an important fact: the teachers of physics in the *lycées* are the 'providers' of physicists. If they do not know how to sustain the enthusiasm of their students and to awaken an interest in a career in physics, it is useless to have excellent physics programmes in universities and *grandes écoles*, because the good students will not enter them. For this reason, little by little, one detects a growing national interest in the recycling of teachers of physics in the *lycées*, and all of the 'users of physicists' are making efforts to organize courses for them.

Vocational education. In order to use human resources fully to renew and develop the national scientific and technical manpower, programmes in vocational education have been organized for workers. This instruction for the up-grading of work abilities should parallel traditional instruction, but should not be confused with it, because the age and the situation of the students are not comparable. It is necessary to adopt quite different methods. In France, the Conservatoire National des Arts et Métiers provides for the upgrading of work abilities at the level of higher education. It accepts those who have reached the level of the baccalaureat, either by the conventional route or by that of vocational secondary education, and allows them to acquire diplomas of higher education, all while continuing as workers. The French Government is making a considerable effort to develop vocational education, particularly the up-grading of work abilities at the higher level of education. It has

145

granted funds not only for the support of 'traditional' students but also students in the higher programmes of improvement of work abilities.

The Conservatoire National des Arts et Métiers (CNAM) is a public educational establishment founded in Paris in 1794 that is probably unique. (There are also seventeen provincial annexes). Organizationally, it is the analogue of a university. The instructional programmes are grouped into Chairs, directed by a titular professor who is responsible for the courses, the laboratory instruction, personnel, and research laboratory. One important difference, however, is that the Chairs are oriented toward technology, for example, aeronautics, general radioelectricity, internal combustion engines, etc. Another important difference lies in the fact that all of the instruction of the CNAM takes place in the evening and Saturdays and Sundays. The students are usually young workmen who desire to return to their studies. This is why no diploma is required for admission and natural selection is allowed to operate. This method requires a very special teaching technique. (There are sometimes 800 registrants at the beginning of the year and, at the end of a month, the number of those continuing has fallen and stabilized at about 500.)

The students have to receive instruction from several Chairs, as in a university, to obtain a diploma—the *diplome d'études superieures techniques* (DEST). It is awarded to every student possessing a certain number of certificates delivered by the Chairs (usually three). Each Chair organizes an instructional programme that comprises, on the average, 120 hours of course work and exercises and 120 hours of laboratory work. Certain Chairs provide 150 hours of course work and 180 hours in the laboratory.

The instruction of one Chair is distributed over two years (sometimes over three). At the end of each year the students pass an examination dealing with the course and another on the laboratory work. A student who possesses the certificate of a Chair has thus undergone successfully four or six examinations during the two or three years. One sees the analogy between the educational programme of the universities and that of the conservatory. In the faculty of science of the universities, the possession of the certificate of the *propédeutique* and two other *certificats d'études superieures* leads to the granting of a *diplome d'études superieures techniques*. At the Conservatory, the possession of three certificates also leads to the delivery of the DEST. The only difference is that in the university less choice is left to the student. He is compelled to begin with the *propédeutique*, and then to choose the two other CES (for example, technology and electronics). At the CNAM, on the contrary, the choice of the students is very free. The structure resembles that of the American universities. The Conservatory students have at their disposal a catalogue of the courses from which they choose freely those in which they enrol. If, for example, a student has already acquired what he thinks is enough mathematics, he is not obliged to enrol for a course in mathematics and to pass an examination. He is allowed to enrol immediately in a technical course. If he is not able to do the work of the course, because of lack of preparation, that is his misfortune; he must go back and obtain the necessary preparation. The CNAM is very proud of this liberal structure, which seems to give good results, and which is well adapted to these students.

Once in possession of the diploma of higher technical studies, the student of the CNAM can continue. He prepares a thesis, obtains some results in technical research, and about two years after the DEST, he can obtain the title of engineer of the Conservatoire National des Arts et Métiers. The average total time required is about seven years, reduced to five years if the student has scholarship aid. To receive his engineer's degree he must not only sustain his theses with success but also undergo written and oral examinations on the material of the DEST. The diploma of engineer of the CNAM is equivalent to that of the *grandes écoles* and is placed at about the level of the *licence* of the university. Thus the Conservatory has the role of a technological university, which does not deliver a *licence*, but an engineering diploma, awarding about one hundred such diplomas per year.

Special programmes in the U.S.S.R.

In the academic year 1960/61 the total number of evening institutes of higher education (independent and departments of day institutes) was 265, and the total number of extramural institutes of higher education 564. The evening and extramural institutes include a few which are very large, catering for as many students and having as many provincial departments as the well-known French evening institute, Conservatoire National des Arts et Métiers. In 1961, the total number of students in the evening and extramural system of higher education was 1,240,000. The system thus existed on a large scale and had many ramifications in the academic year 1960/61.

Its large capacity nevertheless failed to meet the country's requirements in evening and extramural education, and it was therefore decided to expand both branches, particularly the latter. At present, much attention is being given to solving the problem rapidly and effectively, and the Soviet Union is now approaching a position where every institute of higher education will have its own evening and extramural department. There are at present 1,600,000 persons attending evening and extramural courses.

Students graduating from evening or extramural institutes receive diplomas on a par with those granted by day institutes of higher education. This is because the syllabus in the day, evening, and extramural systems of higher education is basically identical. The differences lie mainly in the methods of instruction, particularly in the extramural institutes. Evening students are obliged to attend all the types of instruction provided by the institute; evening education is thus internal, not extramural. Extramural students living in towns or suburbs may attend institute classes, but there is no obligation to do so: the student decides for himself if he wishes to become a student in the evening class department of an institute.

A special system of instruction has been devised for extramural students living a long way from urban centres. We shall describe this as it applies to physics.

Instructions on methods, to go with the physics textbooks, have been specially published for extramural students in view of their isolation from tutors and institute. In the course of a semester the students do a series of exercises from the textbook, send these to the department of physics, and get back written comments and advice on their work. This form of education by correspondence is based on self-study. In addition, the student has the possibility of consulting on the spot a physics assistant specially allocated to him, or he may be called to the nearest town, where he can attend revision lectures, perform laboratory work, attend tutorials, and sit for tests and examinations at some institute of higher education.

In view of their special difficulties in academic work, extramural students receive a great deal of care and attention. Various forms of assistance have recently been inaugurated: certain types of teaching machines specially suited to extramural instruction have been devised for trial purposes; machines which provide tape-recorded lectures on physics, accompanied by visual aids in the form of lantern-slide graphs, tables, diagrams and so forth, periodically setting questions on the lecture material and supplying marks according to the answers given; training machines for particular subjects in the course, and so forth.

The Moscow Institute of Railway Engineers has organized, for example, a physics teaching laboratory in a railway carriage. This travelling physics laboratory is sent, according to a schedule, to the most distant points on the railway line, for use by extramural students as a centre for laboratory work, seminars, examinations, and so forth.

Special programmes in the United Kingdom

It is perhaps in this field of work outside the main stream of full-time education that the flexibility of the British approach to education is seen to best advantage. Especially in industry, there has always been in Britain a very great respect for the man who has 'come up the hard way' and who has acquired qualifications by part-time study, or has reached a senior position on the strength of achievement which may in exceptional cases rest on virtually no formal technical education. Indeed, this attitude of mind may well have some bad effect on development of the British educational system. Apart from the universities and the colleges of advanced technology, there are about five hundred technical institutions in the United Kingdom that offer courses in science or technology; probably about two hundred of these would provide courses that would be suitable for men and women who are engaged in industry or elsewhere as physics specialists, usually as technicians. They can take part-time courses for the London external degrees but there are also many courses for other awards more specifically intended for technicians. For example, Ordinary and Higher National Certificates in Applied Physics are awarded jointly by the Ministry of Education and the Institute of Physics and the Physical Society to students who successfully complete prescribed part-time courses. The standard of the Higher National Certificate is roughly that of a pass degree and these awards are widely recognized in industry. The more able of the successful candidates can go on to higher qualifications, again by part-time study, such as the Graduateship of the Institute of Physics; some universities will accept holders of the Higher National Certificate for entry to honours degree courses.

The City and Guilds of London Institute awards certificates for which many thousands of students enter each year. Many of these certificates are for craftsmen but others, in subjects such as laboratory technicians' work or instrument maintenance, are for technicians, and all may be obtained after part-time study.

An equally important part of the work of the colleges of technology lies in providing specialized courses of evening lectures for qualified engineers, physicists and others, in order to bring them up to date on particular branches of new knowledge or new applications. These courses commonly consist of ten or twenty weekly lectures, and in the big centres of population throughout the United Kingdom a wide range is available in the various colleges. In the London area it is possible to find a course on almost any branch of pure or applied physics and the London and Home Counties Regional Advisory Council for Technological Education publishes twice a year a Bulletin[1] of all the courses available. Similar bulletins are published elsewhere in the country.

Conferences and societies. For almost every branch of pure or applied science one or more learned societies or professional institutions exist in the United Kingdom. These bodies organize lectures and conferences, and publish journals. The most famous of the societies is the Royal Society whose work is highly distinguished. Of the societies dealing with individual sciences, physics is served by the Institute of Physics and the Physical Society, previously two

1. *Bulletin of Special Courses in Higher Technology*, London and Home Counties Regional Advisory Council for Technological Education, Tavistock House South, Tavistock Square, London W.C.1.

separate organizations but amalgamated since 1960. The institute and society organizes each year about a dozen two- or three-day conferences attended by physicists from all over the United Kingdom and from abroad, and more than a hundred lecture meetings. Its monthly scientific journals publish papers dealing with new knowledge or with new applications of physics. One of the institute and society's principal activities is education in physics, and it is associated with the various activities at present being undertaken to improve physics teaching in schools. In association with the Ministry of Education, it has for many years been active in the development of technical education in physics.

Special programmes in the U.S.A.

Post-doctoral programmes, institutes, conferences. The continuing education of the physicist is accomplished in both formal and informal ways. Among the formal means of education beyond the doctoral degree are post-doctoral fellowships and fellowships for senior physicists. Post-doctoral fellowships—such as those supported by the National Science Foundation[1]—are increasingly in demand among the most promising young physicists who want to pursue research and advanced study at one of the world centres of research in their specialities after receiving the doctorate, and before accepting academic or industrial appointments. The fellowship provides support for a period up to two years. The senior post-doctoral fellowships of the National Science Foundation are for scientists who are at least five years beyond the doctoral degree; these fellowships also provide support for periods up to two years. The college physicist, who has concentrated on teaching and who is not qualified for one of the senior post-doctoral fellowships, can apply for a science faculty fellowship which permits 'refresher training' in physics. In addition to the support provided by the National Science Foundation, fellowships are provided by other government agencies and by private foundations, such as the Guggenheim Foundation.

There are also summer conferences and institutes at colleges and

1. *National Science Foundation Programs for Education in the Sciences*, Nationa lScience Foundation, Washington, 1961.

universities for college physics teachers and high-school physics teachers. For example, Cornell University sponsored a conference for college physicists on the teaching of relativity, and some five or ten other conferences were held in other areas of physics during the summer of 1963. Some three hundred summer institutes and academic-year institutes for high school teachers of science and mathematics are supported at colleges and universities each year by the National Science Foundation; many of these include study opportunities for physics teachers. There are also 'research participation' grants and summer fellowships for high school teachers under the NSF programme. Experimental programmes of in-service science institutes for elementary school personnel are also being supported by NSF.

The subject of fellowships, scholarships, institutes, conferences, etc., in the United States is a large one and cannot be treated with any degree of completeness here. In general, many physicists and other scientists have been the beneficiaries of such support at all levels of training.

Meetings of professional societies, journals, research conferences. The informal, self-educating ways of keeping up to date in physics are the most important. They include one's research and teaching, reading the journals and other scientific literature, correspondence with colleagues, attending meetings of the physics societies, and attending research conferences in one's field. It is not necessary in this report to dwell on these activities, but some statistics may be of interest. The five principal physics societies in the United States are the Member Societies of the American Institute of Physics: the American Physical Society, the Optical Society of America, the Acoustical Society of America, the Society of Rheology, and the American Association of Physics Teachers. The number of major meetings of these societies each year are on the average as follows (in the order named above): APS, eight; OSA, two; ASA, two; SR, two, and AAPT, two. In addition, approximately forty local sections of these societies have one or more meetings each year, and there are thirty or forty conferences on special physics topics within the United States as well as international conferences. Eighteen physics journals are currently published by the American Institute of Physics for the member societies or for itself, or are published by the member societies.[1] In addition, the AIP publishes seven translation journals. The problem of information storage and retrieval is one to which much attention is being given by scientific societies in this country.

Evening programmes, extension courses and junior colleges. Most major universities in the United States have evening programmes in which students can obtain bachelor's degrees, advanced degrees, or refresher education by part-time study. In general, the average time required in a degree programme is about double that required for completion of the work of a full-time schedule. Many such programmes are carried out with the encouragement and support of local industrial laboratories whose employees form a large part of the clientele in evening programmes in physics. The work is roughly comparable in quality to that of the day-time programme although some concessions are made to the special situation of the fully employed student. Similarly, many universities operate extension centres in nearby towns and cities that are without universities of their own, so that opportunities for higher education will be available in those places. Students who begin their work in evening programmes or extension divisions often transfer to full-time studies on the main campus for the final years of their studies; for the doctorate there is usually a residence requirement of this kind.

Junior colleges are post-secondary institutions offering two years of college-level work, which is formally similar to the first two years of work in the four-year colleges. Students in the junior colleges usually have one of the following objectives: (a) general education for two years beyond high school—the objective of many women students; (b) preparation for careers that do not require a baccalaureat degree—as technicians in industry, secretaries in offices, etc.; (c) transfer to a four-year college at the beginning of the third year—the objective of the more academically talented students. In certain states, especially California, the rising demand for college admission is being met to a considerable extent by founding junior colleges which relieve the load of the existing four-year institutions

1. *Journal Information*, American Institute of Physics, New York, 1962.

during the first two years, and allow the more able students to continue their education by transferring to a four-year institution at the beginning of the third year. Technical institutes are also two-year post-secondary institutions, but their educational programmes are usually directed entirely toward the training of technicians in a variety of engineering, scientific, and medical specialities.

Summary

The problems of continuing education in physics and of extension of educational opportunity are receiving increasing attention. The activities of professional societies in physics—the publication of journals and the holding of meetings and conferences—furnish one of the chief means of keeping the professional physicist up to date in his field. However, opportunities for formal education of physicists and engineers in mid-career are also being developed to enable them to shift from one field of specialization to another.

Evening programmes and extramural programmes broaden the base of education in physics and make it possible for the worker to study physics on a part-time basis. As the shortage of scientific personnel grows more acute, most countries will have to develop more effective ways of ensuring that scientific ability is found and developed. Special programmes with modest entrance requirements, good scholastic standards, flexible scheduling, and an understanding of the special problems of these students provide means for doing this.

VIII. Teachers of physics in universities

Introduction

The preceding chapters have dealt with the procedures and goals of physics teaching in universities—the selection of students, the educational objectives, the educational programmes at the several levels, the role of academic research, and so on. Now we turn to the means of converting educational hopes into real accomplishments, directing our attention first to the teachers and then, in the next chapter, to the material that they must use.

The importance of the physics teacher—the professor, the docent or the assistant—cannot be over-emphasized. Upon his competence as a physicist and a teacher, his devotion to his work, his communicable enthusiasm for physics, and his personal qualities rests a major part of the success of the university in educating young people in physics. Wise policies and adequate support can make the work of the able professor effective; they cannot compensate for his absence. The first objective of a developing programme in university physics is to secure a core staff of able physicists to whom other able young physicists will be attracted and about whom the physics programme can form. Sometimes the 'core' consists of one unusually competent man.

The terms 'chair', 'department', 'professor', and so on are used with somewhat different meanings from one country to another. An effort has been made in this report to use these terms correctly within the context of each national description. A word of caution must be uttered, however, concerning the equivalence of these terms from one country to another. Before assuming that the terms are equivalent, the reader should refer to such sources of detailed information on this subject as the *World Survey of Education*, published by Unesco.

This chapter contains reports from countries participating in the survey concerning the physics teacher, including: (a) brief descriptions of the ranks and conditions for appointment, emphasizing those things that are specific to physics; (b) the duties of teachers at the various levels of university teaching and in the various ranks; (c) the kinds of supporting personnel who are available to assist the teachers.

Teachers of physics in universities of Czechoslovakia

Professor. The word 'professor' signifies, on the one hand, the highest category of teacher at a university or other institution of this level and, on the other hand, a scientific-pedagogical degree. This means that even scientific workers who have the necessary qualifications, but are not employed at a university, may obtain the degree. Again, a university teacher must, in order to attain the rank of professor, have previously been awarded the scientific-pedagogical professorial degree. In exceptional cases, if no applicant with a professorial degree is available to fill a vacant professorial post, a suitable applicant may be appointed 'deputy professor' for a temporary period and with a reduced salary.

The decision whether the candidate's qualification corresponds to the requirements for the professorial degree rests with the university at which the particular branch of science is taught. A review commission of qualified scientific workers decides this with the approval of higher administrative levels in the university and the State. Applications for a professorial post are invited through the public press. Eligible for the 'function of professor' are, in the first place, scientific workers who have already obtained the professorial degree, and 'appointed professors', or docents, holding the D.Sc. degree. Should applications for this post be received from several qualified applicants, the appropriate commission of the university

156

will list the applicants in the order of their suitability for the vacant post. The selection of an applicant who does not possess the professorial degree is also simultaneously subject to the procedure for the 'appointment of professor', described before.

A professor's work at the faculty entails lecturing in basic courses as well as giving special lectures. He supervises seminars and diploma projects, and acts as scientific instructor in the training of scientific workers. The extent of his teaching duties for each academic year is established by the dean of the faculty. As far as a professor's teaching duties and other work (for example, as head of a Chair, member of a scientific council, etc.) are concerned, they are, as a matter of principle, not to take up more than two-thirds of the legal forty-six hours working week, leaving one-third for scientific work, which forms an inseparable part of his obligations. His hours of teaching may even be temporarily reduced in order to enable him to complete some important scientific work, write a textbook, a monograph, etc. And he may be exempted from all his regular duties if a longer sojourn abroad proves necessary. The retirement age of a professor is 70 years.

Docent. As in the case of the 'appointed' professor, the 'appointed' docent is the holder of the scientific-pedagogical degree of 'docent' which, however, must not be confused with the docent's function, i.e., a docent's post at a faculty. The docent is appointed by a procedure—the *habilitation*—that resembles that of a professor's appointment. The work of docent, especially of the more experienced ones, is similar to that of professors. The extent of their teaching duties and scientific work is likewise determined by the same principles. The status of this category of university teachers equals approximately that of the so-called associate professors or readers at some foreign universities.

Assistant, instructor and others. Expert or senior assistants are selected by public contest to fill a vacancy. Holders of the promoted physicist's degree are considered suitable applicants, provided they have at least three years of practical experience, working at either a university or some other research establishment. Secondary school physics teachers are also eligible. Decisive for the final choice from among the applicants is the standard of the professional and scientific work they have carried out so far. Senior assistants are mostly in charge of the calculating and laboratory exercises. The more experienced of them also give lectures. Their teaching activities are supervised by the head of their Chair, their scientific work by a professor or docent of the Chair.

Applicants for the post of assistant must also have completed their university training, but may be employed immediately after having graduated. They are appointed by the dean of the faculty and assist in teaching by helping with laboratory exercises, preparing certain demonstration experiments, and in other similar manner. They also participate in the scientific work of their Chair.

Instructors are not required to have university training. They are mainly experts who instruct the students in various workshop and laboratory technics, in working with glass, etc. Some instructors also assist in demonstration experiments and scientific work.

Apart from the already mentioned teaching personnel, the Chairs and, in particular, the faculties' scientific institutes employ university-trained physicists for scientific work. They are not expected to teach.

Ancillary personnel. The Chairs and institutes further employ a technical and administrative staff, the first consisting of skilled workers for expert tasks in workshops, technicians for laboratory work, but also of university-trained specialists (for example, chemists and engineers, some of whom are also in charge of special and ancillary laboratories).

The ancillary services at the mathematico-physical faculty are at present organized in the following way: there are mechanicians, machinists, glass-blowers and joiners' workshops shared by all Chairs of physics and the Institute of Physics. At the same time, each Chair, as well as the institute, has, for example, at the mechanical workshop (supervised by a shop foreman) its own group of workers, catering primarily for its needs. A smaller specialized workshop is attached to the Chair of astronomy, geophysics and meteorology. The material needed by the workshops and for the current work of the Chairs and institutes is kept in a common store. The department for designing and constructing special electronic instruments and devices needed by the faculty is part of the Institute of Physics, but also works for the Chairs. The chemical laboratory which prepares and analyses samples for research work, is organized along the same lines. The roentgenographic laboratory, serving all Chairs as well as the institute, however, is attached to the Chair of Solid State Physics.

Each Chair also employs a secretary for current administrative work and correspondence. Working at the faculty's large mathematical and physical library are numerous librarians and documentarians.

Teachers of physics in universities of the Federal Republic of Germany

Career of university teacher. The career of the university teacher generally begins after the doctorate and after advanced research leading to the recognition by the faculty of his right to lecture (*Habilitation*).

Those physicists who intend to take up a university career in general spend a few years after obtaining the doctorate *(Promotion)* as assistants at a university or a research institute (for instance at a Max Planck Institute). There they assist with the practicals and experimental physics lectures, together with the professors and *Dozenten.* They participate in supervising the work for the doctoral and diploma theses and the thesis work of the candidates for secondary-school teaching. They share in the administration or expansion of the institute and in the construction of more elaborate apparatus for research projects. When they have given proof of their ability, by scientific publications, they undertake a more extensive scientific work than for the doctorate and, if adjudged by the faculty to meet the standard, they are appointed *(habilitiert)* to *Privat-Dozent.* After a number of years, generally about six years, the *Privat-Dozent*, provided he has acquitted himself well in the meantime, is appointed *ausserplanmässiger Professor (a.pl. Professor)* upon proposal of the faculty. The qualification *a.pl.* means that it carries with it no remuneration. The appointment to a Chair, either as an *Ordinarius* or *Extraordinarius*, is made in accordance with the very careful appointment procedure of the faculty.

159

Exceptionally, a direct appointment on merit may be made, e.g., in the case of someone of outstanding ability coming from industry, but the course described is the normal career ladder. An appointment depends upon scientific accomplishment and teaching ability, but also upon personal qualities.

The teaching staff. At the majority of German universities at present there exist Chairs in the following ratio for approximately three hundred students of physics: three to five Chairs in experimental physics (including applied physics and nuclear physics); two to three Chairs in theoretical physics; and in some cases a Chair for special branches such as biophysics. The majority of these Chairs are *Ordinariate*, others are *Extraordinariate*.

In general, the *Ordinarius* is also the director or co-director of an institute. Most institutes have the administration of their own affairs.

Apart from professors holding Chairs, there are also *Wissenschaftliche Räte* and *Dozenten*. The ratio is as a rule approximately one *Dozent* to three Chairs. The number of *Wissenschaftliche Räte* is to be greatly increased in accordance with recommendations made to the *Wissenschaftsrat*.

The professors and lecturers supervise the work for the diploma and doctorate theses and the thesis work of the candidates for secondary school teaching.

The institutes have a number of assistants. The majority of *Privat-Dozenten* are simultaneously *Oberassistent*. There are some *Kustoden* and permanent employees, too. Some institutes, in addition, employ *wissenschaftliche Hilfskräfte*. Besides the positions of institute assistants, there are research posts for limited periods, paid for by institutions such as the Deutsche Forschungsgemeinschaft (German Research Association). Technical personnel—glassblowers, mechanicians, shopmen and technicians—are also employed. In addition, there are caretakers for the larger institutes, office personnel and typists.

Recommended size of staff. A memorandum of the Deutsche Forschungsgemeinschaft, published in 1958, contains guiding principles established by prominent physicists and representatives of the ministries, concerning personnel requirements. The following establish-

160

ment data were obtained. For three hundred students of physics, one hundred of whom are employed on a *Diplomarbeit* in experimental, fifteen on a *Diplomarbeit* in theoretical physics, and providing for lectures on experimental physics and practicals for beginners in various fields of study (i.e., mathematics, chemistry, biology, geology, mineralogy, medicine, veterinary medicine and agriculture), the following listed personnel are required: six *ordentliche* and *ausserordentliche* professors for experimental physics, three *ordentliche* and *ausserordentliche* professors for theoretical physics, eight *Dozenten* and *Wissenschaftliche Räte* (section chiefs), twenty-five scientific assistants, four *Kustoden*, forty technical employees, eight typists.

Teachers of physics in universities of France

The first academic post of a young physicist, the holder of a *licence* of instruction, is that of *assistant*. He has the duty of guiding the efforts of students who are preparing certificates of higher education, either in laboratory sessions or in discussion and exercise sessions. He devotes half of his time to preparing a doctoral thesis.

Once he has acquired the doctorate in his speciality, the *assistant* can become a *maître-assistant*. It is now his responsibility to conduct the instructional laboratory, direct the *assistant*, arrange credits, and maintain the experimental equipment and create new apparatus. He spends, theoretically at least, half of his time in continuing his research toward a thesis for the *doctorat ès sciences*. It should be noted that holders of *licences* who have passed the highest-level competitive examination for teachers in the *lycées*—the *agregation* —can also become *maîtres-assistants*.

Only physicists holding the *doctorat ès sciences* can obtain positions as *professeurs d'universités*. Each faculty recruits its personnel by co-optation among physicists, whether or not they have any teaching experience. The instructors begin with the rank of *maîtres de conférences* and then can become *professeurs*. They are required to give three hours of course per week for twenty-five weeks each year. The rest of their activity is, in principle, devoted to research. In practice, administrative tasks are often important, especially for the *professeurs* who direct the services involving many students.

161

Let us note a final category of teachers consisting of the huge group of 'lecturers'. The great majority of courses of the *grandes écoles* and, to a somewhat lesser degree, those of the universities are given by physicists or engineers who have no pedagogical training nor usually any dedication to teaching.

Teachers of physics in universities of the U.S.S.R.

As a general rule, the lectures on physics in the high schools of U.S.S.R. are delivered by professors (doctors of physics) or assistant professors (Candidats of Science). The examinations are conducted by the same persons.

The teaching assistants and teachers (tutors) conduct laboratory studies and exercises on solving problems whilst the laboratory assistants prepare the equipment for laboratory work.

During the industrial practice periods, teachers are assisted by specialists appointed by the administration of the plant.

Teaching of physics in secondary schools requires graduation in physics.

Teachers of physics in universities of the United Kingdom

The title of 'professor' is very sparingly used in British universities. In most subjects the title would be borne only by the head of the department or by holders of one or two endowed Chairs. In the past few years additional Chairs have been created in science departments, but even now in a large physics department with perhaps forty full academic staff, only about six would be professors. Other ranks within the department would be reader, senior lecturer, lecturer and assistant lecturer. In addition, there would usually be research fellows, holding awards with various conditions of tenure, often for a limited period of time.

There are no formal qualifications that must be held before a candidate can be appointed to a post in a British university, although in practice the pattern is fairly clear and generally applicable. Universities aim to recruit their staff from among those who

162

have obtained good (bachelors) honours degrees and have subsequently taken a Ph.D., but a doctorate is not formally an essential
requirement and, indeed, there are some very distinguished British
academic physicists who did not, for one reason or another, take a
doctor's degree. The main recruitment of the university staffs is into
the lecturer or assistant lecturer grades and promotion is dependent
upon ability, particularly ability in research. There is some direct
recruitment to the higher posts from physicists who have achieved
distinction in industrial or Government research. A fair amount of
movement takes place between the United Kingdom universities
and it is particularly common for professorial vacancies to be filled
from the staffs of other universities. This is made easily possible
because, although university teachers are not civil servants, a common scheme of superannuation exists for all the universities so that
movement can take place without any loss of pension rights.

In the colleges of advanced technology the academic hierarchy is
similar to that of the universities except that, so far, the heads of
departments in these colleges have not had the title of professor.
Recruitment from industry is comparatively common and many
heads of departments and readers in the colleges of advanced
technology have had senior research experience in industry or
government research establishments. Movement from these colleges to university staffs is not common.

Teachers of physics in universities of the U.S.A.

Description of academic ranks. The academic ranks in colleges and
universities in the United States in order of increasing rank are:
graduate assistant, instructor, assistant professor, associate professor, and professor. Teaching assistantships and research assistantships are held by graduate students while they work toward advanced degrees. Toward the end of their work as graduate students,
some may be appointed as instructors and given somewhat greater
teaching responsibilities. Both assistantships and instructorships
are appointments for one academic year, renewable at the discretion of the institution. Most Ph.D.'s enter the academic ranks as
assistant professors with three-year appointments. After two such

three-year appointments, a meritorious faculty member is usually
raised to the level of associate professor, and after a roughly corresponding period as associate professor, to the rank of full professor. Exceptionally distinguished persons hold endowed professorial Chairs, and some are named 'university professors', a designa-
tion that gives them the freedom of the university in teaching and
research. Visiting professors from other institutions in The United
States and abroad are also frequently appointed as members of
physics staffs.

What has been described is what might be called 'average' progress toward full professorial rank. Individuals obviously differ
greatly in their rate of advance. In physics, progress through the
ranks tends to be somewhat more rapid than in other disciplines
because of the desire of the universities to maintain their competitive positions in securing and retaining the services of productive
physicists.

About 5,600 physicists in 1962 held academic positions in the
United States at the rank of instructor or above, distributed in
rank about as follows: instructors, 28 per cent; assistant professors,
24 per cent; associate professors, 21 per cent; and professors, 27
per cent. About 70 per cent of teaching physicists hold doctoral
degrees; about 25 per cent of new Ph.D.'s in recent years have
accepted academic appointments as their first employment. The
sizes of the physics staffs (rank of instructor and above) of the four
institutions surveyed, in relation to the numbers of undergraduate
majors and graduate students, are as follows:

Institution	Physics staff	Physics majors (3rd and 4th year)	Graduate students
California (including medical physics)	79	233	400
Columbia	37	78	216
MIT	80	237	245
Swarthmore	6	19	—

Teaching assistants in physics are employed in the following
numbers: University of California, Berkeley, seventy-five; Columbia,
forty-four; and MIT, thirty two. These institutions also employ a

large number of research assistants (MIT has ninety-six), some of whom have some teaching duties.

Teachers of introductory undergraduate courses. Demonstration lectures are usually given by senior professors. There is a tradition that these courses deserve the attention of the most competent and experienced men on the staff, and the tradition is more often honoured than not. Teaching assignments of this kind are rotated so that the members of the major staff do not ordinarily give the courses for more than a few years consecutively. Fresh viewpoints are thus brought to the teaching, and the work of supervising the course does not bear too heavily on one person. These contacts between beginning students of physics and senior physicists are usually mutually beneficial.

Recitation or quiz sections are taught by instructors, by the more advanced graduate student assistants, and not infrequently by members of the professorial staff. (In the smaller institutions, these classes are usually taught by the professorial staff.) Dividing a large group of students into smaller groups for recitation and laboratory work brings with it the necessity of co-ordination, so that the instructors in the smaller groups do not get too far ahead of, or behind, the discussion in the lectures, and that standards of instruction are maintained throughout the course. The lecturer is usually the co-ordinator. He prepares the schedule or assignment sheet (Appendix III F2), gives the recitation instructors copies of his lecture notes or in other ways informs them about topics that require special emphasis, brings them together occasionally for staff discussion of teaching problems, and supervises the grading of examinations and the preparation of final grades for the course.

Graduate assistants are usually in charge of laboratory sections in introductory courses in the large universities. Since there may be one hundred such sections, taught by twenty or more first-year graduate students, the problem of co-ordination is a large one. Most large universities assign to members of the professorial staff the work of co-ordinating the introductory laboratory. The graduate assistants sometimes receive good training as apprentice teachers in the laboratory. However, the result is usually not beneficial to students in the introductory laboratory the following year, because in their second year of graduate work the graduate students move into other kinds of teaching or into research. The co-ordinator must start each academic year with an almost totally new group of laboratory instructors. Nevertheless, the laboratory teaching is often good, the young instructors making up for lack of experience by enthusiasm and an understanding of the difficulties their students are encountering in physics. In the smaller institutions, the laboratory sessions are taught by members of the professorial staff, and the laboratory work of students sometimes becomes really inspired under the stimulus of an experienced and enthusiastic teacher.

Teachers of upper-division undergraduate courses. The more advanced physics courses are taught by the members of the professorial staff. Teaching assignments for these courses are usually rotated; one person may have the course for two or three years before turning it over to a colleague. A fairly common observation is that the teacher learns how to teach the course the first year, teaches it well for a year or two afterwards, and then develops a routine approach to the course and—certain individuals excepted— should be relieved of it for a few years. The advanced laboratory sessions are supervised by the professorial staff or, in large universities, by research fellows.

Graduate teaching. Members of the professorial staff give the graduate courses in physics and supervise thesis research by graduate students. The teaching of the basic graduate courses—advanced analytical mechanics or advanced electricity and magnetism, for example—is usually rotated among the members of the staff. The more specialized courses are given by those whose research interests fall into those areas. However, since there are usually several full professors in each major area of research at each university—rather than one, as in some other countries—even the more specialized courses are handed around to some extent. In general, under the prevailing practice, courses are usually not 'proprietary'.

Occasionally, universities call upon distinguished physicists on the staffs of nearby industrial or governmental laboratories to give graduate courses in specialized areas to their students. Arrangements are also made sometimes for a graduate student employed in industry to carry out his thesis research under the supervision of an industrial physicist who holds an appointment as an adjunct professor or an associate.

Work loads. To quote from the booklet *Careers in College Physics Teaching*:[1] 'Many conditions determine the amount of time a physics teacher spends in actual classroom teaching: the type and the size of the institution in which he is employed, the size of the physics staff, his other academic responsibilities, and his rank on the staff. However, a teaching load of about twelve hours per week of classroom teaching is common practice. A full professor at a large university may spend only six hours per week in classroom teaching whereas an instructor at a small college may teach formally twenty hours per week.

'Classroom contact hours alone do not give a complete picture of an individual physicist's work load. Few academic physicists work less than the standard forty hours per week, and for most —such is their commitment to their work—the hours of formal classroom instruction are followed by hours spent on research, writing, preparation for classes, course planning, colloquia and seminars, committee assignments, and other professional activities. The line between 'work' and 'leisure' cannot be easily drawn, and the physicist seldom bothers to do so. When his classroom teaching load is less than twelve hours per week, the academic physicist usually has major responsibilities in research, course planning, or administration. An instructor in a small college, on the other hand, may teach twenty hours per week, but his schedule usually includes several class sessions in a single course so that his preparation is not excessively heavy.'

The prevailing practice in large universities with extensive research programmes is to assign not more than two courses, about six classroom hours per week, to each member of the professorial staff in physics. A few large universities have reduced this to one course, about three classroom hours per week.

Graduate assistants have a work load of about twenty hours per week, of which about ten hours are spent in classroom or laboratory

1. *Careers in college physics teaching*, American Institute of Physics, New York.

teaching, and the remaining time is spent in grading, assisting in laboratory preparations, etc. Instructors in large universities have work loads of about twelve classroom hours per week.

Supporting personnel. The services of machinists, technicians, librarians, secretaries (typist-stenographers), and other assistants are available to academic physicists. Representatives of the universities surveyed laid great stress on the desirability of a high level of support by service personnel. The numbers of supporting personnel within the physics departments of the four institutions surveyed are as follows:

Supporting personnel	California	Columbia[1]	MIT	Swarthmore
Machinists	10	6 (29)	7	1
Technicians	12	5 (45)	7	—
Librarians	—[2]	1 (2)	—[2]	—[2]
Secretarial and clerical	10	9 (21)	12	—[3]
Administrative assistants or business managers	3	2 (4)	—	—

1. Numbers in parentheses are the numbers of supporting personnel attached formally to other groups at Columbia, but whose services are available to the professorial staff in research.
2. Services of librarians supplied by central library.
3. Part-time secretarial help available.

It must be emphasized that the numbers recorded above do not include the numbers of supporting personnel in the universities who are employed in organizational units other than the physics departments, often under research contracts, but whose services are available to the members of the professorial staff in physics in research. To make this clear, the numbers of supporting personnel at Columbia University in research groups in physics are given in parentheses beside the numbers for the Physics Department. Quite similar situations exist at California and MIT.

Smaller institutions do not have supporting personnel in these numbers, of course, although many have a physics machinist and a departmental secretary. The smallest colleges have no assistance of this kind, and their educational programmes in physics are severely hampered as a result.

The services of supporting personnel are organized in two ways. Some individuals—secretaries, shopmen, and technicians—are affiliated with a particular project, course, or professor. For example, at MIT, the freshman physics laboratory and the sophomore laboratory each has a technician and shares the services of a secretary. It is common in large departments for there to be one technician (usually with an assistant) in charge of equipment for demonstration lectures in introductory physics. Large physics departments also often have a student shop with a machinist in charge of it. The chairman of the physics department usually has a secretary who handles his correspondence and departmental paperwork. People hired under a research contract are attached to that project. Otherwise, the supporting personnel operate within a centrally organized facility—a departmental library, secretarial 'pool', stockroom, machine shop, etc.

Greater attention is being paid nationally these days to the problem of providing adequate numbers of technically trained supporting personnel in physics as a means of extending the efforts of physicists themselves, who are in short supply.

Summary

It is not possible to establish uniform recommendations for the size of the physics staff of a university. The numbers of students and the kinds of instruction being given to them, and the size and scope of the research programme differ greatly from one university to another. Only the most general guidelines can be provided.

The foregoing national reports indicate that the average teaching load of a full-time member of the physics staff of a major university ranges from three to six classroom hours per week for a full professor and from twelve to fifteen hours per week for a junior member of the teaching staff. Class sizes must be considered also, however, in arriving at an estimate of the size of the physics department. It is reasonable to assume that the lecture classes of the first year or two of university physics will generally be large (two hundred or more students) and the laboratory classes will be small (twenty to forty students). Classes in the more specialized courses range in size from about one hundred in the less advanced courses to five

169

to ten in the most advanced courses. These criteria, applied to the local situation, can be used to develop some rough estimates based upon total teaching load.

Another approach is to use the number of physics concentrators who are studying for their first professional degree. Inspection of the data provided earlier leads to the estimate that the ratio of the number of physics concentrators to the number of academic physics staff is approximately seven or eight to one.

'Critical size' is another useful concept. Very small faculties or departments suffer from the disadvantage of not being able to stay abreast of developments over the wide advancing frontier of physics. The critical size is reached when there are enough physicists teaching, carrying on research in various branches of physics, and following the physics literature, to ensure that the department is kept informed of current developments.

In addition to professional physicists, university physics faculties require the services of auxiliary personnel—librarians, secretaries, technicians, shopmen, and others. In the absence of such services, the physicists are required to devote a disproportionate share of their time to non-professional tasks. Conservation of valuable scientific talent requires that these auxiliary services be provided.

The quality of the physics staff, as stated at the beginning of this chapter, is more important than its numbers. The assistance of consultants physics professors from established universities can enable developing universities to judge their progress in this respect.

IX. Material

Introduction

Material used in the teaching of physics in universities includes scientific apparatus, shop tools, stock materials, books and journals, films and many other things in addition to rooms in which to use them. The shopping list of physics faculties is a long one. Unlike the teachers of such subjects as economics and philosophy, the physics teacher needs more than a well-stocked library to present his subject. He must introduce his student to the natural world with which physics deals. Since the concern of contemporary physics is with the very large and the very small, the apparatus needed to carry on experimental work in the more advanced parts of physics can be obtained and used effectively only by means of careful planning, the expenditure of not trivial sums of money, and a proper regard for maintenance. Equipment needed for the introductory courses in physics is less elaborate and, thanks to mass-production techniques, less expensive.

This chapter will serve as introduction to the material of university physics. Included will be information provided by participating countries concerning: (a) policies concerning the use of material in teaching; (b) lists of typical material—shop equipment, books, etc.; (c) references to sources of further information.

Books listed in this report were selected as textbooks by educational institutions in the countries participating and not by the authors of this report or the sponsoring organizations. Except for lists of books and shop equipment, it has not proved possible to provide detailed information concerning apparatus, commercial sources of these materials or the prices. The reader is referred to the Unesco Division of Science Teaching for such information, or to the offices of the physics societies in the various countries taking part in this survey, as listed on page 196.

Material in the universities of Czechoslovakia

Only part of the instruments, apparatus, and devices needed in physics research are being produced in Czechoslovakia; others are imported from abroad.

Some special new apparatus is also produced in workshops of various research institutes and laboratories. These pieces of apparatus are mostly developed on the basis of the result of research work, carried out in these institutes. The Academy of Sciences has a special Institute for Instrumental Technics for this purpose. Such original research instruments and devices are also produced in some workshops of university faculties. The same is valid for special demonstration instruments for university education.

Material in the universities of the Federal Republic of Germany

Apparatus. Several important firms in the Federal Republic of Germany supply universities and schools with instructional materials.

Workshops. Experimental physics work requires more or less spacious and well-equipped workshops. At most of the universities, each institute has its own workshops with its own personnel. At other universities, several institutes have joint use of the workshops. Both alternatives have advantages and disadvantages.

The largest workshop is that of precision mechanics. In addition there are plants for galvanizing and lacquering, workshops for welding, plastics material, joinery, and electricity; furthermore, an electronics workshop, and a glass-blowing plant.

172

Appendix IX B1 lists as an example, the equipment of these workshops for a university with 300 physics students.

Books. At the majority of universities there exists, besides a general university library, which lends books, still another library jointly used by all institutes of physics, equipped with physics books and some mathematical and chemistry literature. Occasionally, individual institutes possess fairly extensive specialized libraries. The students themselves, unfortunately, in general do not own more than a few basic textbooks, since they are too expensive. Appendix IX B2 contains reading lists recommended to the students during lectures and practicals.

Films. In the Federal Republic, widespread use has not hitherto been made of films in physics teaching. The basic reason for this is that in teaching physics, there is at our disposal the whole range of the highly developed art of practical experiments (which are in themselves visual aids). There are, however, a few special cases where the film can fill a gap in the experimental technique, namely in the representation of processes. The film is better able to demonstrate how glass shatters on impact from a projectile, or how wavefronts build up in gases flowing from the nose of a projectile in flight, and so on. The film too, is of value in making abstract concepts more comprehensible by visual representation, e.g., by trick films. For example, trick films enable the velocity of transmission for the phase and signal to be distinguished in the case of signal transmission over waves in certain media, or illustrate the Fourier analysis of sweep oscillations visually. It is certain, however, that even now, the full possibilities of the instructional film in physics teaching have in many respects not been fully exploited, and there is room for extension of their use.

Where films are used in physics teaching in the Federal Republic, only films with a few minutes' running time are selected in order that the main emphasis remains on the lecturer's explanation and commentary. In practice, too, only silent films are considered.

Physics instructional films of the type produced in America, in which a teacher is shown demonstrating an experiment, do not conform to the style of teaching developed in the Federal Republic.[1] Their use is considered, as an inadequate substitute, only where there simply are no physics teachers available. Such films could be profitably used in teacher training in the Federal Republic if the film demonstrations are stimulating and are good examples of how to demonstrate. Until now hardly any use has been made of these films in this context. The reasons for this would appear to be chiefly ones of expense.

The Institute for Science Films, University of Göttingen, Göttingen, supplies physics films for university teaching.

Space requirements. In order to accommodate 300 students of physics and additional students of physics of other faculties, it has been calculated that, depending on the field of physics, the space required varies from 5,000 to 10,000 square meters. These calculations include rooms for practical work, laboratories, administration offices, rooms for special purposes, seminars, workshops, a library, and several spare rooms. In addition, space must be provided for four lecture halls with space for from 100 to 600 seats. The larger lecture halls must be well equipped for experiments.

Material in the universities of France

The universities draw on industry for the equipment of their teaching laboratories. The aim is to bring students as soon as possible into contact with the type of equipment with which they will later be working in industry or research. Moreover, such mass-produced material, manufactured according to precise standards, is of excellent quality and cheaper than specially manufactured 'teaching material'. In other words, there are no industrial firms specializing in physics teaching equipment in France.

Films are very little used in the physics courses, but numerous class experiments are made and there is increasing use of wide-screen closed-circuit television, enabling a whole lecture hall audience to follow the experiments.

There is, of course, a large number of physics teaching manuals,

1. W. Kroebel, 'The Film and University Physics Teaching', *Communication of the Institute for Science Films*, Vol. 15, 1962, p. 4.

but absolute freedom of choice is the rule. The universities never interfere by recommending the use of a particular book.

Material in the universities of the U.S.S.R.

The precision-measurement industry, which is very advanced in the U.S.S.R., especially in the fields of electronics and optics, along with the precision tools industry, is able to supply all the requirements of the teaching and research laboratories in all branches of physics.

Appendix IX D1 contains a list of physics books used in the general physics course and the theoretical physics course in universities of the U.S.S.R.

Material in the universities of the United Kingdom

Well-equipped workshops are an essential part of any physics laboratory, not least in a university. The existence of active research in all British university physics departments ensures that there will be good workshop facilities, and these are available also for the production of equipment for teaching purposes. Most departments will also expect their physics students to take a course in the workshop.

It is hardly necessary to elaborate upon the use of equipment for instructional purposes. British universities have traditionally attached very great importance to experimental work done by the students themselves and there is no problem of obtaining equipment either commercially or from the departments' own workshops, except sometimes the problem of finance. Over the past few years there has been a tendency for fewer demonstration experiments to be done in lectures but a good deal of new thinking has now been given to this question and some interesting experiments have been tried. In Manchester, for example, closed-circuit television is being used for demonstration experiments.[1]

A typical list of physics books is given in Appendix IX E1.

1. Conway, Mendoza and Read, 'The Seminar Method of Teaching Experimental Physics', *Bulletin of the Institute of Physics and the Physical Society*, London, 1963.

It is difficult to give realistic figures for the amount or cost of the equipment of an existing university physics department. However, figures are available for the physics departments of two newly established universities in the United Kingdom. In the University of Sussex, the first of the physics buildings is completed and has an area of 50,000 square feet, including 6,000 square feet of lecture rooms, 2,000 square feet of workshops and 19,000 square feet of laboratories for teaching and research. This accommodation will be used for practical classes for two hundred first-year students, eighty second-year students, seventy third-year students and about forty post-graduate students.

In the University of Essex a building is being planned for the following numbers of students: first-year students of chemistry, physics, mathematics and other subjects—four hundred and fifty who will each spend about one-third of their time on physics; second-year students—eighty full-time physics honours students and three hundred and sixty students taking physics courses for other degrees (chemistry, mathematics, etc.); third-year students— eighty full-time physics students; post-graduate students—one hundred in all. The building will have a floor area of 140,000 square feet.

Material in universities of the U.S.A.

Scientific apparatus. Effective instruction in physics requires that an adequate supply of materials, components, and apparatus be available to physics teachers and students. Materials include the stocks of brass, aluminium, glass, stainless steel, etc., in a variety of forms that are used in the physics shop to construct apparatus. Components include such things as resistors, capacitors, lenses, vacuum tubes, transistors, wave guides, etc., that are assembled into apparatus. Apparatus itself includes such things as potentiometers, spectrographs, linear amplifiers, scalers, etc. By apparatus systems, we mean assemblages such as Van de Graaff generators and other 'machines'. A survey by the American Institute of Physics revealed that there are some 2,500 categories (not items) of material within these four major divisions used by physicists in teaching and research in this country. The rich variety of material for experimentation that is made available by a technologically based economy is extremely important to the vitality of physics.

The specific requirements for material vary greatly from one university or college to another, depending upon the nature of the teaching and the research programme, the number of students and staff, the organization of teaching and research, and so on. One cannot compile a list of apparatus that will be universally appropriate for physics departments. Nevertheless, apparatus in its broad sense is so important to physics that an attempt will be made in this report to illustrate the ways in which apparatus is used by referring to practices in the institutions surveyed. Additional information about specific requirements and practices can be found elsewhere.[1]

In the introductory undergraduate courses, apparatus is used in lecture demonstrations and in the student laboratory. The number of lecture demonstrations given in a physics department depends upon the enthusiasm and ingenuity of the staff in this kind of teaching, but might well range between one hundred and two hundred demonstrations in a large physics department in which four or five physicists share the lecturing in the introductory courses. This means that between 100 and 200 set-ups for demonstrations must be available—either in the form of items of assembled apparatus that can be moved directly from the stockroom shelves to the lecture table, or assembled from components by the demonstration technician. The demonstrations that are given at one time or another throughout the country are therefore quite numerous; their description occupies a sizeable fraction of the physics educational literature. One should note that much demonstration 'apparatus' is very simple; good physics demonstrations do not always require

1. T. B. Brown, ed., *The Taylor Manual of Advanced Undergraduate Experiments in Physics*, Reading, Addison-Wesley Company, 1959.

   Apparatus Drawing Project. A complete set of shop drawings and construction notes for constructing thirty pieces of modern physics apparatus developed in academic physics departments, New York, Plenum Press.

   'Apparatus Notes and Reviews of Apparatus', Published regularly in the *American Journal of Physics*.

   R. Resnick and H. Meiners, *Demonstration and Laboratory Apparatus. Report of the* 1960 *Summer Visiting Professor Workshop at Rensselaer Polytechnic Institute*, Rensselaer Polytechnic Institute, Troy, 1961.

   Apparatus for physics teaching. AAPT Committee on Apparatus. Reprints of articles from *American Journal of Physics*, 1961.

   W. C. Kelly, 'The Study of Apparatus for the Teaching of Physics', *American Journal of Physics*, Vol. 26, 1958, p. 311.

expensive apparatus. Such things as a tin-can induction motor, uncooked and hard-boiled eggs, soda straws, and table-tennis balls can be used very effectively in physics demonstrations.

The student laboratory in the introductory course is usually organized on the basis of one set-up of apparatus for each pair of students. Two experiments are usually in progress at any one time. This means that for a laboratory class of twenty students, five complete set-ups of each experiment must be made. (If a 'single-front' laboratory is being conducted—one in which the entire laboratory class works on one experiment—ten set-ups must be provided.)

In the upper-division undergraduate physics courses, the laboratory work is again usually organized on the basis of one set of apparatus for each pair of students, but there is ordinarily one set-up for each of many experiments that may be going on at any one time. This is necessary because the apparatus is more elaborate and expensive. The procedure is feasible because the laboratory classes are smaller and because it is not necessary that the laboratory work keep in phase with lectures. The apparatus is more nearly 'research-grade' than that in the introductory course; in fact, it is sometimes equipment that has been lent or donated to the teaching laboratory by a research laboratory. It consists of standard instruments—potentiometers, oscilloscopes, etc.—plus locally constructed parts, e.g., a demountable-target X-ray tube, a Stern-Gerlach apparatus, etc.

Apparatus for research by graduate students and by members of the staffs of physics departments is as large a subject as that of physics experimental research itself and cannot be discussed here. It is mentioned simply to remind the reader that, in a university, research is a form of teaching and learning. Equipment must be provided for this purpose in a strong physics programme as much as for the more didactic activities.

Apparatus is obtained for teaching purposes from many sources. Much of it is made in physics shops, particularly in large physics departments.[1] This is true of the pieces of 'pedagogical equipment' in particular. (Standard apparatus such as decade resistance boxes

1. *Apparatus Drawing Project.* A complete set of shop drawings and construction notes for constructing thirty pieces of modern physics apparatus developed in academic physics departments, New York, Plenum Press.

is usually, although not always, purchased.) Physics teachers have a great need for apparatus that enables them to teach the newer concepts of physics, especially in atomic, nuclear, and solid-state physics.[1] The more inventive departments find that only by constructing apparatus themselves can they obtain with reasonable speed the equipment they want for teaching. Their shops are usually large enough to manufacture without great difficulty ten or twenty sets of a given piece of apparatus. All four of the institutions surveyed—California, Columbia, MIT and Swarthmore—construct a large part of their laboratory and demonstration apparatus. Commercial apparatus for teaching and research in physics is supplied by some 5,000 commercial companies in this country. (This does not include the local hardware stores that, as we saw above, can supply simple things for physics teaching.) The number of commercial suppliers that deal in educational equipment in physics is relatively small: there are about four or five major suppliers and distributors of educational equipment in physics and perhaps twenty others that produce one or two items for physics teaching. Finally, one should note that donations of equipment to physics departments by industry and the Federal Government have been very helpful. The Federal Government surplus property programme provides for the low-cost distribution of government property to educational institutions; the property distributed includes scientific apparatus that has become excess to the needs of the government agencies that purchased it.[2]

Shop equipment. The reader is referred to the book *Modern Physics Buildings: Design and Function*, by R. R. Palmer and W. M. Rice, for a discussion of physics shops.[3] The book was the result of a project conducted by the American Association of Physics Teachers and the American Institute of Physics. Of special interest here are the tables in the book listing the floor area and the number of technicians provided in the physics shops of eight colleges and

1. *Apparatus for Physics Teaching*, AAPT Committee on Apparatus, reprints of articles from *American Journal of Physics*, 1961.
2. W. G. Rhoten, L. K. Barry and W. C. Kelly. 'Report to Physics Teachers on Procedures for obtaining Surplus Government Property', *American Journal of Physics*, Vol. 27, 1959, p. 34.
3. R. R. Palmer and W. M. Rice, *Modern Physics Buildings: Design and Function* New York, Reinhold Publishing Corporation, 1961.

universities, the major shop tools in the shop of the Electronics Research Building of the Lawrence Radiation Laboratory at Berkeley, the major tools in the physics shop at Pomona College, and the major tools for a shop for seven machinists at Berkeley.

Physics books and journals. The reader is referred to the report entitled *Check List of Books for an Undergraduate Physics Library*, published by the American Institute of Physics in 1962.[1] The check list contains some 300 physics books that appear most frequently on the shelves of a physics library in an undergraduate college, plus some 1,500 additional ones that are frequently in such libraries. Also of interest is the booklet *The Periodical Literature of Physics: a Handbook for Graduate Students*.[2] Chapter 11 of *Modern Physics Buildings: Design and Function*, referred to above, contains a detailed treatment of the physics library in educational institutions. Textbooks are quite important in physics teaching in the United States. Although some observers believe too great a reliance is placed upon the use of a single textbook in a course, textbooks continue to be important teaching tools. A list of typical textbooks used at one of the three universities surveyed will be found in Appendix IX F1.

Physics films. Physics teachers in the United States in the past have not made much use of teaching films to supplement their lectures. There were two reasons for this: the physics films available were not very good, and the procedure of using them in a classroom was cumbersome and time-consuming. Recently, much better films have become available—through the efforts of such organizations as Educational Services Incorporated, of Watertown, Massachusetts— and cartridge-loading film projectors now promise to eliminate much of the tedious work of showing a film. Articles listing films of interest in physics teaching, written by Professor Robert Weber of Pennsylvania State University, have been published in the *American Journal of Physics*.[3]

1. *Checklist of Books for an Undergraduate Physics Library*, American Institute of Physics, New York, 1962.
2. *The Periodical Literature of Physics: Handbook for Graduate Students*, American Institute of Physics, New York, 1960.
3. R. L. Weber, 'Films for Physics Students', *American Journal of Physics*, Vol. 29, 1961 p. 222; and 'Films for Students of Physics', supplement I, *American Journal of Physics*, Vol. 30, 1962, p. 321.

180

Physics buildings. The book *Modern Physics Buildings: Design and Function*[1] contains detailed information and recommendations for the planning, construction and furnishing of physics buildings or those parts of science buildings that are devoted to physics. The chapter headings will indicate the scope of the book: 'Space requirements of physics'; 'The role of administration, physics staff, and architect'; 'The building'; 'Floor plans'; 'The lecture room'; 'Classrooms and seminar rooms'; 'Teaching laboratories'; 'Research laboratories'; 'Shops and auxiliary rooms'; 'Offices and conference rooms'; 'The library'; 'Laboratories and classrooms for high school physics'.

Summary

The national reports stress the importance of an adequate supply of apparatus and materials for constructing apparatus, of shops and libraries, of films, of books for students, and of well-designed classrooms and laboratories for effectively teaching physics in universities. Material is the reverse of the coin of which the obverse is the teaching staff. Good teachers without the materials for teaching are helpless in an experimental science such as physics. Fine apparatus without well-qualified teachers will be left unused or will be damaged through improper use. The teaching staff and the physical plant of a university must develop together.

Maintenance is as important to apparatus as continuing education is to the physicist. Adequate attention must be given to the problem of storing apparatus, repairing it when it is damaged, replacing failed components, and, in general, seeing to it that the apparatus will be available and ready when the physics teacher wants it. Climatic hazards—corrosion, damage by fungi, etc.—must be anticipated in some countries and guarded against. These are not trivial problems in countries whose industrial establishments are developing at the same time as their universities, and special measures have to be taken there.

1. R. R. Palmer and W. M. Rice, op-cit.

X.   The improvement of physics teaching

Introduction

The preceding chapters have described the teaching of physics as it was practised in 1962 in the universities of the six participating countries. The rapid growth of knowledge and the rising demand for instruction in physics, however, have led physics teachers everywhere to feel a great concern for better ways of teaching. Although much has been accomplished in educating future physicists and other students of physics, there is little complacency among those who have the responsibility for planning and carrying out educational programmes in physics.

The years ahead would seem to be years of change, bringing new emphases and new methods into teaching. The relations of physics to other scientific and technological fields are changing, and what is generally considered to be proper content for a physics course today may well move into the teaching domains of other disciplines to be replaced by new physics now emerging from the laboratories. Similarly, course content will move down from the universities into the schools.

This chapter contains reports about new developments and probable new directions in the teaching of physics—some of them beginning to have an effect, others just becoming apparent.

The situation in Czechoslovakia

The main characteristic of the present period is not only the still insufficient number of trained physicists for research and the continuously extending scope of research in all branches, but also the growing demands for physicists for the laboratories of industrial enterprises—an outcome of new production technology and the introduction of new kinds of products.

The long-term State plan also demands in the near future a substantial increase in the number of professional physicists for research and, very particularly, for industrial enterprises. The organization of the training of professional physicists is still mainly directed at training research personnel. In this field, too, demands on the quality of the scientific workers are rapidly increasing. All this necessitates the devising of measures permitting us to train increased numbers of physicists for research and industry, and raise the level of their university education simultaneously.

Discussions concerning the most effective methods to achieve this goal in the given situation are going on at universities, the academies of sciences, etc. The Union of Czechoslovak Mathematicians and Physicists, mentioned earlier, also plays an important part in these discussions.

Regarding the raising of the educational level at universities, some principles have already emerged from these talks and will probably soon be put to a practical test. There is, for example, the tendency to lay greater weight on independent studies and, consequently, to reduce the number of obligatory weekly hours in the curricula without, of course, at the same time lowering the standards of knowledge demanded in the examinations. A principal prerequisite for the realization of this suggestion is a greater number of textbooks, not only for the basic physics courses, but also for the special parts of modern physics. There is further the endeavour to let students take part in practical scientific work even earlier than hitherto. Another of the most important problems is the selection and special training of especially talented students. Physicists at present are discussing the possibilities of a new conception of teaching physics, concerning the introductory course at the universities as well as at the general secondary schools. Among other things, a principal rearrangement of the subject matter is considered, in order to introduce modern material and examples as widely as possible from the very beginning of the course.

The large number of physicists to be trained in the near future by our universities represents a problem that provides ample food for deliberation and discussion. It seems as if the practice of training all these physicists by the same methods will have to be abolished. It has been suggested that a two-stage training scheme be substituted for it. One part of the students would study only four years and, after graduating as physicists, would mainly work in industry. Another part—especially gifted graduates of these four-year courses—would continue in their physics studies immediately or at a later date, thus attaining a higher qualification.

It has become obvious, too, that a considerable improvement in the training of physicists at the universities can hardly be effected without reforming physics instruction in the secondary schools. This involves, in particular, a new conception in teaching physics as far as content and arrangement of the subject matter are concerned, as well as new teaching methods which would considerably enhance the ability of the pupils independently to recognize physical phenomena and laws, and to engage in critical logical thinking.

The situation in the Federal Republic of Germany

In university education and especially in physics, much is in a state of flux. A number of suggested improvements are at present in the process of being introduced.

The development of university education, which in the Federal Republic is closely tied up with research, is proceeding rather slowly. It is generally admitted that promotion of science and advancement of university education as a whole is one of the most important problems facing this country. The logical outcome of such awareness, namely the provision at individual State level and at Federal State level of adequate means to meet this need, remains a problem for which as yet no solution has been found.

Nevertheless, some progress is being made. Institutes to accommodate the increased numbers of students are being built, although personnel is still in short supply. Endeavours are being made to loosen the academic organization and to distribute responsibility among several holders of Chairs of equal authority.[1]

The compulsory duration of courses has steadily increased since the war, partly because of unfavourable conditions, insufficient space, finance and personnel, partly through additional material to be taught. Pains are being taken now to reduce the time required by concentrating on physics and by reducing the time spent, for instance, on chemistry.

Simultaneously, an improvement of studies is being striven for. The transition from school to university is to be improved by a change or addition to the course during the first term. The steadily increasing importance of theoretical physics is to be taken into consideration. Several universities have proposed different solutions to these problems.

Several organizations are concerned with the teaching of physics. For universities the *Diplomprüfungskommission* (diploma examination commission) calls regular annual meetings with the purpose of giving recommendations for the improvement of teaching, and the reduction of study time by concentration and selection of material. At present, together with the Ständige Konferenz der Kulturminister (Permanent Conference of Ministers of Education) and the Rektorenkonferenz (University Rectors Conference), a uniform examination order is being worked out for the Federal States.

Most universities have a students' association of physicists and mathematicians, some on a voluntary basis, some for all students in these subjects. These associations are sections within the Natural Sciences Society within the Society of German Students' Organizations. These associations, too, are studying the educational problems intensively and seeking to suggest improvements.

The situation in France

There are a number of problems engaging the attention of those who have the responsibility for university education in physics in

---

1. W. Walcher, *The Personnel Structure of the New Universities*, Göttingen, Verlag Otto Schwarz, 1962.

France. Some of them will be mentioned briefly here to indicate areas in which changes are being discussed and in which developments can be anticipated.

The education of teachers of physics at the secondary level in France is generally satisfactory. It is imperative, however, to provide means for continuing education and research participation for these teachers, who cannot arouse the enthusiasm of their students if they themselves do not possess the enthusiasm that comes from taking part periodically in research programmes.

The tendency of the university physicist to become preoccupied with research, to the detriment of his teaching responsibilities, is causing concern. Since the National Centre for Research offers opportunities for pure research, unaccompanied by formal teaching, it may be desirable to maintain a clear separation between positions in pure research (those at the centre), and professorial appointments with teaching duties (those at the universities).

Many believe that the best education for an engineer is one in basic physics, acquired at a university, with an introduction to research. The development of faculties of science and technology would lead to educational programmes of this kind.

Committees representing the universities and industry have been discussing the educational preparation of future employees of industry, planning the development of educational programmes that are directed more toward industrial needs. To accomplish this, Chairs of technology will have to be created, and special laboratories equipped. In turn, industry is attempting to provide support for the universities by: (a) providing place within the industrial laboratories for thesis research by students; (b) by allowing specialists on their staffs to serve as adjunct professors, thereby strengthening the staffs of the universities; (c) the establishment of laboratories of pure research, open to all qualified persons.

The universities are considering the official recognition of educational attainment before the *licence* by introducing a new diploma —called perhaps the Diploma of General Studies—to permit their students of average attainment to enter professional life with an official diploma instead of merely abandoning their studies. There would then be three levels: the diploma referred to, the *licence*, and the *doctorat*.

186

Much thought is being given to the problem of continuing education (see also Chapter VII). Industrial companies increasingly give 'service guarantees' with their products so that the purchaser is assured that the device will be maintained in good working order. It is being proposed that institutions of higher education should do the corresponding thing by periodically organizing refresher courses to permit their graduates to bring themselves up to date. Some of the fields of physics that have been proposed by industry to universities as being appropriate for such refresher courses are the physics of plasmas and its applications, automation, new principles of the conversion of thermal energy, the physics of solids, and modern mathematics. During September of 1962, the University of Paris launched two such courses, each of two weeks' duration and accommodating thirty participants. The courses dealt with modern mathematics and the physics of solids.

Lastly, a few words on the use of television are in place here, although what follows applies not only to physics teaching but to the teaching of all subjects. At present, two educational institutions are equipped for television reception, the Paris Faculty of Sciences and the Conservatoire National des Arts et Métiers. The course follows classical methods without any modification; three cameras are used, and a producer regulates the signals so as to ensure that the most suitable image reaches the antenna at any given moment during the class.

Reception is confined to classroom sets distributed throughout the Paris region (for the time being). Students are thus drawn into a university atmosphere. An assistant lecturer is present at each receiving point to answer questions. This experiment is still in its infancy, but the promising results already achieved show that higher education can be dispensed over a very large number of places provided there are enough assistant lecturers to guide the students. Self-instruction will probably have to be rejected on the grounds that the student, left to himself, would not be able to find the answers to the numerous questions which he will normally find himself asking during the course.

The situation in the U.S.S.R.

The chief aim in training physicists is to give the students a thorough and clear understanding of the fundamental ideas and methods of modern physics on a mathematical basis. This can be achieved only by continuously improving the teaching of physics both in the secondary and in the higher schools.

The main condition for fulfilling this aim is active participation of all members of the physics department in scientific research work. Without this, it is impossible to teach modern physics at advanced level, for the subject is being continually enriched with new scientific data and new methods of scientific research involving the use of very complicated, up-to-date equipment and precision measuring instruments. Only a person directly engaged in scientific research in physics is in a position to give students an understanding of this science.

For this reason, great importance is attached in the U.S.S.R. to the selection of scientific material for teaching physics in the schools and institutes of higher education, because it is essential to use the modern achievements in physics in the process of teaching the subject. This task is made complicated by the continuous flow of new material, from which the departments in the institutes of higher education must, and do, select scientifically verified material, without too much detail. This is one of the main tasks of the physics departments in the institutes of higher education. On the basis of consolidated scientific work they must select such new data as will meet the needs of the course and introduce these into the syllabus, taking into account the general line of studies provided by the institute in question. It should be noted that this job must be done in conjunction with methodical processing and discussion of the new material in the physics departments. For this reason, the physics courses in institutes of higher education of a particular type are not themselves uniform, although the departments are run on the principle of a general standard syllabus laying down the basic scientific and theoretical line of the physics teaching. The content of the instruction is subject to discussion at inter-institute conferences, leading to the definition of a main line of study, which in the last resort is also helpful in determining the structure of the physics course. Much depends on the character of the physics laboratory, which has to be taken into account in allocating the number of hours devoted to lectures, practical work and laboratory teaching.

As an aid in solving the problem of bringing physics closer to the requirements of practical life, with allowance for the particular type of higher education institute concerned, the regular physics course at many of the institutes is supplemented by subsidiary courses devoted to particular branches of physics to meet the requirements of specialized disciplines.

In a number of branches of higher education there are plans for the further expansion of the physics course; for example, a decision has been taken to make further improvements in the physics training of students in the medical institutes.

At present, arrangements are being made to develop the experimental part of the course and increase the amount of laboratory work so as to ensure mastery of modern methods of scientific research in physics in the universities and technical, teacher-training, and medical institutes, taking into account the specific aims of a future practical or scientific research career. Here the teacher-training institutes have a particularly heavy task if they are to train physics teachers capable of involving secondary school pupils in the problems of modern physics, develop in them a capacity for 'thinking physically', and give them a taste for taking part in physics societies and laboratories; this is bound to have a good effect on the teaching of physics in institutes of higher education in the very near future. The goal is to reach a position where it will not be necessary to refer to secondary school material in the higher schools.

The higher schools must give more assistance to the secondary schools. Among other things, it is planned to conduct the physics olympiad in the institutes of higher education on a wider scale (the physics and mathematics olympiad for the European part of the U.S.S.R. finished at the beginning of 1963). The plan is to draw secondary school pupils who have shown ability in physics into physics societies attached to the institutes of higher education, and also to develop a system whereby such students are individually attached to professors and lecturers at the institutes of higher education.

As a rule, physics lectures for entrants to institutes of higher education in the U.S.S.R. are accompanied by good visual aids. Because of the great importance of visual aids in teaching physics we are paying more attention to the development of lecture demonstrations. The State University of Moscow and a number of other institutes of higher education have done a good deal to standardize visual aids for use in lectures, and have devised for this purpose special equipment, which has been demonstrated at a special extended conference, attended by representatives of the departments of physics in the institutes of higher education of the U.S.S.R. A special design bureau, attached to the Ministry of Higher and Secondary Specialized Education of the U.S.S.R., is working on, among other things, instruments (not for batch production) for physical laboratories in the institutes of higher education.

Several films for the teaching of physics have been prepared and are being shown.

In the immediate future the Ministry of Higher and Secondary Education will announce a competition for the best student of physics at an institute of higher education. All these steps must improve the teaching of physics.

In all this, the main purpose is still to ensure that the physics course has a modern content in all branches of higher education. What kind of scientific material should be introduced into the syllabus, how it should be prepared from the point of view of teaching method, what sort of laboratory work should be done in an institute of a particular type, how it should be directed without interfering with the student's independence—these and many others are the questions now facing the departments in the institutes of higher education.

The situation in the United Kingdom

In the United Kingdom, as elsewhere, the past few years have seen great concern for increasing the number of well-qualified scientists and for improving the means whereby they are trained. Substantial expansion has already taken place in university physics departments and further expansion has been planned for the next three or four years. However, even this planning has been made out of date by the report of the Robbins Committee to which reference has already been made. The proposals of this committee have already received the general approval of the British Government and it is clear that expansion will be on a scale far greater than has hitherto been thought possible. Academic physicists in the United Kingdom have given a great deal of thought to the problems that such expansion creates, problems of how to train more students without sacrificing quality of teaching, and how to expand carefully selected university staffs without diminution of quality and without adverse effects on the capacity of the universities to prosecute research. Reference should be made to the previously quoted report of the Institute of Physics and the Physical Society for a detailed discussion of these questions.[1]

Apart from a consideration of changes that could usefully be made in the techniques of university teaching, university physicists have contributed much to the discussions and experiments that have taken place on the improvement of physics teaching in schools. The approach to this problem has been quite fundamental, and the Nuffield Foundation is at present sponsoring a project which is as comprehensive as that of the American Physical Science Study Committee but, of course, framed to meet the different needs of the United Kingdom.

Much new thinking in physics teaching has also shown itself in the courses in the colleges of technology, especially for those leading to the Diploma in Technology. In particular, much has been learnt about different ways in which practical work can be incorporated into physics courses of this level.

In work of this kind, the United Kingdom is fortunate in having an extremely active and enthusiastic organization of science teachers now known as the Association for Science Education, with a membership in excess of 6,000. Its annual conference includes an exhibition of new experiments and equipment designed by members. Also, the Institute of Physics and the Physical Society takes a leading part in the development of new ideas in this field and its own annual Exhibition of Scientific Equipment and Apparatus includes a section devoted to educational exhibits.

The broad structure of physics education in the United Kingdom,

1. *Problems facing University Physics Departments*, The Institute of Physics and the Physical Society, London, 1963.

including the form of the university courses, is not likely to change significantly, but it is so flexible that change and experiment within it are comparatively easy to achieve. At the present time, new thinking is evident at all levels of education in physics, and physicists are conscious of the need to develop new methods that will allow them to meet the demands created by the large increase in the number of students, by the rapid expansion of physics and by its enhanced importance in a modern community.

The situation in the U.S.A.

Activities of the universities. Leadership in the improvement of physics teaching has come from the stronger universities and colleges. Physicists in these institutions realize that the educational process in physics must be more closely coupled with the rapid advance of physics itself. Unless this is done at all levels in physics teaching, the preparation of students for advanced study in physics and related sciences and engineering will be seriously deficient, and—by failure to educate the non-scientist in physics—lack of public understanding of physics will lead to serious consequences for physics and for society. Accordingly, there is a strong spirit of innovation among the leading physics departments in this country.

Some of the major efforts can be briefly mentioned as examples of the kinds of activities. At the University of California, Professor Charles Kittel is leading a project to produce a new introductory university physics course that will take advantage of the preparation that students have received from the Physical Science Study Committee (PSSC) high school physics course.[1] The six parts of the course are tentatively titled: I—Symmetry, relativity and particle physics; II—Electricity; III—Waves and oscillations; IV—Quantum physics; V—Statistical and thermal physics; VI—Epilogue. Professor Harvey White of the Berkeley staff has shown leadership in the exploration of film and television teaching of physics by producing a complete high school physics course on film, and by conducting a year-long nationally broadcast television physics course for high-school teachers called 'Atomic Age Physics'. At

1. 'A College Physics Course Working Committee', *American Journal of Physics*, Vol. 30, 1962, p. 843.

Columbia University, equipment development is going forward. One of the pieces being developed there under the direction of Professor Allan Sachs, with a grant from the National Science Foundation, is a spark chamber for teaching use. The activities of MIT physicists in the improvement of physics teaching are numerous and well known. The development of the physics course for high schools by the Physical Science Study Committee under the chairmanship of Professor Jerrold Zacharias has already been referred to; it has been productive of many good things. Educational Services Incorporated, a separate non-profit corporation formed to implement the work of the PSSC and other educational groups, continues to be active in many areas, including the making of additional physics films, the development of science courses for junior high schools, and the writing of additional text material for high schools.[1] The Science Teaching Center at MIT is working on a new introductory university course and on the development of a new approach to laboratory work in the introductory physics course, including the development of home-study kits of apparatus and other apparatus.[2] Professor Sanborn C. Brown of MIT is the chairman of a group of physicists who have prepared the outline of a course in plasma physics with the encouragement of the Commission on College Physics.[3] Swarthmore College has taken a prominent part in the Apparatus Drawings Project of the American Association of Physics Teachers and the American Institute of Physics.[4] Four pieces of physics apparatus developed by Professor W. C. Elmore of Swarthmore were described in that project. The California Institute of Technology is preparing an introductory university course in physics that integrates modern and classical physics thoroughly and carefully, emphasizing the quantum mechanical nature of the universe and using symmetry arguments. Washington University at St. Louis is developing an introductory course that will stress particle physics throughout. A number of colleges, including Beloit College and Wabash College, are experimenting with courses that combine chemistry and physics during the first two years. New

1. *Quarterly Report*, Educational Services Incorporated, Watertown, Winter 1962–63.
2. *A Progress Report*, Science Teaching Center, Massachusetts Institute of Technology, Cambridge, 1963.
3. C. Brown, 'Outline of a Course in Plasma Physics', *American Journal of Physics*, Vol. 31, 1963.
4. *Apparatus Drawing Project*, op. cit.

courses are in preparation at Rensselaer Institute of Technology, Princeton University, and Cornell University. In addition to these projects, much ferment is taking place generally in colleges and universities, leading to course revision, apparatus development, textbook writing, etc., on a broad scale. For example, in 1962/63 an experiment of merging one section of Physics 121 (Introduction to Atomic Physics) and Physics 115 (Introduction to Quantum Mechanics) into a full year's course will be tried at the University of California to amalgamate the discussion of quantum mechanical methods and quantum phenomena.

Activities of the professional societies. Although the primary responsibility for physics teaching rests with the schools, colleges and universities, collective action through the professional societies in physics, often with the support of the National Science Foundation, proves helpful in many ways. The American Association of Physics Teachers and the American Institute of Physics, of which the AAPT is a member society, have jointly and severally carried on a wide variety of educational projects. Recently the Commission on College Physics was established by the AAPT to stimulate revision of course content.[1] Among the current activities of the AAPT are the publication of two journals, the *American Journal of Physics* (for college teachers) and the *Physics Teacher* (for high-school teachers), the holding of two national meetings each year for the discussion of physics and physics teaching, and the sponsorship of a project at Rensselaer Polytechnic Institute for the preparation of a book on lecture demonstrations in physics. Among the joint activities of the AAPT and AIP are: the Visiting Scientists Program in Physics, which arranges visits by physicists to schools, colleges and universities;[2] the Project on Physics Faculties in Colleges, which involves a study of the problems of the smaller institutions in obtaining physicists for their staffs; the Regional Counselor Program in Physics[3] and the Center for Teaching Apparatus in Physics, which

1. 'Report of Conference on the Improvement of College Physics Courses', *American Journal of Physics*, Vol. 28, 1960, p. 568.
   W. C. Michels, 'Progress Report of the Commission on College Physics', *American Journal of Physics*, Vol. 30, 1962, p. 665.
2. W. C. Kelly, 'The Visiting Scientists Program in Physics', *Physics Today*, Vol. 11, 1958, p. 21.
3. *The Regional Counselor Program in Physics*, American Institute of Physics, New York.

stimulates and co-ordinates the development of physics teaching apparatus.[1] The AIP also includes among its current educational activities, in addition to activities mentioned earlier in this report, a project on documenting the recent history of physics in the United States[2] and the distribution of the AIP Educational Newsletter. The Commission on College Physics has just concluded a series of conferences on the undergraduate curriculum in physics. The Commission has stimulated the preparation of *Resource Letters*—annotated bibliographies in areas of interest to contemporary physics teaching that enable the college physics teacher to prepare new course materials.[3] The activities mentioned, although not the only ones, are illustrative of the educational programmes of the three organizations.

Summary

There is a drive toward improved physics teaching in all of the countries that have taken part in this survey. Long-established traditions are being questioned, and many of them superseded by new approaches to the teaching of physics. Changes are taking place in the objectives of physics teaching, the curricula and the content of physics courses, the relative emphases on the different branches of physics, the kinds of practical work, and the kinds of specialized study.

There is a strong desire to couple the teaching of physics more closely to the research process, both by introducing new material more rapidly into university courses and by making it possible for students to take part in research at an earlier age. Greater flexibility is a characteristic of the newer arrangements; efforts are being made to allow each student to work at his own pace and to develop his abilities as fully as possible without the hindrance of artificial restrictions. The laboratory and lecture demonstrations, supplemented by films when necessary, are being emphasized to a

1. *The Center for Teaching Apparatus in Physics*, American Institute of Physics, New York.
2. W. J. King, 'Source Materials for the History of Recent Physics', *Physics Today*, Vol. 15, 1962, p. 44.
3. Gerald Holton, *et al.*, *Resource Letters*.
   W. A. Shurcliffe, 'Polarized Light', *American Journal of Physics*, Vol. 30, 1962, p. 227.
   Sanborn C. Brown, 'Plasma Physics', *American Journal of Physics*', Vol. 30, 1962, p. 303.
   Gerald Holton, 'Special Relativity Theory', *American Journal of Physics*, Vol. 30, 1962, p. 462.

greater degree to enable students to have direct experience with the phenomena and the strategies of physics. The connexions between physics and technology are being strengthened in the educational programmes of many countries, so that the physicist will be prepared to contribute to the solution of problems of applied science when his career brings him into contact with them.

It has not been possible here to examine all of the developments toward improved teaching in the survey countries. For this reason, the national representatives decided that sources of further information about these trends should be indicated here so that additional questions of the reader would find answers. The reader is therefore referred for further information about the teaching of physics to:

In Czechoslovakia: Jednota cěskoslovenských matematikú a fyzikú (Union of Czechoslovak Mathematicians and Physicists), Maltézské nam. 1, Praha 1, Czechoslovakia.

In the Federal Republic of Germany: Deutsche Physikalische Gesellschaft e.V., z.Hd. Hauptgeschäftsführer Herrn Dr. Karl-Heinz Riewe i.Hs. W. C. Heraeus GmbH, 6450 Hanau, Postfach 369.

In France: Société Française de Physique, 33 rue Croulebarbe, Paris-13e.

In the U.S.S.R.: Ministry of Higher and Specialized Secondary Education, Department of Methodology, Uliza Gdanowa, 11, Moskwa, U.S.S.R.

In the United Kingdom: The Institute of Physics and the Physical Society, 47 Belgrave Square, London S.W.1.

In the U.S.A.: The American Institute of Physics, 335 East 45th Street, New York 17, N.Y.

International Union of Pure and Applied Physics: Professor C. C. Butler, General Secretary, Imperial College, South Kensington, London S.W.1.

Professor S. C. Brown, President, International Commission on Physics Education, Massachusetts Institute of Technology, Cambridge 39, Mass.

Mr. N. Clarke, Secretary, 47 Belgrave Square, London S.W.1.

Unesco: United Nations Educational, Scientific and Cultural Organization, Place de Fontenoy, Paris-7^e.

In one sense, the changes that are occurring present a problem for the developing university: there are fewer time-tested solutions to be adopted. But in another sense, changing practices represent an opportunity to build a new educational programme upon the best of the old and to take part in an educational development that all countries share. It is the hope of the authors of this report that it will serve as a chart for some adventurous exploration into better ways of teaching physics.

Appendixes

Notes on the educational system of Czechoslovakia

In Czechoslovakia all schools and educational establishments without exception are State institutions, directed and supervised by the Ministry of Education and Culture. The school system forms a unit in which the individual grades and types of schools organically link up with one another, enabling every citizen to acquire the highest possible level of education according to his abilities and the requirements of the nation.

Figure 1 shows schematically the main structure of the present Czechoslovak school system. (Art schools and other forms with which this report is not concerned are not referred to.) The Czechoslovak Education Act distinguishes pre-primary education, basic school education, secondary school education, full secondary school education, and university education. Voluntary pre-primary education is provided for children up to the age of 6 years in crèches and kindergartens. Basic education, lasting from the 6th to the 15th year, is compulsory for all children and received in the 'basic nine-year schools'. Secondary education, offered by apprentice training centres, apprentice schools, vocational schools and other educational installations, is of varying length and directed at various different objectives. The so-called 'full or complete secondary education' is either general or specialized, and terminates in a 'school-leaving examination' (school certificate).

'Secondary general education schools' offer young people who have completed the ninth year of a basic nine-year school a complete general and polytechnical education combined with basic training in some simple craft. One of the main tasks of these schools is to prepare the young people for further studies at universities in various fields. These schools are three-year schools. There are three branches at this type of school; one of them is the 'mathematico-physical branch'. 'Secondary vocational schools', lasting four years, offer complete specialized education and the necessary general education, preparing young people for medium-grade technical, commercial, medical, administrative and other positions in various branches of the national economy and culture. They end with a school certificate. The pupil may then enter a university or other institution of higher education, preferably one where he continues to study the branch for which he has prepared himself at the vocational school. During the past few years, many employed persons have been endeavouring to enhance their education and attain full secondary level. For this purpose, they enrol in a special type of secondary general or vocational school with facilities for extramural studies. Most of these schools run evening classes.

The training of specialists takes place at various types of schools of university level. Each faculty of these schools trains certain kinds of specialists according to the instructions of the Ministry of Education and Culture who, in conformity with the State plan, also specify the number of students to be admitted at each faculty, as well as the number of specialists to be trained for the various branches, in order to satisfy the requirements of society.

The oldest classical type of higher educational institutions are the traditional universities (Charles University in Prague was founded in 1348). At various faculties of these universities, research in mathematics, natural, humanistic and medical sciences is carried out, and professional specialists and teachers in these sciences are trained.

Engineers for industry and other branches of the national economy are trained at technical universities and colleges. The older technical universities (the oldest is the Technical University in Prague, founded in 1707) have several faculties, offering education in a number of technical fields. A newer, more specialized type of university-level school for the training of engineers in individual narrower fields are such specialized schools as the College of Textile Industries, the College of Agriculture and Forestry, the College for Mining and Metallurgy, etc. In addition to the instruction courses, fundamental and applied research work is also carried out in all schools of this type.

Only very recently another type of university-level school was established, the so-called pedagogical institutes, training teachers for the basic nine-year schools.

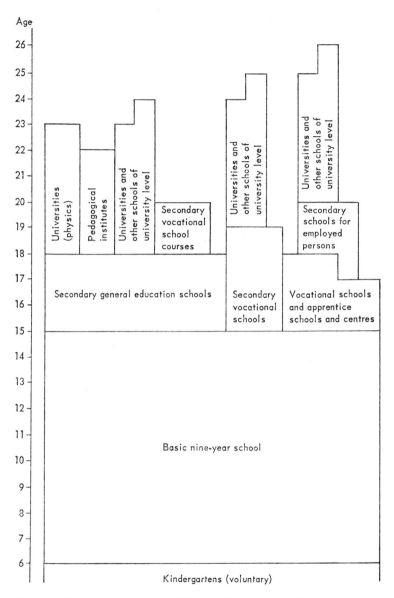

Figure 1. Main component parts of the Czechoslovak school system.

Notes on the educational system
of the Federal Republic of Germany

Readers are referred to the *World Survey of Education*, Volumes II, III, and IV, published by Unesco, for a description of the basic system of education in the Federal Republic of Germany. Figure 2 summarizes the relationships of the various parts of the educational system from the primary school *(Grundschule)* to the university. The horizontal lines indicate the ages at which the examinations should be normally taken, the double vertical arrows the most frequently observed deviations. (Where the student, in higher semesters, is simultaneously working as assistant at an institute, naturally the completion of his studies takes longer.) The single arrows indicate the most frequent ways taken towards the most important branches of physicists' professions.

The secondary school education is completed with the school-leaving examination *(Abitur)* in the *Gymnasium* at the end of the thirteenth class, at the age of about 19. According to an agreement of the Ministers of Education (Saarbrücken 1960), physics has become an optional subject in the last two classes of the ancient- and modern-language type of the *Gymnasium*. In the lower classes of *Gymnasiums* of this type, and in the mathematics and science type of the *Gymnasium*, physics is a compulsory subject from the eighth class onwards (corresponding to an age of approximately 13 years).

There are at present twenty-seven centres for the advanced study of physics. Eighteen of these are universities and nine are institutes of technology *(Technische Hochschule)*, one of which bears the name Technical University. Education in physics is rather similar at all German universities. Slight differences which exist are partly due to historical development and depend in part on individual appointments, specialized lines of study or particular emphasis in specialized programmes. However, there is no essential difference in the quality of education offered at the different universities. Moreover, endeavours are made to match education and requirements, in order to enable students to have the widest possible freedom in changing universities.

There are two paths open to the student. These two paths differ in aims and details of courses. The one way leads, via the preliminary education, to the diploma in physics and the qualification *Diplom-Physiker*. Students heading for careers in industry, who form the majority of students of physics, receive this training. The other way leads to the examination to become specialist science teachers in secondary schools *(Staatsexamen, Staatsprüfung für das höhere Lehramt)*. Both possibilities are offered at each of the universities.

The duration of a course of study is calculated in semesters, i.e., two semesters per year. The summer semester lasts approximately twelve weeks, the winter semester lasts about fifteen weeks. Thus one period per week results in twelve to fifteen lectures per semester.

During the summer semester 1961, the total number of students was about 225,000. The number of students in physics were about 14,000; about 35 per cent of these intended to take the *Staatsexamen* to become teachers in the *Gymnasium*.

205

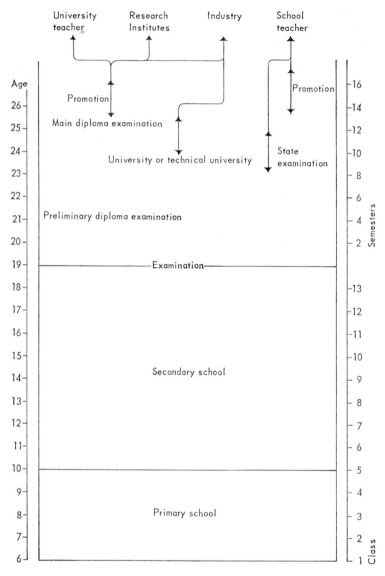

Figure 2. Main component parts of the school system in the Federal Republic of Germany.

Notes on the French educational system

School attendance is compulsory from the ages of 6 to 16; the school-leaving age will be raised to 18 within a few years. Higher education usually starts at about the age of 18, therefore a start must be made by listing the university entrance qualifications acquired by the student in the course of his primary and secondary education. All State schools follow the same syllabus, laid down by the *commissions nationales* (National committees) in Paris and promulgated by administrative regulation.

Figure 3 shows the basic system of pre-university education. As can be seen, there are several 'switch-points' during the child's career. The channel leading to the university is shown on the extreme left of the diagram. The child attends primary school from 6 to 11 years of age; he then takes the *cycle d'orientation* (orientation course). If he shows the necessary aptitude he goes on to the *premier cycle* (first part) of secondary education, which lasts until the age of 15, and then completes his pre-university training, from 15 to 18 years of age, in the *second cycle* (second part) of the secondary course.

The *baccalauréat*, which is, in fact, the secondary school-leaving certificate (advanced level), is awarded to candidates who have passed two examinations, including written and oral tests. The first of these examinations is taken at the end of the second year and the other at the end of the third and last year of the second part of the course *(second cycle)*. It is worth pointing out that this is a uniform nation-wide examination; the same papers, set by the Ministry of National Education, are taken at the same time on the same day throughout the country. Candidates have a choice of several subjects, biased heavily in favour of either arts or pure science. The subjects are as follows: *Litterae humaniores (philosophie)* (for careers in the arts and literature); experimental sciences (medicine, biology); economics (for careers in law or economics);

207

elementary mathematics, mathematics and engineering (for careers in science and technology).

At present one-third of the total number of secondary school leavers take the science options for the *baccalauréat*.

The whole French higher educational system is divided into two parts (figure 4). On the one hand, there are the nineteen traditional universities, each under a rector nominated by the State and not elected by the professors; these universities award *licences* and *doctorats* (figure 5). On the other hand, there are the colleges for specialized higher education *(grandes écoles)* and institutes *(instituts)*, which award what are generally known as *diplome d'ingénieurs* (engineering diplomas). The prime purpose of the *grandes écoles*, entrance to which is by competitive examination, is to train the experts the country needs; their second task is scientific research. In other words, the order of values is reversed by comparison with the traditional university, which never had the training of individuals for a particular requirement of the outside world as one of its aims. The Conservatoire National des Arts et Métiers is the sole institute of higher education which specializes in the education of young workmen who wish to return to their studies. It is open to those who do not hold the *baccalauréat*, although in practice a large minority of its best students have that qualification (figure 6).

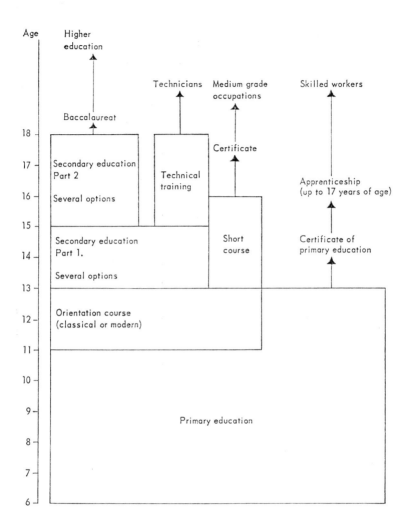

Figure 3. Main component parts of the French school system.

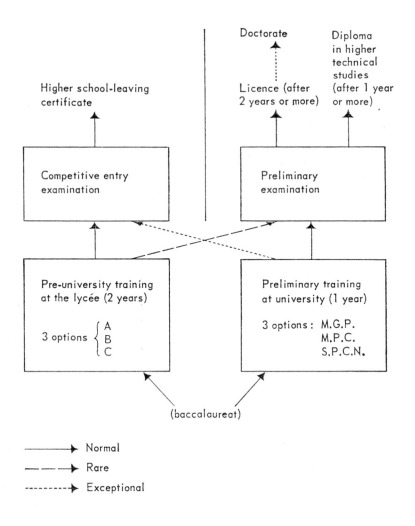

Figure 4. Two parallel systems in French education.

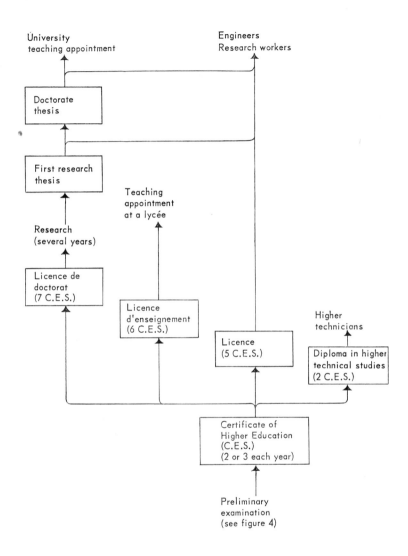

Figure 5. French degrees.

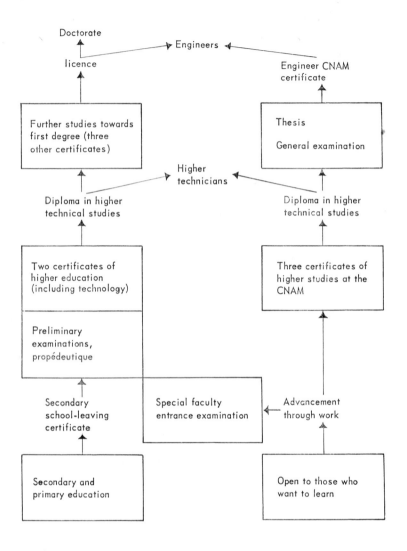

Figure 6. Different formations of technicians and engineers.

Notes on the educational system
of the U.S.S.R.

One of the basic principles of the Soviet national educational system, apart from the fact that it is a State system of universal and compulsory secondary education, is that all forms of education, at all levels, are free and that there is also a wide range of State educational grants and allowances.

Children under school age may either be educated at home or may take advantage of the immense network of day nurseries and kindergartens, at the discretion of the parents. School starts at the age of 7.

There are two main types of secondary schools in the U.S.S.R., the eight-year school and the complete eleven-year school (see figure 7). The full eleven-year secondary course can be taken at any of the following: (a) a general education labour polytechnic; (b) a technical or other specialized institute of secondary education; (c) a young people's urban or rural evening school.

In addition, there is an extensive network of urban and rural vocational technical colleges, offering one- to three-year courses in various skilled trades to former pupils of the eight-year schools.

An adolescent leaving the full secondary school at the age of 18 or 19 has the State-recognized right of admission to an institute of higher education.

Matriculation students are prepared for the competitive examinations either independently or, if it is felt necessary, within the system of preparatory courses or in a department of an institute of higher education.

Higher education is provided both for internal (day-time and evening) and for extramural students by a network of universities, technical, teacher-training, medical and agricultural institutes and other specialized institutes of higher education (academies, colleges, conservatoires and so forth), reflecting all aspects of the national life.

213

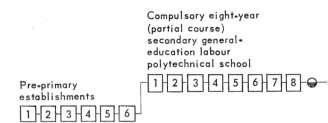

1 2 3 4 5 6   7 8 9 10 11 12 13 14

Pre-primary establishments

Compulsory eight-year (partial course) secondary general-education labour polytechnic school

○ Eight-year secondary school leaving certificate.

◑ Vocational - technical college leaving certificate.

● Certificate of general secondary education (eleven-year school).

○ Diploma of special secondary education and award of certificate of competence in subject of specialization.

◕ Diploma of higher education and award of scientific degree in a specialization (equivalent of degree of Master of Sciences, or second degree and corresponding award in institutes of higher education in the West).

* As a rule, the course takes one year longer, but not more than six years in all, at extramural and evening institutes.

+ The alternation of theory and practice in the institutes of higher education depends on the subject of specialized study.

Figure 7. The Soviet educational system.

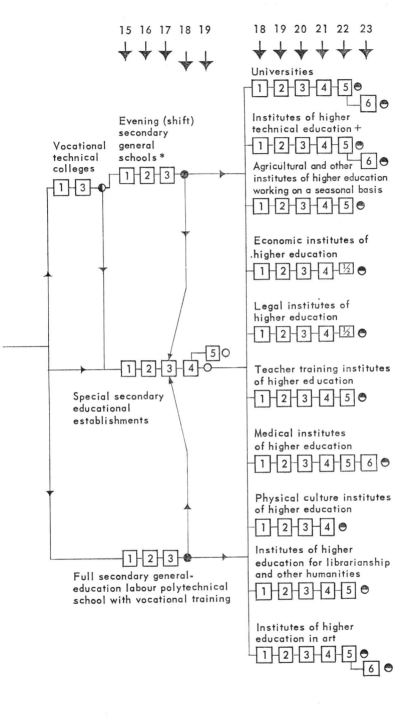

A reform of the national education system was started in 1958, under the Law of 24 December 'On strengthening the relationship of the schools with outside life and further developing the national education system in the U.S.S.R.', and is now practically completed. This law lays down that the most important task of the secondary and higher educational system at the present stage is to achieve a balanced combination of theoretical training in science with preparation for the student's practical career as a member of society. Revulsion from social parasitism, respect for work, and understanding of the necessity for preparing for an active career of useful work are instilled into children from their earliest consciousness and on adolescents in the U.S.S.R.

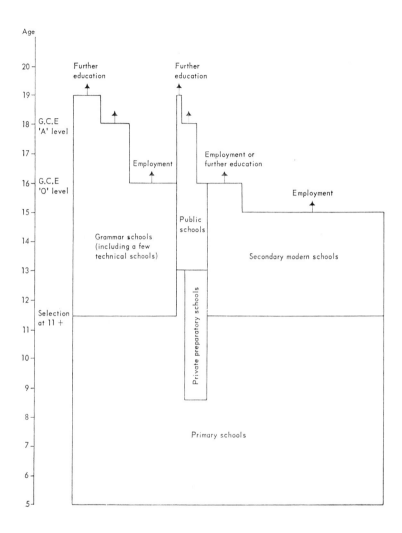

Figure 8. School education in the United Kingdom (England and Wales). (There are some differences in Scotland.)

Notes on the educational system of the United Kingdom

Figures 8 and 9 summarize the relationships of the various parts of the educational system of England and Wales. The Scottish system is somewhat different.

It is probable that the English schools whose names are best known outside the United Kingdom are the small group of 'public schools'. These are independent, i.e., private schools. The majority of British children, however, attend schools maintained by the State and it is the organization of the State system that needs to be explained. Primary education is compulsory from the age of 5 and secondary education from the age of 11 plus until 15. An increasing proportion of children stay at school beyond the age of 15. In their eleventh year all children in the State primary schools are graded by tests decided upon by local education authorities, in a process that has popularly become known as the '11 plus examination'. The brighter children, about 22 per cent of the total, enter grammar schools and, in the main, these are the children who enter the educational paths discussed in this report, although it is possible for children not initially selected for grammar schools to enter institutions of higher education, including the universities.

It is impossible to understand the position of physics in British universities without some general picture of the provision of higher education in the country. This provision cannot be described easily because, as with many British institutions, the educational system has not been built up by a simple logical process. For example, over the past half-century a good deal of work of university standard, especially in science and technology, has been undertaken successfully by institutions that are not themselves universities. Moreover, there are some significant differences between the arrangements in Scotland and those in the rest of the United Kingdom.

Finally, a document has been published in Britain during the days when the final draft of this survey was being agreed that may well transform much of the provision of higher education in the United Kingdom in a very few years. The Government has already accepted the main proposals of that document,[1] which is the report of a committee under the chairmanship of Lord Robbins that was set up to make recommendations for the future organization of all higher education in the country. Among the recommended changes are the granting of university status to the colleges of advanced technology, and the development of five new technological institutions modelled on the Massachusetts Institute of Technology.

Policy relating to university education in England has often been considered to have been dominated by the reputation of the universities of Oxford and Cambridge. They are two of the most ancient centres of learning in Europe and for more than six centuries they were the only two universities that England possessed. Scotland has four universities, the youngest being Edinburgh, which dates from 1582.

The remaining universities of England and Wales date only from the nineteenth or twentieth centuries, although at various times in the previous two centuries attempts had been made to establish other universities. The most notable foundation of the nineteenth century was the University of London, significant particularly because it became primarily an examining rather than a teaching body. The establishment of 'external' degrees, open to any student who passed the appropriate examinations, was to have an outstanding influence upon the development of other university institutions both in Britain and in the British Commonwealth overseas. A pattern that was to become common in the early twentieth century was the establishment in various cities, usually through local effort or the benevolence of some single local citizen, of 'university colleges' which provided courses of degree standard for students who took the examinations set by the University of London and qualified for degrees of that university. Among universities that have now achieved full independence but which began in this way are Bristol, Southampton, Leicester, Nottingham and Hull. Since the Second World War this practice has, however, been discontinued, and it is now the custom to create new universities that from the start are independent with power to confer their own degrees.

In Britain a university can claim this title only when it has been granted a Royal Charter from the Queen, on the recommendation of the

1. *Higher Education.* Report of the committee appointed by the Prime Minister under the chairmanship of Lord Robbins, London, Her Majesty's Stationery Office, October 1963. Price 15s. (Cmd. 2154.)

Government, entitling it to award degrees. Local authorities, private organizations, charitable foundations or, indeed, commercial bodies can establish colleges and can submit candidates to the University of London for external degrees, but, without a Royal Charter, they may not call themselves universities and they cannot award degrees of their own. One consequence of this is that, although variations must inevitably exist between universities in the standards demanded for degrees, these differences are comparatively small, and it may reasonably be taken that a bachelor's degree in a subject will be of broadly the same standard in all the universities.

In any country of the world, the method by which the universities are financed has important influences on the structure of the courses. The British arrangements are unique.[1] There are no 'State' universities, although all the universities now derive a very large proportion of their income from grants from the Government. The Ministry of Education has no control whatever over the universities; government grants are administered through a body termed the University Grants Committee, which receives its income direct from the Treasury and not through the Ministry of Education. The composition of the University Grants Committee is determined by the Government, but it has been the practice to appoint to it distinguished scholars and other educationists, and not to appoint to it anyone whose public reputation is primarily that of a politician. The revenue income of the universities is fixed for five-yearly periods. The whole purpose of the arrangement is to secure for the universities an appropriate income without challenging their essential autonomy. In academic matters, the universities are virtually independent corporations.

University students are widely subsidized from government funds, and this is financially possible only because admission to British universities is restricted. Severe competition exists for places, especially in those universities which have high reputations, and above all in Oxford and Cambridge. This is one of the biggest differences between the British system and that of most of the rest of the world. In many countries the universities that receive State support are required to take all students who satisfy minimum entrance conditions. This is not so in Britain, and the universities have complete discretion in their selection. In physics, for example, a university department that normally takes one hundred students each year into the course leading to its honours degree may be able to select from ten times that number who have applied for admission. At present, over the country as a whole, almost all students of adequate

1. At the time of writing the future of the present arrangements is uncertain in view of the Robbins Committee report.

ability do secure places in physics departments, but the students whose examination performance in the 'A' level of the General Certificate of Education has not been much above the minimum pass mark are unlikely to secure entry to the better known departments. This situation is of crucial importance in understanding many of the factors that determine the pattern of our school education system and of our university courses.

It is partly the pressure on university places in the years since the war that has led to an increase in the more advanced work of the technical colleges. Many of these colleges were founded in the latter part of the nineteenth century, and until about thirty years ago there were very few that did any appreciable work at a level above rather specialized courses for technicians in engineering, textiles, industrial chemistry, and so on. Since then, the technical institutions have been organized into something approaching a rational system. About a dozen of them have recently been designated as colleges of advanced technology, and these undertake almost exclusively full-time work of university standard. At present they work mainly for a nationally recognized diploma known as the Diploma in Technology which is awarded in individual sciences including physics. Other technical colleges do a fair amount of advanced work, commonly for the external degrees of the University of London. All these technical institutions, unlike the universities, come under the Ministry of Education. The colleges of advanced technology have a high degree of academic autonomy under independent governing bodies but the whole of their income is derived through the Ministry of Education. Other technical colleges are controlled by local educational authorities under the general direction of the Ministry of Education.

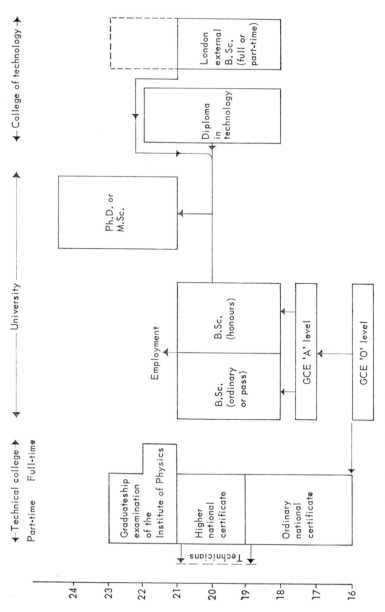

Figure 9. The education of physicists in the United Kingdom.

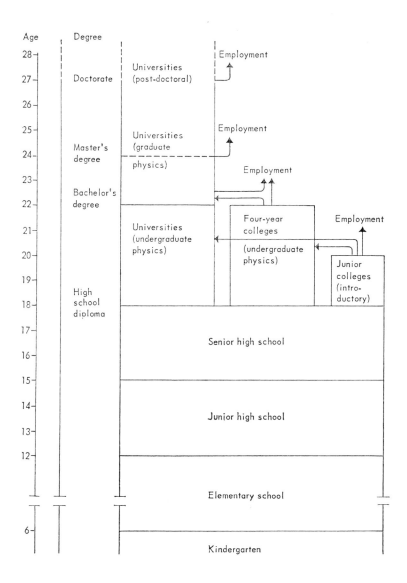

Figure 10. Education in the United States of America.

Notes on the educational system
of the U.S.A.

With few exceptions, students who apply for admission to a college or
university in the United States have had twelve years of prior education
in elementary and secondary schools (figure 10). The twelve years comprise twelve grades, usually divided as follows: grades 1–6 (ages 6 to 12
approximately) are in the elementary school; grades 7–9 (ages 12 to 15),
in the junior high school; and grades 10–12 (ages 15 to 18), in the senior
high school. (For some purposes, the twelve years are divided somewhat
differently: grades 1–8 are the elementary grades and grades 9–12 are the
secondary grades.) Education up to the age of 16 is compulsory for children
in all but three of the states. About 90 per cent of the schools are publicly controlled by local school boards with some state supervision. The
others are privately controlled, many of them by the Roman Catholic
Church.

There are two primary objectives for education in the elementary and
secondary schools: (a) to provide each child with the basic knowledge,
skills, and orientation needed by all in a technological society, and (b) to
provide a more intensive preparation in certain areas for children whose
later educational and career plans require it. The first of these is common
to education in all modern societies. In the United States it includes such
studies as the English language (including reading, grammar, writing,
spelling and speaking), modern foreign languages, the history of the
United States and the world, government, geography, economics, and
the fine arts. These subjects are grouped in various ways—history, government, geography and economics are often called social studies—and are
pursued at levels of increasing sophistication throughout the twelve years.
The programmes in science and mathematics are discussed in Chapter II
of this report.

Higher education in the United States includes undergraduate college and university education, graduate education (called 'post-graduate' in other countries), and post-doctoral and continuing professional education. Higher education thus encompasses all formal education beyond the age of about 17 or 18 years, for which satisfactory prior completion of twelve years of elementary and secondary studies is ordinarily required.

Local autonomy is a tradition long and firmly established in the United States at the lower levels of education as well as in higher education. American education is rather unique in this regard. Centralized control of education of any kind is kept to a minimum. There are no national certificate examinations administered by the Federal or state Governments to set standards for the granting of degrees at any level of higher education, and only mild requirements for the granting of diplomas upon completion of earlier stages of education. There are no Federal Government inspectors of education with broad regulatory powers. State control of colleges and universities within each state is limited to the institutions that are totally supported by state funds. Even here, following the practice of the private colleges and universities, the institutions themselves enjoy as much autonomy as is consistent with the responsibility of the state to oversee the use of its funds.

Educators enjoy a considerable amount of freedom to develop educational programmes that best serve the needs of their students, as the needs are interpreted by the institutions themselves, and that best employ local educational resources. The first result of this freedom is that there are many institutions of higher learning—a total of 2,028, of which about 700 offer bachelor degree programmes in physics and about 120 offer doctoral programmes in physics.

The second result is that there is diversity of educational philosophy and educational programme. Experimentation in the development of educational programmes is possible and is regularly engaged in—not so much as the most ardent educational pioneers would wish, but more than pleases the most entrenched conservatives. Also, a variety of educational environments, differing in the rigour of the educational programme, in the social milieu and in orientation toward various careers, is open to the prospective student of higher education.

Although colleges and universities in the United States have considerable freedom to determine their own policies, there are factors that act to reduce the amount of diversity. Among these factors are: (a) educational requirements for careers as set by employers and, in many professions, by professional organizations; (b) the financial exigencies that make it necessary for educational institutions (even the privately controlled ones) to seek support from the state and Federal Governments and thereby to conform to certain standards; (c) a competitive spirit

among institutions that causes them to emulate the 'best' among themselves and thus leads to the setting of standards; (d) various stimuli that
result from public and professional debate about the objectives of higher
education. These standardizing factors produce their effect upon education through an intricate network of associations, councils, professional
societies, grants panels, committees, commissions, educational service
organizations, and so on. By means of meetings (large numbers of
participants), conferences (smaller numbers), publication of journals and
magazines, the visits of representatives of regional and national associations, nationally standardized (but not nationally required) examinations,
surveys, projects, reports and speeches, the accomplishments of education
are noted, improvements are suggested, and these improvements are
carried out with varying degrees of expedition. In all of this, Federal and
state Governments take part as partners in education—financially powerful partners, but without the unique responsibilities for education that
are held by Governments in other countries. Private industry, labour
organizations, civic groups of private citizens, and educational foundations also have an influence upon education.

Outline of subject matter in mathematics and physics for the mathematico-physical branch of secondary general education schools in Czechoslovakia

Physics

First form

Mechanics: basic concepts, units; elements of kinematics. Elements of dynamics; work, mechanical energy; circular motion of a mass point. Gravitation field; orientation on the sky, measurement of time. Dynamics of solid body; simple machines; friction; statics of liquids and gases; flow of liquids and gases.

Second form

Molecular physics and heat: elements of kinetic-molecular theory; structure of solid materials and their elasticity; molecular structure of liquids; temperature and thermal expansion; heat and work; thermal processes in gases, changes of state; thermal machines.

Vibrations and waves, acoustics: simple vibration motion, wave-motion; sound waves.

Electricity and magnetism: electric charge and electric field; electric current in metals; direct current laws; electric current in semi-conductors; electric current in electrolytes; electric current in gases and in vacuum.

Third form

Electricity and magnetism (continued): magnetic field; electromagnetic induction; alternating current; production and transmission of electric energy; electric oscillations and electromagnetic waves.

Optics: wave properties of light, light as electromagnetic wave-motion, formation of images by mirrors and lenses, the eye and other optical instruments; quantum properties of light; energy of light; electromagnetic spectrum.

Structure of atom: structure of atomic envelope; structure of atomic nucleus; peaceful exploitation of nuclear energy.

Astronomy: importance of astronomy; evolution of concepts concerning the Earth and solar system; solar system; stars and star systems, origin and evolution of stars.

Importance of Physics: for the development of technics, especially for mechanization, automation and electrification; for other sciences; for the materialistic world view.

Mathematics

First form

Algebra: linear equations, linear and quadratic inequalities, equations of the second degree, powers and roots, real numbers, linear functions, quadratic functions, $y = ax^n$.

Geometry: basic properties of geometric figures, congruency, rotation, shifting (vector), similarity of triangles, Euclid theorems, theorem of Pythagoras, homology; basic geometrical formations in space and their properties.

Second form

Algebra: exponential and logarithmic functions, properties of the logarithm, use of logarithms, slide rule, exponential and logarithmic equations. Complex number and vector, computation, geometrical representation of complex numbers, the trigonometrical form of complex numbers, quadratic equations with real coefficients. Binomial equation, reciprocal equation. Combinatorics; arrangements, permutations, combinations, binomial theorem.

Geometry: trigonometric functions of the general angle, their properties, relations between trigonometric functions, trigonometric equations, trigonometrical solution of triangle.

Third form

Analytical geometry of the straight line and of conic sections (forty-five lessons).

Introduction to differential and integral calculus (thirty lessons).

Introduction to probability theory (twenty lessons).

Congruency in space, symmetry, rotation, shifting. Introduction to stereometry (twenty lessons).

Axioms, definitions, theorems and their proofs (ten lessons).

The mathematical and physical olympiads as conducted in Czechoslovakia

Run on the basis of voluntary participation, the Mathematical and Physical olympiads not only stimulate interest in physics and mathematics but also help to sort out the most talented pupils. The participants have to solve a certain number of problems in the course of the school year. The problems are different for each form. In solving their tasks, the pupils have the advice of their mathematics and physics teachers when necessary. They may also attend a special course of lectures organized especially for them and open throughout the school year. Those pupils who have successfully solved the given problems are, at the end of the year, invited to participate in the next round of the olympiad—the regional competition—and, finally, in the national contest. Both regional and the national competition demand of the competitors the solution of a number of problems allocated to him on the spot and to be solved that very day. The physics contest demands, in addition to calculation problems, several prescribed experiments and some measuring to be performed by the pupil. The successful participants in these olympiads are awarded books and other prizes. They also have priority when applying for acceptance at universities to study mathematics and physics, or when seeking permission to enrol for studies with a mathematical and physical base at technical universities and colleges.

Pre-university mathematics syllabus
in France and a typical test paper

The following is a brief summary of the syllabus designed for approximately 500 hours' teaching time; the full text will be found in the pamphlets published by Vuibert (63 boulevard Saint-Germain, Paris-5e). An idea of the ground covered in each part of the syllabus can be obtained by referring to such textbooks as that of Lentin and Maillard (Hachette, 79 boulevard Saint-Germain, Paris-5e). The order of teaching is, of course, adapted to the age of the pupils, starting with the simpler ideas.

Arithmetic, Algebra. Successive extensions of the notion of number, as far as complex numbers; practice in arithmetical and algebraic calculation; first and second degree equations.

Analysis. Elements of function theory (continuity, primitives); study of simple functions and their graphical representation; second degree algebraic functions, trigonometric functions, logarithmic and exponential functions; linear differential equations with constant coefficients.

Geometry. Euclidean plane geometry (straight line, triangle, circle, cone); three-dimensional geometry (plane, trihedral, simple figures); descriptive and dimensioned geometry; vectorial geometry, vector dependent on a parameter, vector derivatives; transformation theory; plane analytical geometry.

The following question paper, to be completed in four hours, will give the reader an idea of the level of knowledge required from a candidate who has just been admitted to the second part of the *baccalauréat* (during the four hours the candidate is required to produce a written answer to the question, solve the problem and prepare a fair copy of his answer).

Test paper

(Answer one of the following)

1. Prove the theorem that angles are conserved under inversion.
2. Prove Dandelin's theorem which states that the plane sections of a cone of revolution are conics.
3. Perform an orthogonal transformation of a circle. Calculate the area of the ellipse.

Problem

1. Study the variations of the function

$$y = \frac{-6x^2 - x + 1}{6x^2 + 3x - 3}$$

carefully determining the positions of the maximum and minimum, the poles and the limit value of the function when x tends towards infinity.
2. Plot the graph taking 2 cm as the unit in each direction.
3. We now consider the second degree equation

$$6(m+1)x^2 + (3m+1)x + (3m-1) = 0$$

in which m is some parameter.

Discuss the existence of real roots of this equation as a function of m, and their sign.
4. Show that the curve constructed in the second question makes the preceding discussion much easier.

Pre-university physics syllabus
in France and a typical test paper

The following is a brief summary of the syllabus designed for approximately 210 hours' teaching time; the full text will be found in the pamphlets published by Vuibert (63 boulevard Saint-Germain, Paris-6^e). An idea of the ground covered in each part of the syllabus can be obtained by referring to such textbooks as that of Cessac and Treherne (Nathan, 18 rue Monsieur le Prince, Paris-6^e). Classes I, II and III relate to the syllabuses for the last three pre-university classes, class III being the last.

Class I

Units and systems of units. Measurements; experimental error; the calculation thereof.

Measurements of length. Basic conceptions of statics. Balance; measurement of masses and specific masses. Statics of liquids and of gases.

The conception of temperature; the conception of quantity of heat; its measurement. Specific heat of body. Various states of a pure substance; equation of state of perfect gases; compressibility and expansion of solids and liquids. Diagram of equilibrium of a pure substance. Change of state; latent heat.

Class II

Geometrical optics; applications of the laws of Descartes to Gaussian optics of lenses and mirrors; the prism and the decomposition of light. Conventional optical instruments (magnifying glass, microscope, spectacles).

Basic ideas of electrostatics. Continuous current and its effect. Resistance, e.m.f., Ohm's law. Electrolysis; some ideas on ionic

233

theory (in co-ordination with the chemistry teaching); batteries and accumulators.

Magnetic field; action on a current, Laplace force; field created by a current; some very simple examples of magnetization. Electromagnetic induction phenomena. Self-induction.

Class III

The basic law of dynamics. Theorem of kinetic energy. Applications to simple movements (falling bodies, pendulums, uniform rotation, etc.). Study of sinusoidal periodic movements and their propagation; waves in a string, in the air, in an organ pipe.

Principle of the equivalence of heat and work. The first law of thermodynamics. The steam engine and the combustion engine; Carnot's theorem.

Acoustics; the physiological qualities of sounds. Vibrating strings; natural frequencies; organ pipes. Light waves; nonlocalized interference. Polarization of light.

Alternating electric currents; study of the influence of an induction coil and of a capacitor. Oscillation circuit; principle of electron emission; applications to photoelectric cells and radio valves. Electromagnetic waves; continuity of the electromagnetic spectrum (from radio waves to X-rays).

The atom and its structure; Mendeleyev's periodic table. The nucleus; natural radioactivity. Simple ideas in nuclear physics. Nuclear energy and fission.

The following question paper, to be completed in three hours, will give the reader an idea of the level of knowledge required from a candidate who has just been admitted to the second part of the *baccalauréat* (during the three hours the candidate is required to produce a written answer to the question, solve the problem and prepare a fair copy of his answer).

Test paper

(one of the following three questions to be attempted)

1. State the theorem of kinetic energy. Applications thereof.
2. The photoelectric effect; interpretation thereof.
3. X-rays.

Problem

1. A variable capacitor is constructed by placing a flat, semicircular metal plate P_1 in front of and parallel to another such plate P_2; the centres of the semicircle formed by the plates are O_1 and O_2 respectively and the radius r of both plates is 6 cm. The plate P_2 can turn about the vertical axis O_1O_2. The distance O_1O_2 between the two plates is 0.5 mm and is noted by e. Calculate the maximum capacity C_0 of the capacitor. When the two armatures (plates P_1 and P_2) overlap only at angle $\theta < \pi$, what does the C of this capacitor become?

   It will be recalled that in the MKSA system the capacity of a flat air capacitor is given by the formula

$$C = \frac{1}{36\pi 10^9} \frac{S}{e}$$

2. The capacitor C and a coil of resistance $R = 1$ ohm and inductance $L = 480. \ 10^{-6}$ henry constitute an oscillation circuit. An alternating electromotive force e of frequency ω is produced in this circuit by a source emitting waves of length λ. Let us assume that the circuit is represented by the following diagram.

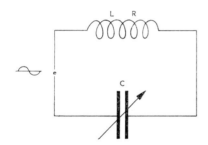

Figure 11

   How do the values of ω and λ, corresponding to the resonance, vary as a function of the angle θ?

   Calculate ω and λ for the following values of θ:

$$\theta_1 = \frac{\pi}{6} \text{ and } \theta_2 = \frac{2\pi}{3}$$

3. The circuit being tuned to the wavelength λ of an emitter absorbs a power of 10^{-10} watts. Calculate the effective values of the electromotive force and the current.

4. Let us slightly disturb the oscillation circuit, which is exactly adjusted to a certain value of C, by taking a new value $C + \Delta C$. Calculate ΔC knowing that the power absorbed will then be only half as great as when the adjustment is correct. Calculate the corresponding rotation $\Delta \theta$.

Calculate $\Delta \theta$ for the following cases:

$$\theta_1 = \frac{\pi}{6} \text{ and } \theta_2 = \frac{2\pi}{3}$$

5. Show that $\Delta \theta$ is proportional to λ^3 and draw conclusions regarding the ease of tuning of such a circuit as a function of wavelength.

II C3 Syllabus of practical or laboratory exercises in pre-university physics instruction in France

The following are a few of the operations which the pupil will perform. Classes usually last for one hour. The list follows the syllabus order of Appendix II C2.

Class I

Use of the vernier and micrometer calliper.
Calibrating a dynamometer.
Establishing the sensitivity of a balance; double weighing.
Measurement of specific mass of a liquid and of a solid.
Verification of the Principle of Archimedes.
Verification of Mariotte's law.
Measurement of a quantity of heat by the adiabatic calorimeter.

Class II

Verification of Descartes' laws.
Verification of the laws of the prism; minimum deviation.
Laws of conjugate points of a lens.
Measurement of the enlargement of a microscope.
Construction of the caustic curve of a spherical mirror.
Study of Faraday's law.
Operation of an ammeter and of a voltmeter.
Measuring resistances with a Wheatstone bridge.

Class III

Study of the fall of bodies (graphs).
Study of oscillations of a pendulum.
Melde's experiment with a vibrating cord.
Examination of interference produced with Young's slits.
Influence of an inductance coil and of a capacitor on an alternating current.
Study of the characteristic of a triode valve.
Examination of the spectrum emitted by a hydrogen tube.
Examination of tracks in a 'nuclear' photographic plate.

The necessary equipment is manufactured under the supervision of a government committee which is responsible for distributing it to the schools. Information can be obtained from the Centre d'Equipement, 29 rue d'Ulm, Paris-5e. Further, the Union des Physiciens, 44 boulevard Saint-Michel, Paris-6e, publishes instruction leaflets for the guidance of students performing experiments.

II D1   Physics syllabus for preparing students
for entrance examinations to
higher educational establishments in the
U.S.S.R.

General

The physics papers must be designed primarily to bring out the examinees' understanding of the nature of physical phenomena, their ability to interpret the physical meaning of quantities occurring in a particular formula and their ability to solve problems relating to matter covered by the syllabus, with appropriate analysis of the results and inferences to be drawn from them.

Examinees must show that they know the history of the most important discoveries and inventions in physics (within the scope of the syllabus).

Mechanics

1. Addition of forces operating along the same straight line. Addition of forces operating at an angle to one another (by graphs). Breakdown of a force into two forces operating at an angle to each other. Condition of equilibrium of a body on an inclined plane. Addition of parallel forces operating in one direction. Condition of equilibrium of a lever. Simple machines. Centre of gravity of a body. Types of equilibrium of bodies attached at a single point. Conditions of equilibrium of a body resting on an horizontal plane.
2. Uniform rectilinear motion. Velocity. The equation for this motion. Curve for the path and velocity of this motion as a function of time. Variable motion, mean velocity. Velocity at a given moment. Acceleration. Uniformly accelerating motion without initial velocity. Velocity curves in this motion. Velocity formula.

Deriving the path formula $S = \dfrac{at^2}{2}$, using the concept of mean velocity.

3. Newton's first law (the law of inertia).
4. Newton's second law of motion: ratio between force, mass and acceleration. Weight and mass of a body. Density and specific gravity. The CGS system of units. The unit of force—the dyne and its ratio to weight units (g and kg). Free fall. Acceleration of a freely falling body. Influence of air resistance.
5. Newton's third law: equality of action and counteraction. The principle of the jet engine. Tsiolkovsky, founder of the doctrine of reactive motion. Principle of construction and operation of a jet engine.
6. The law of universal gravity.
7. Mechanical work. The work formula. Power. Energy. Kinetic and potential energy. Conversion of potential to kinetic energy and vice versa. Law of the conservation of energy in mechanics.
8. Uniform circular motion. Linear velocity. Angular velocity. Centripetal acceleration. The formula for centripetal acceleration (not derived). Centripetal force, its point of application. Examples from engineering.
9. Elastic bodies. Spring balances. Dynamometers.

Oscillations and waves. Sound

1. Examples of oscillatory motion. Period. Number of oscillations. Number of oscillations per second. Amplitude. Connexion between period and number of oscillations per second. Formula for the period of oscillations of a pendulum (not derived). Mechanical resonance effects. Transverse and longitudinal waves. Velocity of propagation of oscillations. Wave lengths. Relationship between wave lengths, velocity of wave propagation and number of oscillations per second (or period).
2. Vibration of a sounding body. Atmospheric waves. The sound barrier. The speed of sound. Reflection of sound. Acoustic resonance.

Liquids and gases

1. Pressure. Pascal's law for liquids and gases. The principle of construction of an hydraulic press. The pressure of a liquid on the bottom and walls of a vessel. Law of communicating vessels for an homogeneous fluid.
2. Atmospheric pressure. Torricelli's experiment. Normal atmospheric pressure. Technical atmosphere. Mercury and metal barometers.
3. Archimedes' law for liquids and for gases. Conditions of buoyancy of a body.

240

4. Physical principles of aeronautics. Motion of a liquid and a gas. Zhukovsky and the world importance of his work in aviation.

Principles of the kinetic theory of the structure of matter

Basic propositions of the kinetic theory and its experimental validation. Brownian movement. Diffusion in gases, liquids and solids. Movement of the molecules of gases, liquids and solids. Mass and size of molecules. Molecular interaction.

Heat

1. Thermometers. The centigrade scale.
2. Coefficients of linear and volumetric expansion. Peculiarities of the expansion of water. Expansion of gases. Gay-Lussac's law. Boyle's law (Mariotte's law). Curves for this law.

   Formula for combining Boyle's and Gay-Lussac's law. Absolute zero. The absolute temperature scale.
3. Quantity of heat. Unit for measuring the quantity of heat. Formula for calculating the quantity of heat required to heat a body.

   Determining the specific heat capacity of a body experimentally. Calorific value of different types of fuel. Efficiency of a heater.
4. Convection in gases and liquids. Thermal conductivity of gases, liquids and solids.
5. Melting. Determining the melting point experimentally.
6. Vaporization and condensation. Boiling. Dependence of boiling point on pressure. Determining the heat of vaporization experimentally.
7. Saturated and unsaturated vapours. Their properties. Dependence of pressure of a saturated vapour on temperature.
8. Absolute humidity. Relative humidity. Hydrometers.
9. Liquefaction of gases.
10. Lomonosov theory on the nature of heat. Mechanical equivalent of heat. Heat equivalent of work (for kg-m, joule and erg). Diagram of a steam engine and of a steam turbine. Internal combustion engine.

    Efficiency of a steam engine and of an internal combustion engine.

Electricity

1. Two kinds of electricity. Interaction of electric charges. Coulomb's law. Electrostatic and practical unit of charge. Construction of the electroscope. Distribution of electricity on the surface of a conductor. Induction.

2. The electric field of a charge. Field strength. Calculating field strength for a point charge. Potential and potential difference; the volt. Capacitance. The unit of capacitance. The capacitor, its construction and purpose.
3. Electric current. The unit of current, the ampere. Potential difference at the ends of a conductor. Ohm's law for part of a circuit. Resistance of conductors. The unit of resistance—the ohm. Resistivity. Formula for calculating resistance. Dependence of resistance on temperature. Rheostats. Series and parallel connexion of conductors. Ohm's law for a whole circuit. Parallel and series connexion of sources of current.
4. Work and power of a current. The unit of work and power of a current: the volt-coulomb (joule), the volt-ampere (watt), the watt-hour, the hectowatt-hour, the kilowatt-hour. Energy of an electric current and its conversion into other forms of energy. The Joule-Lenz law.

   Electric bulbs. Lodygin's incandescent bulb. Heating instruments. Fuses.
5. Electrolysis. Faraday's laws of electrolysis. Yakobi, inventor of galvanoplastics.
6. Electric current in gases. Emission of electrons by incandescent bodies. Cathode rays, their nature and properties. Petrov's discovery of the electric arc. Slavyanov, inventor of electric-welding.
7. Magnetic field of direct current and live coil. Action of magnetic field on current. Magnetic field strength. Magnetic flow.

   Iron in a magnetic field. Electromagnetic relay. The principle of construction of the ammeter and voltmeter. The microphone, the telephone, the loudspeaker.

   Faraday's discovery of electromagnetic induction. Generation of induced electromotive force. Conditions determining the magnitude of induced electromotive force.

   Lenz's law.

   Self-induction. Inductance. Dependence of the inductance of a coil on a number of turns and the presence of an iron core. The unit of inductance, the henry.
8. Producing alternating current. Period, frequency, phase of alternating current. Root-mean-square value of tension and current strength. Resistance in alternating current.

   Rectification of alternating current. Direct current generator. Construction of an electron valve. Electron valve as rectifier. Construction and operation of a transformer. Yablochkov's invention of the transformer.

Transmission and distribution of electric energy. Soviet progress in electrification.

9. Electromagnetic oscillations and waves. The oscillatory circuit. Conversion of energy in an oscillatory circuit. Dependence of the period of oscillations in the circuit on inductance and capacitance (without mathematical deduction). Resonance. Producing undamped oscillations. The electron valve as a generator.

Open oscillatory circuit. Studying electromagnetic waves. Length of electromagnetic waves and their propagation velocity.

Popov's invention of the radio.

The principle of radiotelephonic transmission (amplitude modulation). A detector circuit and a very simple valve radio receiver circuit.

The electron valve as amplifier.

The cathode ray tube. The principle of radar.

Optics

1. Source of light. Rectilinear propagation of light. The velocity of light. Determining the velocity of light by the Michelson method.
2. Illumination. The unit of illumination. Formula for the dependence of illumination on distance from the source of light and on the angle of incidence of the rays. Comparison of the luminosity of various sources. The unit of luminosity. Photometers.
3. Laws of the reflection of light. Construction of the image in a plane mirror. Diffused reflection. Construction of the image in spherical mirrors. Focus of a mirror. The projector.
4. The laws of the refraction of light. Refractive index. Path of rays in a prism and a plane-parallel plate. Total internal reflection. Critical angle.
5. Collecting and diffusing lenses; the lens formula (without deduction). Construction of the image in lenses. Power of a lens.
6. The projector. The camera. The magnifying glass. The microscope. The telescope. The path of rays in these instruments. The eye as an optical instrument. Spectacles.
7. Breakdown of white light by a prism. The spectrum. The spectroscope. Invisible rays. Emission spectra. Absorption spectra. Fraunhofer lines. The solar spectrum. Spectral analysis. Principle of the methods of producing X-rays and their properties.
8. Principle of the wave nature of light. Interference of light.
9. The action of light. The photoelectric effect. The work of Stoletov on the photoelectric effect. The concept of quanta. Photocells and

their use. Chemical effects of light and their use in photography. Luminescence and its application in optical engineering. Importance of Vavilov's work on the study of light.

Atomic structure

1. Phenomena confirming the complex structure of the atom. Methods of observing particles.
2. Atomic structure—the electron shell and the nucleus. Radiation and absorption of energy by the atom.
3. Component parts of the atomic nucleus—protons and neutrons.
4. Splitting the uranium nucleus. Chain reaction. Release of energy in atomic decay.

II E1   Oxford and Cambridge Schools
Examination Board. General
Certificate Examination Advanced
Level (special paper), 1963, Physics III

(To be completed in three hours)

Answer *five* questions, including at least *two* from Section A and at least *two* from Section B.

Candidates are advised that they are not expected to derive standard formulae unless specifically told to do so.

$$[g = 981 \text{ cm sec}^{-2}]$$

Section A

1. A gravity conveyer consists of two parallel bars at an angle of $5°$ to the horizontal, between which are mounted rollers of diameter 5 cm and moment of inertia 25×10^3 gm cm² about their axes, evenly spaced at ten rollers per metre length of conveyer. The rollers, initially at rest, have rough surfaces, but may turn without friction on fixed bearings mounted on the bars, and their axes are horizontal and perpendicular to the bars. A long flat-bottomed box is placed at the top of the conveyer, exerting pressure on eight rollers, and is released so that it starts from rest and runs down under gravity. If the mass of the box is 40 kg, calculate its initial acceleration, by energy or other considerations.

   Explain why the speed which the box can attain on a long conveyer is limited, and why this limiting velocity cannot be calculated by the energy method.

   Discuss the effect of launching a second, similar box close behind the first.

2. On what grounds would you anticipate some connexion between the surface tension of a liquid and its latent heat of vaporization?

A vertical capillary tube 10 cm long tapers uniformly from an internal diameter of 1 mm at the lower end to 0·5 mm at the upper end. The lower end is just touching the surface of a pool of liquid of surface tension 60 dyne cm⁻¹, density 1·2 gm cm⁻³ and zero angle of contact with the tube. Calculate the capillary rise, justifying your method.

Explain what will happen to the meniscus if the tube is slowly lowered vertically until the upper end is level with the surface of the pool.

3. A powerful U-shaped magnet is suspended, with limbs vertical, on a torsion wire, at a place where the earth's magnetic field is negligible. It is found to execute torsional oscillations of period 2π sec about a vertical axis through its centre of gravity. Its moment of inertia about the axis of suspension is 10^6 gm cm². Calculate the restoring couple per unit angular displacement.

In an experiment to determine the mechanical equivalent of heat a copper cylinder of mass 270 gm and specific heat 0·095 cal gm⁻¹ deg⁻¹ C is placed symmetrically between the poles of the suspended magnet, with its axis vertical, and rotated about this axis at 20 revolutions per second. The magnet, initially at rest, turns in the same direction until it shows a steady deflection of 6° from its equilibrium position. In the first five minutes of rotation the temperature of the copper rises 3·40° C, starting at room temperature, and with the magnet removed and rotation continued it cools 0·20° C in the next five minutes. Calculate the mechanical equivalent of heat. You may assume the copper to be a perfect thermal conductor.

In a modification of this experiment the magnetic field is caused to rotate while the torque on the copper cylinder is measured, and the heat generated is continuously removed from the copper by a flow of cooling water. As a method for the determination of the mechanical equivalent of heat, what are the *advantages* of these modifications?

4. Two flat metal plates are mounted horizontally, one immediately above the other, about 1 cm apart in a gas at N.T.P. Explain the physical process by which molecules of the gas transfer heat from one plate to the other when the upper plate is the hotter of the two.

Experiment shows that with this apparatus the rate of transfer of heat is independent of the gas pressure over a fairly wide range of pressures. How do you account for this?

In such an experiment each plate has area 1 square metre and they are 1 cm apart. The upper plate is maintained at 100° C and the top surface of the lower plate at a temperature of 20° C by a flow of cooling water of 84 gm sec⁻¹ which is thereby heated 5° C. When the distance between the plates is reduced to $0\cdot5$ cm the same temperatures are maintained when the flow of cooling water is increased to 148 gm sec⁻¹. Assuming that the gas does not absorb any radiated heat, and that all heat flow is normal to the plates, calculate the thermal conductivity of the gas.

5. (a) Parallel rays of light are incident normally on the plane face of a plano-convex lens of refractive index 1·5, whose convex face is a hemisphere of radius 2 cm. Consider the action of this lens on three rays of light, one incident very close to the axis, one distant 1 cm from the axis and one distant $\sqrt{2}$ cm from the axis. Find the point of intersection of the ray with the axis in each case.

(b) Parallel rays of light are incident normally on the plane face of a lens of refractive index μ. The other face of the lens is so curved that all the rays are brought to a focus at a point F on the other side, at a distance f from the point where the axis cuts the curved face. P is a point on the curved face at a distance r from F, and PF makes an angle θ with the axis. Assuming that the time taken by light to travel along a ray, from a plane perpendicular to the axis on the object side of the lens to the focus, is the same for all rays, find an equation relating f, r, θ and μ.

6. Two short vertical line sources of radiation, ABC and DEF, are placed with their mid-points B and E in the same horizontal plane and $0\cdot5$ metre apart. Each source radiates uniformly in this plane. The intensity of the radiation received along a line GH, parallel to BE, at the same horizontal level and distant 5 metres from BE, is measured and is found to be zero at O where the perpendicular bisector of BE meets GH, with a series of maxima and sharp minima on either side of O. The first minima on either side of O are 30 cm from O.

What deductions can be made concerning the radiators ABC and DEF?

When ABC is turned through 90°, to lie along BE, the intensity at points along GH shows negligible variation, but when DEF is rotated also in the same way the maxima and minima reappear. What further information does this give?

Section B

7. A parallel plate air-spaced condenser of capacitance 5×10^{-4} microfarads is charged to a potential difference of 100 volts. It is then isolated and immersed in oil of dielectric constant 2·5. Calculate the new value of the potential difference, and explain as fully as you can

why the presence of the oil causes the potential difference to change. What change in energy stored in the condenser occurs on immersion?

In an experiment to measure the dielectric constant of the oil, the above procedure was followed, but with an electrometer connected across the plates of the condenser the whole time, to measure the initial and final values of the potential difference. The electrometer itself had a capacitance of 10^{-4} microfarads. What value would have been obtained for the dielectric constant if the electrometer capacitance had been neglected?

8. State Ohm's law and Kirchoff's laws for electrical circuits. How far can you account for these laws as applied to metallic conductors in terms of the motion of 'free electrons'?

A Wheatstone bridge consists of four resistors P, Q, R and S, with a driving cell of e.m.f. E_1. The galvanometer is replaced by a second cell of e.m.f. E_2 connected as shown in the diagram.

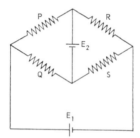

Figure 12

Find under what condition the current through P will be zero, assuming that the internal resistances of the cells are negligibly small.

Show further that if the condition is to be achieved by adjustment of the resistor S only, E_1/E_2 must lie in the range 1 to R/Q.

9. Explain what is meant by (a) the Seebeck effect and (b) the Peltier effect, and describe how each may be demonstrated independently.

Two identical copper wires AB, CD are joined together by a uniform wire BC of different material so as to form a perfectly symmetrical circuit with two junctions at B and C. The positive terminal of a battery is connected to A and the negative terminal to D, and a large current is allowed to flow for about a minute. The battery is then disconnected and a sensitive galvanometer immediately connected between A and D. A small current is observed to flow through the galvanometer, gradually decreasing to zero.

248

Explain these observations. In which direction would you expect the galvanometer current to flow, and why?

10. Derive an expression for the intensity of magnetic field at a point which is at a perpendicular distance p from a long straight wire carrying a current i. State the units in which the quantities in your expression are measured.

A coil of wire of 100 turns forms the perimeter of a rectangle with sides 10 cm by 200 cm. Estimate the magnetic field intensity at the centre of the rectangle when a current of 1 ampere flows around the coil, explaining any approximations you make.

A second small coil with five turns of area 1 sq. cm is placed at the centre of and coplanar with the rectangular coil. Calculate approximately (a) the mutual inductance between the two coils, (b) the r.m.s. value in volts of the electromotive force induced in the small coil when an alternating current of r.m.s. value 1 ampere and frequency 50 kilocycles per second is passed through the rectangular coil.

[1 ampere $= 10^{-1}$ e.m.u.; 1 henry $= 10^9$ e.m.u.]

11. Describe the construction of a simple form of thermionic diode valve, and explain how it may be used to supply unidirectional current to a resistive load from an alternating voltage supply.

The current i through a given diode for various values of voltage V between anode and cathode is given in the following table.

V (volts)	0	50	100	150	200	250	300
i (mA)	0	8	30	55	70	76	78

Sketch a characteristic curve for this valve and explain its general shape.

When a diode with this characteristic is connected in series with an anode resistor to a 100 volt D.C. supply, a current of 8 mA is observed to flow. To what value must the supply voltage be raised in order to increase the current to 30 mA?

Examination paper for entrance
scholarships to six of the Cambridge
colleges. Physics

(To be completed in three hours)

The following examination paper (set in 1962) was for open entrance
scholarships to six of the Cambridge colleges. The candidates sitting this
paper would normally have completed two years and one term in the
sixth form of a grammar school and would be aged 18 years.

A three-hour practical examination is also taken. The problem set is
given at the end of the written paper.

Candidates are required to attempt questions 1 and 2 and three other
questions, of which at least one must be chosen from either section C
or D.

Extra credit will be given for complete answers.

Question 1 is equal in value to any two other questions.

Answers to the four sections should be given up separately.

Electrical quantities are usually stated in both c.g.s. and R.M.K.S.
units but sometimes relevant conversion factors are given instead.

Section A

1. (a) A condenser of capacity C is charged to a potential difference V_0
   and is then shunted by two equal resistances in series each of resistance R. A discharge tube is connected in parallel with one of the
   resistances and starts conducting as soon as the resistances are connected to the condenser. This tube has characteristics such that while
   conducting the voltage across it remains constant and equal to $V_0/3$.
   How long is it before the tube stops conducting?

   (b) Inside a spherical star which is not rotating it is found that the
   gravitational attraction is independent of distance from the centre.

Appendixes

The density of the material at the surface is 1 g cm^{-3}. What will it be half way to the centre?

(c) A piston is fixed at the end of an evacuated cylinder of volume 100 litres so that it cannot move until it lies on the sea floor. The piston is connected to a dynamo and electrical energy is produced when the piston is released. If the sea depth is 5 km and the device is lowered to the bottom on a wire and subsequently brought up to the surface what is the maximum electrical energy which could be produced and whence has this energy been derived?

(Density of sea water $=1$ g cm^{-3}; g $= 1000$ cm s^{-2}; 1 joule $= 10^7$ erg.)

(d) From outside a house air that is saturated with water vapour is sucked through a cooling plant at a constant rate of 5 m^3 min^{-1}. Its temperature is lowered from 10°C to just above freezing point. This results in the condensation of water from the air. The heat thus extracted and the heat due to frictional and electrical losses in the machine are returned to the air as it is pumped into the house. What would be the air temperature if these losses amounted to one third of the heat extracted from the air? It may be assumed that the specific heat and the density of the air are constant over the temperature range involved.

(Latent heat of vaporization of water near 0°C $= 600$ cal g^{-1}; specific heat of air at constant pressure $= 0.25$ cal g^{-1}; density of air $= 1000$ g m^{-3}; water content of saturated air at 10°C $= 10$ gm^{-3}, at 0° C $= 5$ gm^{-3}.)

(e) A ship steams away from a radio transmitter ashore in a straight line at a speed of 36 km h^{-1}. Aboard the ship there is an electrical oscillator of precisely the same frequency as that of the transmitter. Because of the Doppler effect a beat frequency of 10^{-2} c s^{-1} is observed in the ship between the radio transmissions and the oscillator. What is the frequency of the transmitter?

(Velocity of radio waves $= 3 \times 10^{10}$ cm s^{-1}.)

Section B

2. Answer four of the following:

(a) The front wheels of a four-wheeled car are parallel when at full lock. Why does one front wheel have to slip as the car moves in its turning circle of minimum radius? Which wheel is it?

(b) Why does a photograph taken with a telephoto lens appear to lack depth?

(c) Why is a finite force required to roll a cylinder over a smooth flat surface?

251

(d) Why is the standard of length now defined in terms of the wavelength of light from krypton instead of in terms of the length of a metal bar?

(e) What factors limit the intensity of continuous sound in (i) a gas, (ii) a solid?

(f) The fair-skinned races of mankind originate from the middle and high latitudes and dark-skinned races from equatorial regions. From the aspect of maintaining body temperature at a fixed value, is this colour difference what might be expected?

(g) A shunt-wound electric motor drives a load which requires a constant mechanical couple. Why is the motor likely to be damaged by excessive heating if the supply voltage is (i) increased above, (ii) decreased below, the normal value?

Section C

3. Discuss the motion of a satellite travelling in an elliptical orbit around the earth with regard to (a) the forces acting on it, and (b) the conservation of energy principle. You may ignore small perturbations due to effects such as atmospheric friction and the oblate spheroidal shape of the earth.

   A telecommunication satellite of mass 100 kg is to be placed in a circular equatorial orbit such that it remains stationary above a fixed point on the equator. Calculate the radius of the orbit and the energy which must be supplied to place it in orbit.

   (g at the surface of the earth $= 10^{-2}$ km s^{-2}; radius of earth $= 6,400$ km.)

4. How is the rise of water in a glass capillary explained in terms of surface tension? What is the physical origin of the increase in potential energy of the liquid in the capillary?

   A long vertical glass capillary has a small uniform angle of taper. The wider end of radius r_0 is placed in contact with a water surface. The radius of the capillary decreases with height h above the water surface according to the relation $r = r_0 - \alpha h$. Show that there are two possible positions of equilibrium for the meniscus. Which one would you expect to be stable and why?

   (You may assume that

$$\alpha \ll \frac{\varrho g\, r_o^2}{8T},$$

where ϱ and T are the density and surface tension of water.

252

5. Derive the relation between the pressure and volume of a perfect gas undergoing reversible adiabatic expansion.

A hollow cylinder of internal cross-sectional area 1 cm² is closed at both ends. The cylinder is divided into two equal halves, each of length 100 cm, by a frictionless piston of mass 100 g, and each half is filled with a gas at a pressure of 10^6 dyn cm⁻². The cylinder is held horizontal and the piston is displaced a small distance from the centre and released. Show that the piston performs simple harmonic motion. The period of the motion is 0.37 s. Determine $\gamma(= C_p/C_v)$ for the gas. (The cylinder and piston may be assumed to have negligible thermal conductivity.)

6. Discuss the mechanism by which thermal equilibrium is attained when a hot body is placed in an evacuated space with cooler walls maintained at constant temperature. The body is not in physical contact with the walls.

A diode valve consists of two long coaxial cylinders. The inner cathode cylinder, of radius 0.05 cm, radiates heat like a black body. The radius of the anode cylinder is large compared with that of the cathode. The cathode heater element dissipates one watt per centimetre length. If the steady anode temperature is 227° C, estimate the temperature of the cathode. Neglect end effects.

(Stefan's constant $= 5.74 \times 10^{-12}$ watt cm⁻² °K⁻⁴.)

Section D

7. Explain what is meant by the terms *magnification* and *angular magnification* of an optical system, and *luminance* (sometimes called *brightness*) of a surface.

Show that the luminance of an image seen through a simple lens of large aperture is the same as the luminance of the object, if the lens transmits all the light falling on it.

Night binoculars usually have larger objectives than those used during the day. Show that this is necessary because the pupil of the eye is larger at night.

A simple telescope consists of two convex lenses. If the diameter of the pupil of the eye is 5 mm, the angular magnification of the telescope is five times, and the telescope is 12 cm long, determine the minimum aperture of the objective if the field of view is to appear to have maximum brightness up to 1° from the axis (that is, up to 5° as seen through the telescope).

8. Explain what is meant by *interference* in connexion with wave

motion and give four examples drawn from as wide a field as possible.

A radio-navigation system consists of three transmitters A, B and C which are situated 50 km apart on a straight line and two receivers E and F in every aeroplane. A and C transmit with the same phase and power on a wavelength of 150 m and B on a slightly different wavelength and at the same power. E can receive and measure the intensity (power) of signals on a wavelength of 150 m (but does not respond to transmissions from B) and F can receive and measure the strength of signals from B only. For an aeroplane which is known to be about 500 km from A and C the power of the signal received by E is found to be equal to the power of the signal received by F. How far is the aeroplane from the line drawn through B perpendicular to AC?

Would the system as described be satisfactory in principle? (Ignore such practical difficulties as irregular propagation of radio waves over long distances.)

9. Define and explain the terms *magnetic field strength (magnetizing force)* and *magnetic flux density*. How are they related (a) in free space; (b) in weakly magnetic substances such as aluminium and copper; (c) in a ferromagnetic material such as soft iron.

How would you determine the relation experimentally for soft iron? Give rough values for the relevant quantities (for instance, the current used in any magnetizing coil) used in your determination.

10. A copper disc 10 cm in diameter is placed inside a long solenoid so that the axes of the disc and solenoid coincide. A brush touches the rim of the disc and is connected to one end of the coil; a second brush touches the centre of the disc and is connected to the other end of the coil. The coil is uniformly wound with 1,000 turns per centimetre of its length and has a resistance of 100 ohms. It is placed in the earth's field in such a way that the component of the earth's field along the axis of the coil is 0.1 gauss ($= 10^{-5}$ Wb m^{-2}). With the assumption that the disc does not break, describe what happens as the disc is rotated at increasing speed, and show that for one direction of rotation there is a critical speed at about 10^5 revolutions per second.

Explain why such a system would not be suitable for a practical dynamo and describe how it must be modified to make it suitable.

(1 V $= 10^8$ e.m.u.; 1 A $= 10^{-1}$ e.m.u.; $\mu_o = 4 \times 10^{-7}$ henry metre^{-1}.)

11. How has the ratio of charge to mass of a proton been determined?

A space ship has a total mass of 10^5 kg and is propelled by a jet of protons which have been accelerated by a potential difference of

10^7 volts. The current carried by the jet is 1 ampere. What is the acceleration of the space ship and how much hydrogen will it need to increase its speed by 10,000 km per hour?

If to avoid charging up the space-ship a current of electrons that have been accelerated by 10^7 volts is also discharged, how are the acceleration and hydrogen required altered?

[Charge on proton $= 5 \times 10^{-10}$ e.s.u. $= 1.6 \times 10^{-19}$ coulomb; mass of proton $= 1.67 \times 10^{-24}$ g; mass of electron after acceleration through 10^7 volts (to a velocity which you may assume is equal to the velocity of light in free space) $= 1.8 \times 10^{-26}$ g.

$1 \text{ V} = \dfrac{1}{300}$ e.s.u.; $c = 3 \times 10^{10}$ cm s^{-1}.]

Practical physics

(Three hours)

From the rate of change of volume of a mixture of water and ice in a glass conical flask surrounded by a large volume of water at constant temperature, calculate the thermal conductivity of the glass.

Curricula for the education
of professional physicists in
Czechoslovakia

In reproducing the curricula, the following abbreviations are used:

4/2 = Four weekly periods of lectures and two periods of connected exercises (laboratory work and seminars are marked as exercises, e.g. 0/3).

ex = Examination.

mv = Marked validation, used for evaluation of the results of the student's laboratory work and given immediately upon completion of the exercise.

The curricula described here apply at the mathematico-physical faculty of Charles University in Prague. The curricula of the other faculties training professional physicists differ somewhat from these as far as the number of periods per week is concerned, or in distributing certain lectures over the individual semesters.

A. Basic curriculum

Subject	Semester				
	First	Second	Third	Fourth	Fifth
Experimental (general) physics	4/2 ex	4/2 ex	3/1 ex	3/1 ex	—
Selected parts of electricity and magnetism	—	—	—	—	4/0 ex
Introduction to practical physics	2/0	—	—	—	—
Physical laboratory exercises	—	0/3 mv	0/3 mv	0/3 mv	0/4 mv
Theoretical mechanics	—	—	3/1	3/2 ex	—
Theory of electromagnetic field	—	—	—	—	4/2 ex
Special theory of relativity	—	—	—	—	2/0 ex
Mathematical analysis	5/2 ex	4/2 ex	4/2 ex	3/2 ex	—
Introduction to algebra and analytic geometry	4/2 ex	4/2 ex	—	—	—
Analytic geometry	—	—	4/0 ex	—	—

256

Subject	Semester				
	First	Second	Third	Fourth	Fifth
Algebra	—	—	2/0	4/2 ex	—
Mathematics for physicists	—	—	—	—	4/2
Stochastic processes in physics	—	—	—	—	2/0
General education	9	11 ex	9 ex	9 ex	6
Production activity	—	8 weeks	—	8 weeks	—
Excursions	—	—	—	2 days	—
Total number of weekly hours	30	32	32	32	30
Total number of examinations	3	4	4	5	3

B. Common part of the curriculum of specializations

Subject	Semester				
	Sixth	Seventh	Eighth	Ninth	Tenth
Selected parts of optics	3/0 ex	—	—	—	—
Quantum mechanics	4/2 ex	—	—	—	—
Thermodynamics and statistical physics	—	5/2 ex	—	—	—
Mathematics for physicists	4/2 ex	—	—	—	—
General education	5 ex	6	6 ex	—	—
Total number of weekly hours	20	13	6	—	—

C. Curricula of the specializations

Subject	Semester				
	Sixth	Seventh	Eighth	Ninth	Tenth
(a) *Theoretical physics*					
Common part of curriculum	20	13	6	—	—
Introduction to solid state physics	3/0	—	—	—	—
Selected parts of classical physics	4/0	—	—	—	—
High energy nuclear physics	2/0	—	—	—	—
Structure of atoms and molecules	—	3/0 ex	—	—	—
Theory of solid state	—	—	3/0 ex	—	—
Quantum theory of radiation	—	—	4/0 ex	—	—
Quantum theory of wave fields	—	—	—	4/0 ex	—
Seminar in theoretical physics	—	—	0/2	0/2	0/2
Optional lectures (from non-compulsory lectures)	—	4/0	6/0	4/0 ex	—
Numerical methods	0/3	—	—	—	—
Selected part of mathematical analysis	—	4/2 ex	3/2 ex	—	—
Diploma project	—	—	5	10	20
Excursions	3⅔days	—	3 days	—	—
Total number of weekly hours	32	26	31	20	22
Total number of examinations	4	3	4	2	—

257

Subject	Semester				
	Sixth	Seventh	Eighth	Ninth	Tenth
(b) *Solid state physics*					
Common part of curriculum	20	13	6	—	—
Physical electronics	3/0 ex	—	—	—	—
Introduction to solid state physics	4/1	4/1 ex	—	—	—
Structure of atoms and molecules	—	3/0 ex	—	—	—
Analysis of crystal structures	—	2/0 ex	—	—	—
Theory of solid state	—	—	3/0 ex	—	—
Seminar in solid state physics	—	—	0/2	0/2	0/2
Laboratory work	0/4	0/6	—	—	—
Optional lectures	—	—	6/0 ex	4/0 ex	—
Diploma project	—	—	10	15	20
Professional practice	—	—	4 weeks	—	—
Excursions	2 days	2 days	3 days	3 days	—
Total number of weekly hours	32	29	27	21	22
Total number of examinations	5	4	3	2	—
(c) *Electronics and vacuum physics*					
Common part of curriculum	20	13	6	—	—
Physical electronics	3/0	2/0 ex	2/0 ex	—	—
Introduction to vacuum physics and technique	4/0	2/0 ex	—	—	—
Discharges in gases	—	2/0	2/0 ex	—	—
High frequency electronics and physics	—	2/0 ex	2/0	3/0 ex	—
Operator calculus	—	2/0	—	—	—
Special mathematical functions	—	—	2/0	—	—
Seminar in electronics and vacuum physics	—	—	0/2	0/2	0/2
Optional lectures	—	—	2/0	2/0 ex	—
Laboratory work	0/3	0/7	—	—	—
Glass techniques	0/1	—	—	—	—
Professional practice	—	—	4 weeks	—	—
Diploma project	—	—	0/8	0/15	0/20
Excursions	—	3 days	3 days	2 days	—
Total number of weekly hours	31	30	26	22	22
Total number of examinations	4	4	3	2	—

III A2 # Syllabus of the introductory university course in physics in Czechoslovakia

First year

Introduction: objects and methods of physics; elements of vector calculus.

Mechanics

Mechanics of a mass point: rectilinear motion, velocity, acceleration; curvilinear motion, tangential and normal acceleration; circular motion, angular velocity; linear harmonic motion; oblique projection in the gravity field; Newton laws of dynamics; momentum and impulse; work and power, energy; circular motion, centripetal and centrifugal forces; simple harmonic motion, mathematical pendulum; central forces.

Mechanics of a system of mass points; system of mass points and rigid body; external and internal forces; momentum theorem; centre of mass and its motion; kinematics of a rigid body, translation and rotation; moment of force, couples, the resultant of a system of forces; conditions for equilibrium; moment of inertia, Steiner's theorem; angular momentum theorem; equation of motion of a rigid body rotating about an axis; compound pendulum; free axis; gravitation; relative motions, centrifugal and Coriolis forces; motion at the Earth surface; flywheels.

Elasticity: elastic and plastic properties of materials; uniaxial strain, shearing, bulk compression; torsion and bending; impact of bodies.

Hydromechanics and aeromechanics: elementary properties of liquids and gases; hydrostatic pressure, pressure exerted on the bottom and walls; floating of bodies; ideal gas law, gas in gravity field; flow of perfect fluids, equation of continuity, Bernoulli theorem; laminar and turbulent flow; internal friction, motion in a resisting medium, flow of a liquid or gas about bodies; surface tension and capillarity.

Vibrations and waves: principle of superposition of vibrations, superposition of vibration in the same direction, in two mutually perpendicular directions; one-dimensional propagation of transverse and longitudinal waves; interference, standing waves; Huygens principle, reflection, refraction and diffraction; Doppler effect.

Heat

Temperature and heat: temperature scales, thermometers; thermal expansion; specific heat; propagation of heat.

Elements of thermodynamics: equivalence of heat and work; first law of thermodynamics and its application to an ideal gas.

Elements of molecular physics: molecular structure of matter; theorem of Avogadro; Maxwell law of distribution of velocities; kinetic theory of gas pressure; principle of equipartition of energy, explication of specific heats of gases; Brownian motion; solutions, diffusion, osmosis, dialysis.

Changes of phases: Gibbs phase rule; evaporation, boiling; critical point; Van der Waals equation, Clapeyron equation; fusion and solidification; triple point; achieving of low temperatures, liquefaction of gases.

Electricity and magnetism

Electrostatics: electric charge, Coulomb law, units, electric field, dipole; Gauss theorem, conductor in an electrostatic field; electrostatic potential, units; electrostatic induction; capacitance of condensers; dielectric polarization, susceptibility, permittivity, polarization and displacement vectors; Gauss theorem and Coulomb law in a dielectric; ferroelectrics, piezoelectric effect; energy of an electrostatic field; electrostatic measuring instruments.

Electric current in solids, liquids and gases: current in metals; Ohm law in differential and integral form; resistivity, its dependence on temperature; electronic semiconductors; heating effect of current; thermoelectric effect; Kirchhoff laws and their application; electrolytic dissociation. Faraday laws of electrolysis; electrolytic potential, voltaic cells, accumulators; dependent and spontaneous discharge in gases, electric arc, discharge at low pressures, cathode rays.

Magnetic field: force acting on an electric charge in magnetic field;

magnetic induction and flux vectors, the path of a charged particle moving in magnetic field; force acting on a conductor carrying current, current loop in a magnetic field; moving-coil measuring instruments; magnetic field of current, Biot-Savart law, field of a linear conductor, definition of ampere; magnetic field of a circular loop and solenoid; electrodynamic measuring instruments.

Electromagnetic induction: origin of induced electromotive force; Faraday induction law, Lenz rule; mutual induction, mutual inductance, self inductance; transient currents in a circuit with inductance; energy of magnetic field; connexion between electric and magnetic fields, Maxwell displacement current, electromagnetic field.

Magnetic field in material media: influence of medium on magnetic induction in a toroid; magnetization and field strength vectors; susceptibility, permeability; magnetic pole as source of field strength vector; para-, dia-, and ferromagnetic substances; microphysical nature of magnetic properties; ferromagnetics, magnetic circuit.

Alternating currents: producing of a simple harmonic current, effective current and voltage values; A.C. current through a circuit with resistance, inductance and capacitor in series, vector diagrams of circuits; A.C. power transformer; three-phase current, magnetic rotating field; D.C. and A.C. generators and motors; damped electric oscillations, open circuit, electromagnetic waves.

Electronic valves: thermionic emission, diode and its application; triode and its parameters; triode as voltage amplifier, generator of oscillations and detector; oscillograph.

Second year

Optics

Development of conceptions of the nature of light; velocity of light and its measurement.

Fundamental terms of photometry: radiant flux; photometric units, luminous flux, luminous intensity, illumination, luminance.

Reflection and refraction: four basic laws of geometrical optics; reflection and refraction at plane boundary of two media, total reflection; refractometers.

Geometrical optics: optical image; imagery by a plane mirror; refracttion by a single spherical surface; basic elements of image-producing systems, equations of image forming; imagery by spherical mirrors; imagery by two centred systems; thin and thick lenses, aberrations; the eye as an optical system; magnifying glass, microscope, telescope, projector and photographic camera; prism spectral apparatus, spectroscopes, spectrographs and monochromators.

Wave optics: conditions for interference of two beams; Young interference experiment; diffraction of plane waves by a slit, by a grating, resolving power of a microscope; polarization of light by reflection and refraction; double refraction, double refracting crystals as polarizers; interference of polarized light; optical rotation, polarimeters.

Interaction between radiation and matter: absorption and scattering of light; external photoelectric effect; internal photoelectric effect; luminescence of crystals and organic substances; black body radiation laws.

Atomistics

Structure of matter: basic laws of chemistry, atomic weight, valency, gram-atom, chemical equivalent, molecular weight, gram-molecule; Avogadro number; periodic system of elements, atomic number and mass number; development of conceptions of atom.

Structure of electric charge: experiments proving the atomic structure of charge, electrolysis, discharges in gases, cathodic rays; ions, protons, electrons; determination of the charge and specific charge of electron; classical radius of electron; dependence of the electron mass on its velocity, Einstein formula.

Investigation of structure of matter by means of beta-, alpha-, and X-rays; path of beta-rays, reverse diffusion, decrease of velocity, range; absorption of beta-rays; range of alpha-rays, air equivalent, ionization; deflection experiment and atomic model of Rutherford; absorption of X-rays.

Corpuscular and wave nature of radiations: photoelectric effect, Einstein equation; Compton effect; dual nature of electromagnetic phenomena.

Spectra and electronic structure of atom: emission and absorption spectra; spectrum of hydrogen atom and ionized helium; main properties of atomic spectra; atomic model of Bohr; quantum numbers, selection principles, vector model of the atom, correspondence principle; spectra of molecules; X-rays spectra and their interpretation; Moseley law; periodic system of elements; Pauli principle; difficulties of Bohr's theory.

Natural radioactivity: radioactive radiations, spectrum of energies; radioactive transformation series, Soddy-Fajans law, radioactive decay law, isotopes, isobars.

General characterization of atomic nucleus: mass, size, charge, spin, magnetic moment; hypotheses on the structure of nucleus; relation

262

between mass and energy; mass defect, packing fraction; character of nuclear forces and energy of nucleus; the drop and shell model.

Review of elementary particles and their properties.

Measuring methods in nuclear physics: registration of particles, ionization chamber, G.M.-counter, proportional counter, crystal scintillation counter, Wilson cloud chamber, bubble chamber, photographic method; measurement of activity, electromagnetic method; dosimetry; mass spectroscopy and spectrometry; Aston, Dempster and Nier spectrographs.

Nuclear reactions: conservation laws, general classification of reactions, course of nuclear reactions, Breit-Wigner formula, individual types of reactions; beta-spectroscopy; measurement of the velocity of neutrons.

Methods for acceleration of particles: Van de Graaff generator, cascade generator, cyclotron, betatron; self-phasing principle, synchrotron, synchrocyclotron, synchrophasotron.

Use of the nuclear energy: fission of nuclei, conditions for chain reactions; nuclear reactors, heterogeneous, homogeneous, with reprocessing spent fuel elements; thermonuclear reactions. Application of isotopes.

Cosmic rays.

Structure of solids: monocrystals, polycrystalline materials, amorphous materials; space lattices, Miller indices; diffraction of X-rays by crystal lattice, methods of crystal structure analysis; unit cells and symmetry of crystals, examples of crystal lattices; structure of metals and alloys; thermal lattice vibrations, crystal lattice defects; structure of polymers: phase transitions.

Fifth semester

Selected parts of electricity and magnetism

Review of knowledge of the electromagnetic field: Maxwell equation in integral and differential form; systems of units; basic measuring methods.

Electrical networks: D.C. circuits, linear network analysis by means of Kirchhoff laws; method of circuit currents and junction voltages; basic theorems of the theory of linear networks; A.C. networks, operator calculus; A.C. through various elements of networks; impedance and admittance; resonance circuits; A.C. measuring methods; use of the method of circuit currents and junction voltages in the case of A.C. networks; dipolar circuits and quadripoles, basic quadripole equation; use of matrix calculus in the theory of quadripoles; coupling; characteristic impedance, propagation constant; electromagnetic waves along wires; propagation of electromagnetic waves in wave-guides; elements of ultra-high frequency measurements.

Micro-physical nature of electric and magnetic phenomena: mechanism of electric current; resistance, conductors, insulators, semiconductors; energy levels of electrons in metals; insulators and semiconductors, thermal dependence of conductivity; contact potentials; thermo-electric effect; Peltier effect; Hall effect; elements of semiconductor electronics; polarization of dielectrics; ferroelectrics and piezoelectrics; para-, dia-, and ferro-magnetism; electron emission; electron current in vacuum; principles of electron optics; conduction of electricity through gases, elementary process in electric discharges; dependent discharge; Townsend theory; glow and arc discharge; plasma; other kinds of discharge.

Sixth semester

Selected parts of optics

Propagation of light waves: phase and group velocity; measurement of light velocity.

Interference of light: double slit, Fresnel mirrors, biprism; interference in thin layers: fringes of equal thickness and its application; interference with large path difference; two-beam interferometers; Michelson-Morley experiment; Fabry-Perot and Lummer-Gehrcke interferometers; visibility of fringes; width of spectral lines.

Diffraction of light: Fraunhofer diffraction phenomena, single rectangular aperture, circular aperture; limit of resolution and resolving power of a telescope and prism; double slit, diffraction grating, concave grating, resolving power of a grating; Fresnel diffraction phenomena, Kirchhoff's formulation of Fresnel theory; diffraction of microwaves; X-rays diffraction by a crystal lattice.

Polarization of light: linear polarized electromagnetic wave; reflection and refraction of polarized light, Fresnel's formulas, polarization by reflection and refraction; double refraction, wave-fronts in uniaxial and biaxial crystals; polarization by double refraction; interference of polarized light, circularly and elliptically polarized light; analysis of elliptically polarized light; photoelasticity; optically active substances; scattering of light; Raman effect.

Dispersion and absorption of light: theory of dispersion in insulators, in conducting medium; anomalous dispersion; optical properties of metals; measurements of optic constants of metals; dispersion of X-rays.

Magneto- and electro-optic phenomena: Faraday effect; Kerr magnetic effect; magnetic double refraction; Zeeman effect; Stark effect; Kerr electro-optic effect.

Syllabus of the course in theoretical physics in Czechoslovakia

Analytical mechanics

Kinematics of points: position vector of a point; trajectory and velocity of a point (derivative of a vector with respect to a parameter, hodograph of a vector; average and instantaneous velocity, uniform and rectilinear motion; components of velocity in cylindrical and spherical co-ordinates, areal velocity); acceleration of a point (average and instantaneous acceleration; tangential and normal acceleration; components of acceleration in cylindrical and spherical polar co-ordinates; areal acceleration; accelerations of higher order).

Dynamics of a system of mass points: dynamics of mass points without constraints (second Newton law; conservative field of force; concepts of linear and angular momentum, work and kinetic energy of a system; impulse theorems; conservation laws; centre of mass of a system); simple pendulum (first approximation for small amplitudes; integral of mechanical energy for large amplitudes); motion of a mass point in the field of a central force (planarity of this motion; Kepler laws; problem of two bodies); degrees of freedom (classification of equations of constraints; generalized co-ordinates); principle of virtual work (virtual displacement in case of holonomic constraints; constraining forces); d'Alembert principle (inertial force); Lagrange equations for conservative systems (law of conservation of dynamical energy); Lagrange equations for non-conservative systems (generalized force, Lagrangian function); first integrals and cyclic co-ordinates (generalized integral of energy; the case that all co-ordinates are cyclic).

Kinematics of a rigid body: relative motion of a point; Eulerian angles; translation and rotation of a rigid body; Euler kinematic equations;

kinematics of relative motions of a point (relative velocity and velocity of transport; relative acceleration and acceleration of transport; Coriolis, Euler, centripetal acceleration); motion relative to the Earth (apparent forces).

Dynamics of rigid bodies and of bodies having variable mass: Euler equations of motion of a rigid body (moments of inertia and deviation moments); motion of a gyroscope under no torque and of heavy symmetrical gyroscope (interpretation of the solution in moving and fixed co-ordinate system); motion of a body having variable mass (Neshcherski equation, Tchiolkovski formula and number).

Vibrations of a system having one and more degrees of freedom: forced damped vibrations; resonance; normal co-ordinates.

Hamilton principle: fundamental ideas of the calculus of variations; generalization of the d'Alembert principle (concept of a differential and integral principle, action of a system); Euler-Lagrange equations (application to a system of mass points).

Hamilton-Jacobi theory: Hamilton canonical equations (Hamiltonian function; phase space; generalized momentum = impulse; physical interpretation); canonical transformations (point transformations in configurational and phase space; generating function; criteria of canonical transformations); invariants of canonical transformations (Lagrange and Poisson brackets; infinitesimal canonical transformations); Hamilton-Jacobi equation (principal and characteristic Hamilton function; separation of variables).

Mechanics of continua

Tensor of strain and stress: fundamental properties of Cartesian tensors; forces acting at a surface or in a volume (vector and tensor of stress); equations of equilibrium and motion (definition and elemental properties of line, surface and space integrals; Stokes and Gauss theorems; equilibrium conditions for a continuum; symmetry of the stress tensor; equation of motion of a continuum); components of tensors of small strains (displacement vector, volume expansion); kinematics of continuum (finite rotation, velocity field, rate of deformation and finite rotation; Lagrange and Euler variables).

Relation between strain and stress tensors: Hooke law and its generalization (elastic coefficients, anisotropic body, symmetry elements of crystals, isotropic body, Lamé coefficients, elastic constants and moduli); boundary value problems, Saint-Venant principle).

Vibrations of a string (deduction of the equation of motion and its integration).

Equilibrium and kinematics of fluids: elemental properties of fluids; equilibrium conditions (Archimedes law); kinematics of fluids (concept of trajectory, stream line, stream tube, stream filament, verticity, vortex line, vortex tube, vortex filament; strength of vortex line and circulation, their conservation in space; irrotational and vertical flow; Kelvin circulation theorem).

Dynamics of perfect fluids: equation of continuity (integral and differential form); Euler equations; boundary value problems of mechanics of fluids (kinematical and dynamical conditions; differences between perfect and viscous fluids); Bernoulli equation; irrotational flow.

Dynamics of viscous fluids: Navier-Stokes equation; similarity method.

Theory of the electromagnetic field

Electrostatics: point charge; Coulomb field; electric field strength; principle of superposition, Gauss theorem, its differential form; potential; fields of line, surface and volume charges; Laplace-Poisson equation; boundary conditions; dipole; field in conductors; conditions for the potential of a system of conductors, uniqueness theorem; field in a dielectric; polarization; bound charge; induction vector; interaction energy of a system of charges; energy of an electrostatic field, connexion with mass of elementary particles; force effect of electrostatic field.

Magnetostatics: analogies and differences between magnetostatics and electrostatics; magnetic dipole; magnetization.

Stationary fields: stationary electric current; equation of continuity; Ohm's law; impressed electromotive forces; Joule law; magnetic effects of a stationary current, equations describing these effects in integral and differential form; Biot-Savart law; equivalence of a current loop and a magnetic double layer.

Non-stationary fields: equation of continuity; Maxwell current; first series of Maxwell equations; electromagnetic induction law; second series of Maxwell equations; boundary conditions; law of conservation of energy; Ponting vector; force effect of a electromagnetic field; Lorentz force; stress tensor; momentum of electromagnetic field; electromagnetic potentials; gauge transformation: Lorentz condition; Coulomb gauge; plane waves in dielectrics and conductors; Fresnel formulae for reflection and refraction at boundary of two media, total reflection; retarded potentials; field of Hertz dipole; quasi-stationary fields, definition; skin effect, skin depth.

Electron theory: microscopic charges, currents and fields; Lorentz equation; Lorentz interpretation of electric and magnetic properties of substances; averaging of Lorentz equations; motion of particles in an electromagnetic field; radiation reaction; complete equations of motion of an electron, paradoxical solution and approximate solution of the equations of motion; light emission of an oscillator; light scattering on an oscillator; cross section for scattering; resonance fluorescence; Thomson formula for cross section of scattering on an electron.

Magnetohydrodynamics: Ohm's law in case of a moving conductor; equations of magnetohydrodynamics; penetrating and freezing-in of the field in a fluid; flow of a magnetized fluid through a pipe; magnetohydrodynamic dynamo; applications of magnetohydrodynamics in astrophysics.

Classic theory of radiation: solution of wave equation (properties of the Dirac function; Green functions; separation of the radiation part of the field); the field of moving charges (radiation of accelerated charges; radiations in linear and cyclic accelerators; shining electron; Cherenkov radiation).

Application of the Lagrange formalism to an electromagnetic field: Lagrange formalism in the classic mechanics, its extension to a field; Lagrangian; field equations as Euler-Lagrange equations of variation principle; invariants in respect to the infinitesimal transformations; energy, momentum and moment of momentum of the field; separation of proper electromagnetic momentum of the field.

Theory of relativity

Principle of relativity in the classic physics: frame of reference and coordinate system, inertial frames, Galilean transformation, formulation of the principle of relativity, second Newton law; scalar plane wave; velocity of light in vacuum and the concept of a privileged frame; direct measurement of the light velocity; velocity of light in material media, coefficient of drag, Fizeau experiment, aberration of light; de Sitter analysis of double-stars trajectories and independence of light velocity of the motion of the source; Michelson experiment; contraction hypothesis, Doppler effect.

Lorentz transformation: Einstein criticism of the concept of simultaneity, the invariance of the speed of light, derivation of the special Lorentz transformation; physical consequences of the Lorentz transformation; existence of limiting speed, Galilean transformation as limiting case of the Lorentz transformation; relativity of simultaneity and time succession, time and space coincidence of events; contraction of measuring rods and slowing down of clocks; experimental proofs, transversal Doppler effect, half-life of decay; relativistic composition of velocities, coefficient of drag.

Four-dimensional formalism of relativity theory: Minkowski space-time, general Lorentz transformation, space-time interval; vectors and tensors in the space-time, world line, four-velocity, four-acceleration; absolute past, present and future, light cone; geometric interpretation of the Lorentz transformation.

Electrodynamics *in vacuo*: transcription of Maxwell equations into the four-dimensional symbolism; charge-current and intensity tensor of the electromagnetic field; transformation of intensities of electric and magnetic field by special Lorentz transformation, field of a linear-uniform moving point charge; four-potential gauge invariance; plane wave, frequency four-vector, Doppler effect.

Dynamics of point charge and theory of collisions: equations of motion of a point charge in frame of reference at rest, their transcription into four-dimensional form in an arbitrary inertial frame; Lorentz-Minkowski four-force, momentum and energy vector of a particle, rest and relativistic mass of a particle; relativistic kinetic energy; comparison with classic quantities; physical interpretation of equations of motion; hyperbolic motion; concept of a collision of relativistic particles; momentum and energy of a photon; equivalence of mass and energy, examples.

Quantum mechanics

Fundamentals of the quantum mechanics: contradiction between classic theory and experiments; de Broglie theory; Schrödinger equation for a free particle and for a particle in a field of force; concept of an operator; physical interpretation of the wave function, electron diffraction, etc.; postulates of quantum mechanics; average values of functions and operators; uncertainty principle; complementary quantities; experiments for the uncertainty principle; Ehrenfest theorem.

Operators of the quantum mechanics: linear Hermitian operator, its properties; commutator; commutation relationship; Hamiltonian canonical equations; commutative operators; angular momentum operator, commutation relationship between its components; Hamiltonian.

Eigenvalues of energy operator: fundamental definition; boundary conditions; a free particle between walls; a potential trap; parity; normalization in continuum; Dirac function; linear harmonic oscillator; Hermite polynomials; discussion of the probability of finding a particle at a certain point in space; spherically symmetric potential.

Legendre polynomials, spherical functions; orbital, azimuthal and magnetic quantum number.

Two-particle systems: Schrödinger equation for hydrogen atom; Laguerre polynomials, principal quantum number; degeneracy.

Matrix formalism of the quantum mechanics: elemental properties of matrices, their transformation and diagonalization; E-representation; matrix element of an operator; linear harmonic oscillator using matrix method; unitary transformation; equations of motion in quantum mechanics.

Stationary perturbation theory: non-degenerate and degenerate case; ground state of helium atom, two identical particles.

Spin: magneton; motion of a free charged particle in magnetic field; normal Zeeman effect; experimental facts proving the existence of the spin; Pauli matrix and Pauli equation.

Dirac theory of the electron: question of probability density; Dirac equation; positron; antiparticles.

Thermodynamics and statistical physics

Fundamental concepts: thermodynamic system and its surroundings; reversible, irreversible, quasistatic, non-quasistatic processes; adiabatic walls, thermodynamic state of equilibrium.

Properties of substances: equation of state of ideal gas, van der Waals equation; Curie law; thermodynamic diagrams, triple point, critical point.

Zeroth law and the three laws of thermodynamics; empiric and absolute temperature; work, heat, internal energy (physical interpretation of total differential); definition and properties of entropy in case of equilibrium and non-equilibrium states and processes.

Consequences and applications of thermodynamic laws: thermodynamic potentials; Maxwell relations; Gibbs-Helmholtz equation; relations between specific heats; Joule-Thomson experiment; thermodynamics of dielectrics and magnetics, magnetic method of refrigeration; equilibrium conditions; phase transitions (classification, Clausius-Clapeyron equation, Ehrenfest equations); phase rule; chemical potential.

Fundamentals of the probability theory: concept of probability; probability density; addition and multiplication of probabilities; average values; fluctuations; normal distribution.

Fundamentals of the statistical physics: macrostate and microstate; phase space; statistical ensemble; importance of classic and quantum mechanics for statistical physics; Liouville theorem.

Distribution: microcanonical and canonical distributions and their relation; large canonical, Boltzmann, Fermi-Dirac, Bose-Einstein distributions.

Connexions between thermodynamic and statistical concepts.

Some applications: Gibbs paradox; specific heats (equipartition law, specific heats of mono- and diatomic gases, contribution of electron gas in metals, contribution of crystal lattice, phonon gas); black-body radiation.

Fluctuations: Brownian motion, scattering of light.

Thermodynamics of irreversible processes.

Negative temperatures.

Typical schedule of optional lectures
in Czechoslovakia

	No. of hours per week	
	Winter semester	Summer semester
Chair of general physics		
Theory of photographic process	–	2
Elements of photography	2	–
Photographic laboratory work	–	3
Physics of high molecular materials	2	–
Seminar in actual physics problems	2	2
Chair of theoretical physics		
Theory of atomic nucleus	2	–
General theory of relativity	2	–
Theory of dislocations	2	–
High energy nuclear physics	2	–
Aerodynamics	–	2
Advanced optics	–	2
Chair of solid state physics		
Semiconductors and ionic crystals	3	4
Technology of semiconducting materials and devices	–	2
Optical properties of crystalline solids	2	–
Metal physics	3	4
Dislocations and plastic deformation of crystals	2	–
Advanced analysis of crystal structures	–	2

	No. of hours per week	
	Winter semester	Summer semester
Selected parts of magnetism	2	–
Microphysical structure of magnetic substances	–	2
Physics of dielectrics	2	–
Luminescence of crystals	–	2

Chair of electronics and vacuum physics

Electronics of semiconductors	–	2
Electron emission	2	–
Electron optics	2	–
Transistor electronics	2	–
Measurement of centimetre and millimetre waves	–	2
Theory of centimetre waves circuits	–	2
Mass spectrography	–	2
Electric discharges in gases	2	–
Ultra-high vacuum physics	–	2

Mathematical Chairs (selected lectures)

Theory of groups	2	2
Ordinary differential equations	2	2
Variation calculus	2	2
Applied tensor calculus	2	2
Geometrical methods in analytical mechanics	2	2
Automatic computing machines and programming	2	2
Approximative analysis methods	2	2
Partial differential equations of parabolic type	2	2
Operator calculus	2	–
Estimation theory and testing of hypotheses	2	2
Theory of algorithms	4	–

The content of mathematics courses
in the physics curriculum in
Czechoslovakia

Mathematical analysis

From the beginning, emphasis is placed on an exact formulation of
definitions and theorems, although some general theorems are given first
without proofs and the proofs are treated later (e.g., theorem on the least
upper bound, theorems on continuous functions in compact interval,
existence of the primitive function to the continuous function, etc.). The
content is traditional: sequences and series; functions of one or more
variables; continuity and limits; differential and integral calculus; elements of ordinary differential equations (more with regard to the study
of physics than to a systematic exposition).

The exposition begins with the functions of one variable (the sequence
and series theory is developed later) so that the foundations of differential
calculus, the primitive functions, and the definite integral may be studied
as soon as possible. The logarithm is introduced practically as a primitive
function. These are the concepts covered in the first and second semester.
The third semester is devoted mainly to the functions of several variables,
and finally to a more detailed theory of series including uniform con-
vergence and the elements of Fourier series. The fourth semester is
devoted to multiple integrals. First the Riemann integral for continuous
functions with compact support is defined, then the Lebesgue integral is
obtained by the extension of the domain of the Riemann integral. The
main aim is to develop general formulations of theorems important in
the calculation of integrals and numerical training. The theory of real
numbers has not been included in this course of analysis; the prospective
teachers are acquainted with it later in a special lecture. As to the professional mathematicians, it is expected that they will study it on their own

initiative. Examinations are held at the end of each semester, i.e., a total of four examinations.

Algebra and analytical geometry

Instruction begins in the first year with the introduction of Cartesian co-ordinates (visual intuition) and with the elements of analytic geometry in one-, two- and three-dimensional space. Then follows a systematic study of n-dimensional space on the vectorial basis combined with higher algebra, including the solution of linear equations (also using determinants). The course concludes with bilinear and square forms. In the third semester, the course in analytic geometry begins with the study of linear and quadratic geometry in n-dimensional projective space. The main content is the theory of conic sections and quadrics in three-dimensional space. The lectures in the field of algebra during the third and fourth semesters give the elements of modern algebra on an axiomatic basis: commutative ring, integrity domain, field; quotient field; field of integrity of polynomials; the problems of divisibility; root and split of the polynomial above the given field. Elements of group theory. Symmetric polynomials, discriminants. Constructions made by means of a ruler and a compass. The ring of square-matrices of degree n. Further theorems on determinants. Examinations in the subject matter of this partial course are held at the end of each semester, but in the third semester only analytic geometry is examined, and in the fourth semester the topics treated in both the third and fourth semester are examined.

Mathematics for physicists

This course comprises four parts:
1. Theory of analytical functions (theory of holomorphic and meromorphic functions in the given domain, analytical continuation).
2. Elements of variation calculus. Among other variation problems in the plane with free ends, variations problems in parametric form (in connexion with the principles of mechanics), isoperimetric problem, are studied. Only conditions necessary for weak extremum are derived.
3. Tensor calculus (curvilinear co-ordinates in space, concept of tensor operation with tensor calculus, operation with tensors, elements of differential geometry; systems of mass points under constraint). Principles of mechanics.
4. Partial differential equations of mathematical physics (Dirichlet problem in the plane, equation of the string). Examinations, covering the

276

entire subject matter of both semesters are held at the end of the sixth semester.

Responsible for all these courses is the Chair of fundamental mathematical disciplines.

Experiments for basic lectures
on physics in the Federal Republic
of Germany

The experiments listed below are, in the main, those demonstrated in the basic lectures in experimental physics at the University of Giessen. To complete the picture, a few of the experiments demonstrated at the universities of Marburg and Munich and the Technical Institute in Karlsruhe are added. The number and type of experiments change with the course of time since new experiments are added corresponding to the growing advance in knowledge. Similar experiments are also described in books about experimental physics listed below in Appendix IX B2. Due to lack of space we can bring only a number of experiments from a few of the different fields in physics.

Examples from mechanics

Experiments concerning 'rotational movement'

Model demonstrating the flattening of the earth as a result of its rotation. Centrifugal governor. Equilibrium of rotation. Section through a rotating liquid. Centrifuge. Sparks scattering from a grindstone. Rotating bucket filled with water. Dynamic stability of a rotating endless chain. Experiments with a wooden board lying on steel ball-bearings (torque, translation, coupling of forces, rotation). Torque of a motor. Determining the directional moment of a spiral spring. Determining a body's moment of inertia on the torsional axis. Energy of rotation of Maxwell's disc. Uniformly accelerated rotational motion. Different moments of inertia of a solid and a hollow sphere. Experiment showing the conservation of angular momentum with the rotating chair. Conservation of momentum in a closed system (electric train running on a turntable). Demonstrating free axes. Precession and nutation of a gyro. Influence of the gyro's

278

moment of inertia on the angular velocity of its precession. Model of a bicycle. Gyro compass. Model of a Foucault pendulum (conservation of the plane of oscillation). Showing the Earth's rotation with the Foucault pendulum. Quantitative measurement with the Maxwell disc. Frequency and torque of a torsional oscillation. Determining the bullet velocity from its Coriolis deviation.

Experiments concerning 'oscillations, waves, acoustics'

Changing the oscillation period of an elastic spring by varying the mass load. Dependence of the oscillation on the spring constant. Determining the spring constant statically. Determining the spring constant dynamically: by the period of oscillation. Seconds pendulum. Linear motion of a pendulum is the same as the projection of its circular motion. Plotting a sinusoidal oscillation on a luminescent screen. The oscillation period of a simple pendulum is independent of its mass, but is dependent on its length. Influence of atmospheric damping on the oscillation of a pendulum. The roll tank of a ship. Addition of two linear oscillations polarized perpendicularly to each other by means of Pohl's apparatus. Lissajou lines of motion. Vibrational mode of the tongue of a doorbell. Mode of vibration of a steel string. Superposing of oscillations. Characteristic oscillations of coupled simple pendulums. Automatic control of pendulum oscillation. Standing waves demonstrated with a rope. Longitudinal and transverse oscillations of steel rods. Monochord. Standing transversal waves along a wool thread. Chladni's sound figures. Chladni's figures with a soap lamella. Buben's flame tube. Kundt's dust figures. Open and stopped pipes. Lip and tongue pipes. Dependency of the pitch on the length of the pipe. Blowing a pipe with air and with hydrogen gas. Upper frequency limit of the human ear. Demonstrating forced vibrations with Pohl's wheel. Resonance gyroscope. Mechanical resonance of the frame of a motor. Reed frequency meter. Tuning fork on a resonance body. Resonance of an air column. Siren. Demonstrating the velocity of sound. Quantitative determination of the velocity of sound. Propagation of sound in air of reduced pressure. Penetration of sound through different media. Coupled pendulums. Generating beats with a variable sound generator and a tuning fork. Interference of two sound sources. Acoustical Doppler effect; turntable with a pipe. Registering sound with an oscillograph. Experiments with two dimensional wave fields in a tank of water. Wave machine. Oscillations of fluid columns. Reversion pendulum. Oscillation of the surface of a fluid.

Examples from the theory of heat

Experiments concerning 'change of state of real gases'

Liquefying oxygen (Joule-Thomson effect). Liquefying CO_2 by pressure (Andrews-isotherms).

Examples from electricity

Experiments concerning 'electrolysis'

Apparatus for electrolysis of water. Silvervoltameter. Coppering a platinum electrode. Changing the resistance of an electrolyte by raising its temperature. Comparing the conductivity of a highly diluted with that of a highly concentrated solution of copper sulphate. The increase of current upon diluting a concentrated solution of copper sulphate leaving the amount of the soluted electrolyte constant. Melting a glass rod using its electrolytical conductivity. The primary and secondary reaction of electrolyzing sodium hydroxide. Determining the resistance of an electrolyte using the alternating current bridge. Showing the electrolytical polarization of a gas cell. Charging and discharging a lead accumulator. Electrochemical voltage series (potentials of lead and copper, and lead and zinc). Depositing copper on an iron rod by dipping it into a solution of copper sulphate. Different galvanic cells. Poggendorf's compensation electrolytic rectifier. Electrolytic condenser. The migration of ions upon passing a current through a solution of $KMnO_4$. Showing the effect of friction between ions and fluid. Change of density near the electrodes in a conducting electrolyte. Capillary electrometer. Changing the surface tension of a water droplet in an electric field. Changing the surface tension as a result of electrolytic polarization.

Experiments concerning 'induction'

Induction in the field of a permanent magnet. Induction in the field of a current conducting coil. Induction in the field of a coil with an iron core. Experiment showing Lenz's rule. Dependence on the diameter and number of turns of a coil. Showing that there is no induction on moving a coil parallel to itself in the homogeneous part of the magnetic field of a horseshoe magnet. Induction effect upon opening or closing an iron-yoke. Induction in the field of the Earth's magnetism. Eddy currents: braking a rotating metal disk in a strong magnetic field. Eddy currents: carrying along a magnetic needle over a rotating copper disc. This effect

280

stops when the disc is slotted. Eddy currents speedometer. The slow rise of a current effected by self-induction. Self-induced voltage upon cutting the current. Measuring the resistance of a coil with alternating and direct current. Mutual induction of two coils. Capacitance in an alternating-current circuit. Phase relation between current and voltage of an impedance in an alternating-current circuit.

Experiments concerning 'electrical oscillations and waves'

Series resonant and parallel resonant A.C. circuits. Lodge's experiment with resonance. Feedback of a tube transmitter. Tesla transformer. Skin effect. Polarization of electromagnetic waves. Standing electromagnetic waves in a room. Rod-shaped oscillator in water. Demonstration of a magnetron transmitter. Standing waves on Lecher wires. Broadcasting recorded music with a klystron transmitter and receiver. Rotating the polarization plane with a metal screen. Reflection on a metal plate. Refraction in a prismatic paraffin block. Radar detection.

Optics

Centre-shade and half-shade. Picture made with the pin-hole camera. Independence of the image from the shape of the diaphragm. Bunsen photometer. Model of a gypsum-wedge photometer. Measuring light intensity with the photo-electric cell. Law of reflection. Law of refraction. Refraction and the functioning of a lens demonstrated in the wave-tub. Parallel shift of a light beam caused by refraction with a parallel-plane glass plate. Total reflection. Total reflection in a prism. Streak formation by variation of density. Total reflection of light following the curvature of a waterjet and a plexiglass rod. Abbe's refractometer. Crystal refracto-meter. Spectral analysis of light with a 60°-glass prism. Spectral analysis of light with a 60°-water prism. Direct-vision prism. Virtual image of a mirror. Course of rays of a spherical mirror. Image obtained with a concave mirror. Catacaustics. Course of rays of a parabolic mirror. Astigmatism of a concave mirror. Model of a lens. Air lenses in water. Law of image formation by lenses. Focal distance of combinations of lenses. Depth of focus. Spherical aberration. Colour deviation. Astigmatism. Cushion and barrel distortion. Magnifying glass. Microscope. Telescope. Projector. Interference pattern of the superposition of two systems of concentric rings. Fresnel's mirror experiment. Interference with Fresnel's biprism. Newton rings. Haidinger rings. Interference of microwaves. Colours of thin plates. Diffraction with a slot. Diffraction with a wire. Diffraction with a pin point. Diffraction with an edge.

Diffraction with a grating, determining the wavelengths; reflection grating. Zone plate. Polarization by reflecting the light on two black-glass plates. Double refraction with calcite. Passage of light through two adjacent calcspars. Structure of a Nicol prism. Passage of light through a calcite and a Nicol prism. Two Nicol prisms as polarizer and analyser. Polarization with Tourmaline plates. Polarization filters of dichroitic substances. Polarization of light by scattering. Dissecting polarized light into two components polarized perpendicularly to each other with a polarization filter. The same experiment as above, with microwaves. Turning the polarization plane with a quartz crystal. A double plate of quartz between polarizer and analyser. Small gypsum plates between polarizer and analyser. Making elliptically polarized light with a quarter-wave plate. Two quarter-wave plates after each other in polarized light. Quartz-wedge interference. Faraday effect shown with a glass rod. Kerr effect in nitrobenzol. Double refraction caused by tension in a rapidly chilled glass, a glass cube under heavy pressure, and in a bent glass rod. Analysing calcite, quartz, and aragonite in a polarization microscope. The continuous emission spectrum of a carbon arc. Absorption spectrum of various colour filters. Absorption spectrum of didymium glass. Absorption spectrum of a solution of $KMnO_4$. Spectrum of a mercury lamp analysed with a glass and a quartz prism. Showing the ultra-violet lines with a fluorescent screen. Prism and grating spectroscope, pocket spectroscope. Double monochromator. Interferometer. Interferometer of Perot and Fabry. Colorimeter. Polarimeter. Filtering out a spectral colour of a spectrum. Complementary colours by recombining the residual spectrum. Additive mixing of colours; substractive mixing of colours. Coloured bodies in the light of different spectral lamps. Veiled colours. Coloured spinning top. Interference filter in a spectrum. Reflection of light on a copperplate, glass, and frosted glass. Tyndall effect; Rayleigh scattering. Curved beam of light in a salt solution under a layer of water. Coloured rings of a halo. Black bodies. Heat radiation even in vacuum. Colour of a strip of redhot platinum as a function of the temperature (Wien's law). Planck's law of radiation. Pyrometer. Analysing the spectrum of a carbon-arc with a thermopile. Focusing heat radiation with a concave mirror. Leslie tube. Kirchhoff's law. Infra-red light barrier. Quasi-'optical' experiments with microwaves. Resolving power of prisms and gratings. Foucault's experiment for measuring the velocity of light. Velocity of light with an ultrasonic method.

282

Atomic and Nuclear Physics

Beam of electrons curved by a magnetic field in hydrogen gas. Photo-effect. Reducing the starting voltage by ultra-violet radiation. Stoke's law applied to fluorescence. Resonance fluorescence of sodium gas. Experiment of Franck and Hertz. Emission spectrum of sodium. Reversal of the yellow sodium line. Analysing the spectrum of a mercury arc with an ultra-violet-sensititive photo-electric cell. Discharging a condenser with X-rays. Radioscopy; Roentgen dosimeter. Absorption by Fe, Al, and Cu. Diffraction with a rotating crossed grating. Testing of materials with X-rays. Field-electron microscope. Temperature dependency of the resistance of a semi-conductor. Photo-electric conductivity of a CdS-crystal. Photo-electric conductivity of ZnS. Hall effect of Au and Zn. Conductivity of CuI with excess of I. Photo-electric conductivity of a rectifier diode. Running a small motor with a photo-electric cell of silicon. Different phosphorescent materials in the light of a UV-lamp. Freezing-in of luminescence. Quantitative demonstration of a glow curve. Quenching of a luminescent material by exposing it to infra-red rays. Deflecting beta-rays in a magnetic field. Models of diffusion tubes. Construction of a Geiger-Müller counter. Maximum range of alpha particles. Absorption by a thin Al-foil; residual range. No uniform range of beta-particles. Comparison of the absorption of gamma rays of radium by Al and Pb. Law of distance for gamma rays; Alpha tracks in an expansion cloud chamber (Wilson). Alpha tracks in a diffusion cloud chamber. Demonstration of a scintillation counter. Demonstration of a spark counter. Activation of rhodium with neutrons and determining the half-life period of the two components. Reducing the null-effect of a Geiger-Müller counter by shielding with lead. Neutron chamber. Radioactive uranium pitch-blend. Thorium emanation. Canal rays. Compton effect. Zeeman effect. Dispersion and polarization of light and X-rays. Laue diagram. Electron diffraction.

Example of syllabus in physics
for the *propédeutique* in France

(Teaching time about 150 hours)

Units, systems of units; dimensional equations.

Speed, acceleration; basic law of mechanics; kinetic energy and potential energy. Examples of classical motions. Movement of a solid; moment of inertia. Basic law of relative dynamics; application to the movement of an electrified particle in an uniform electric or magnetic field.

Hydrostatics; Archimedes' principle. Capillarity.

Principles of thermodynamics; the reversible and irreversible transformations; definition of thermodynamic temperature. Calorimetric coefficients; Clapeyron equations. Physical equilibrium; general laws. Detailed study of a pure substance in one, two and three phases. Boiling of a liquid; of a mixture of liquids; ebullioscopy.

Revision of fundamental principles of lenses and mirrors. Diffraction of light; Fresnel diffraction and Fraunhofer diffraction; application to the resolving power of an optical instrument. Interference; grating; diffraction of X-rays and the Bragg equation. Polarization of light: Malus's law; polaroids. Interference in polarized light. Rotation of the plane of polarization; the polarimeter. Prism-dispersion and diffraction-grating spectroscopes.

Continuous spectra; black body radiation; Planck's radiation formula. Spectrum of rays; example of the hydrogen atom; Bohr's theory. Spectrum of vibration and rotation. Emission and absorption of X-rays.

Vacuum electrostatics; Coulomb's law, Gauss theorem. Electrostatic equilibrium; coefficients of induction and capacity; electrostatic energy, electrostatic force. Influence of a dielectric on a capacitor. Electric currents; intensity, potential, Ohm's law. Thermal effect,

284

Joule's law. Electrical energy and power. Force exerted by a magnetic field; induction vector; conservation of induction flux. Calculation of magnetic field produced by a current; classic examples. Electromagnetic induction; coefficient of self-induction. Magnetic energy stored in a circuit. Basic ideas on magnetized media; permanent magnets. Continuous current measurement apparatuses, the galvanometer. Basic laws of alternating current; impedance of a portion of a circuit.

The above is a brief summary of the official syllabus for classes preparing for higher education (*grandes écoles*, option B). The syllabuses vary slightly, according to the option taken.

The reader may refer to the official text of the syllabus in the pamphlets published by the Librairie Vuibert (63 boulevard Saint-Germain, Paris-5e).

An idea of the level of French teaching in the first years of higher scientific education can be obtained from *Traité de Physique* by P. Fleury and J. P. Mathieu, published by Eyrolles (61 boulevard Saint-Germain, Paris-5e). This work covers the whole of physics in eight volumes.

III C2   Example of problem for *propédeutique* students in France

In the circuit shown in the diagram, E is the potential difference between the points A and M, and U is the potential difference between the points B and M.

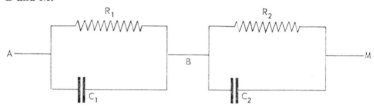

Figure 13

1. Establish the differential equation relating U and E at any moment of time t when:

$$a = \frac{R_2}{R_1 + R_2} \qquad b = \frac{C_1}{C_1 + C_2} \qquad T = R_1 C_1$$

2. Let E undergo an infinitely rapid variation of finite amplitude ΔE at a certain moment t_0. Show, by integrating the two terms of the preceding differential equation over an extremely short time interval including t_0 that U also undergoes an infinitely rapid variation of amplitude $\Delta U = b\Delta E$.

3. Using the preceding result, study the variations of U when E has the following values:

$$E = O \text{ for } t < O$$
$$E = E_0 \text{ for } t \geqq O$$

286

Appendixes

The $U(t)$ curves will be plotted in the following cases: $b > a$, $b < a$.
4. Let E now have the following values:

$$\text{for } t < 0 \qquad E = 0$$
$$\text{for } 0 < t < t_1 \ E = E_1$$
$$\text{for } t > t_1 \qquad E = 0$$

Using the preceding results determine and show to scale on four different graphs the variations of E and U in the following cases:

$a = \frac{1}{2}$	$a = \frac{1}{2}$	$a = \frac{1}{2}$	$a = \frac{1}{2}$
$b = \frac{1}{3}$	$b = \frac{2}{3}$	$b = \frac{1}{3}$	$b = \frac{2}{3}$
$T = 0.30s$	$T = 0.30s$	$T = 4s$	$T = 4s$

Let us take $E_1 = 120\ V$ and $t_1 = 1$ second.
The values of U at times $t = 0$ and $t = t_1$ will be established and the curves will be compared with those which would be obtained if the capacitors did not exist.
5. What is the simple relationship which must exist between R_1, R_2 C_1 and C_2 in order that the variations of U shall be proportional to those of E at any moment?
6. In this question E is a sinusoidal function of time of frequency ω, which is assumed to have been imposed long enough for a permanent regime to have been established. Calculate, using imaginary notation, the ratio U/E.

Express this ratio as a function of a, b, T and ω. Show that the potential differences $U - aE$ on the one hand and $U - bE$ on the other are in quadrature whatever the frequency.

On the complex plane the number U/E is the affix of a certain point P. When ω varies the point P describes a simple curve which we shall determine from the preceding results. Deduce from this that there exists a value ω_m for which the phase shift between the potential differences U and E is maximum. Evaluate ω_m as a function of a, b, T and the maximum value of this phase shift.

287

Some experiments performed
by university *propédeutique* students
in France

Measuring *g* by the oscillation of a reversible pendulum.
Studying torsion; the torsion pendulum.
Measuring the capillary constant by the Jurin rule.
Comparative measurement of viscosity (influence of temperature).
Calibration of a thermoelectric couple.
Measurement of specific heat of a solid and of the melting point of ice.
Measurement of latent heat of vaporization of water.
A cryometrical experiment.
Determination of the cardinal elements of a centred system (Cornu method).
Measurement of the index of refraction of a solid by the prism method.
Study of a diffraction grating.
Verification of Malus's Law and of the law of photometry with the help of a photovoltaic cell.
Study of relaxation oscillations of a neon tube (R.C. circuit).
Measurement of galvanometer constants.
Measurement of e.m.f. with a potentiometer.
Measurement of resistance and resistivity with a Wheatstone bridge.
Characteristic of a semiconductor rectifier.
Resonance of an alternating current L.R.C. circuit.
Auto-oscillating circuit using a triode.
Operation of a Geiger counter.

Each class lasts three hours.

Syllabus for the various CES in France

Each item represents about one hundred teaching hours. The text of the syllabus is very brief, but reference to the textbooks mentioned by way of example at the end of each section will give an idea of the ground covered. The level of the students' mathematics can be estimated by referring to *Mathématiques* by Hocquenghem and Jaffard, published by Masson, Paris, in 1963.

The course includes also exercises and laboratory work (cf. Appendix III C6).

General mechanics[1]

The relationship between kinematics and kinetics.
Forces. Basic principle and general theorems of Newtonian mechanics.
Virtual work and power. Energy theorems.
Problems of statics and dynamics of solids.
Usual types of binding. Friction. Mathematical formulation of specific problems.
Lagrange's equations and canonical equations.
Introduction to the mechanics of continuous deformable media.

Thermodynamics and physical mechanics[2]

Thermodynamics

The first and second laws. Free energy; thermodynamic potential.
Specific heat and the equation of state. Changes of state. Low temperatures; helium.

---

1. See J. Peres, *Mécanique générale*, Paris, Masson, 1953.
2. See G. Bruhmat and A. Foch, *Mécanique Physique*, Paris, Masson; and G. Bruhat and A. Kastler, *Thermodynamique*, Paris, Masson, 1964.

Kinetic theory. The virial law; rarefied gases; transfer phenomena; Brownian motion; the Boltzmann entropy hypothesis; fluctuations.

Statistical mechanics. The Maxwell-Boltzmann distribution law. Specific heat (Einstein, Debye).

Physical mechanics

Recapitulation of the dynamics of a point and of a solid. Example of electron optics.

Oscillations: general considerations. Harmonic and relaxation oscillators. Electrical analogies.

Propagation of vibrations. Longitudinal and transverse vibrations. Propagation, phase and group velocities—Doppler effect. General concept of impedance.

Free acoustic waves. The speed of sound; ultrasonics.

Vibrations in closed systems. Organ pipes; reflection, resonance. Vibrating strings and rods.

Optics [1]

Propagation of a light wave in an isotropic medium. Speed of light; restricted relativity theory. Interference; diffraction; phase contrast. Diffusion; refraction; dispersion.

Propagation of a light wave in an uniaxial medium. Birefringence; polarization; interference in polarized light; thin plates; circularly and elliptically polarized light; accidental birefringence.

Quantum mechanics. Diffraction of X-rays and of particles; matter waves; photons, the Compton effect. The Schrödinger wave equation; simple applications; tunnel effect, harmonic oscillator.

Spectroscopy. Atomic spectra; Bohr's theory; principal quantum numbers (n, l, j, m); selection rules; hydrogen and alkalis; the Zeeman effect.

Radiation. Black body; quantal aspect.

Concepts of nuclear physics and radioactivity.

Electricity [2]

Recapitulation of the differential and integral laws of electrostatics and electromagnetism.

1. See G. Bruhat and A. Kastler, *Optique*, Paris, Masson, 1965.
2. See G. Bruhat and G. Goudet, *Electricité*, Paris, Masson, 1963.

Macroscopic study of dielectric and magnetic media. Magnetostatics, electrical and magnetic energy.

Industrial alternating current. Alternating circuits, filters, energies; transformers; rotating machines.

Maxwell equations. Displacement current; propagation of electromagnetic waves; free waves and waves guided along wires; reflection; resonance; adaptation; wave guides; skin effect.

Electrons and ions. Discharge in gases; ionization potential; mobility; thermoelectric and photo-electric effects. Action of fields on a charged particle; variation of m; $E = mc^2$.

Electron tubes. The diode; space charge; the triode and its characteristics; classical valves; simple connexions.

Theory of solids. Magnetism; diamagnetism and paramagnetism; ordered states; magnetostriction; dielectrics; ferro-electrics; semiconductors —atomic theory; rectifiers; transistors. The Hall and Peltier effects.

Electrical engineering

General

Materials used in electrical engineering.
Electric circuits.
Magnetic circuits.
Alternating fields, rotating fields.
Tracing electrical and magnetic fields.
Symmetrical components. Non-sinusoidal periodic magnitudes.
Maxwell's equations.

Electrical machines

Direct current machines.
The transformer.
The alternator.
The synchronous motor.
Asynchronous machines.
Aerial lines and cables.
Special electrical machines and some special circuits.
Specimen electrical calculation for a machine; the transformer.

Electronics[1]

Classical vacuum and gas valves (15 hours)

Tetrodes, pentodes, special valves; the oscilloscope.
Gas valves; rectifiers, thyratrons, counter tubes.
Photoelectric cells.
The noise in vacuum tubes.
The klystron and the magnetron.

Active electronic circuits with lumped constants (45 hours)

Low frequency, direct current, high frequency amplifiers; feedback.
Oscillators, multivibrators.
Various types of modulation, demodulation, frequency change.
Pulsed circuits.

Semi-conductors (20 hours)

First considerations on semi-conductor theory.
Principal applications; thermistors and varistors; diodes and rectifiers; triodes and tetrodes; base connexions and equivalent circuits; photo-diodes.
Transistor circuits; amplifiers, oscillators, pulsed circuits.

Distributed constant circuits and the radiation of radio waves (20 hours)

Propagation along loss-free lines.
Influence of losses.
Wave guide propagation; resonant cavities.
Typical examples of v.h.f. circuits.
Radiation from a wave projector.
Radiation from a doublet.

---

1. See B. Guillien, *Electronique*, Paris Presses Universitaires de France, 1960–61, 4 vols., and P. Grivet, *Cours d'électronique*, Paris, Masson, 1958–65, 5 vols.

Typical examination questions
for the CES in electronics
at the University of Paris

(To be completed in three hours)

1. Define the following concepts: (a) the principal mode in a rectangular waveguide; (b) the wave impedance for the principal mode, for example the H_{01} mode in a rectangular waveguide; (c) impedance matching at a point in a line; (d) the elements (R, L, C, Q_0) of the parallel equivalent circuit of a resonant cavity.

2. A variable frequency generator, which may be taken to supply a current I, is matched into a waveguide of characteristic admittance Y_0 containing a wattmeter M with an equivalent shunt admittance of $g + jb$. This system is followed by a waveguide of length l terminated by a resonant cavity wavemeter which can be represented by the classical parallel resonant circuit (R, L, C).

What is the actual admittance Y_1 of the cavity when the frequency ω differs slightly from the resonant frequency ω_0? Let Q_0 denote the vacuum quality factor (always very large) of the unloaded cavity, and take $\omega = \omega_0 + \delta\omega$.

For what value of β is the power P_0 absorbed by M a maximum for $\omega \neq \omega_0$? Find that value P_0.

When $\omega = \omega_0{}^1$, a frequency very close to ω_0, the power as measured by M is a minimum $P_{\min}$: why is this? By setting $RY_0 = \beta$, determine the difference $(\omega_0{}^1 - \omega_0)$.

If $\beta = 1$, $g = b = Y_0$, $Q_0 = 24{,}000$ and $f_0 = 10^4$ Mc/s; calculate $P_{\min}/P_0$ and the frequency difference $(\omega_0{}^1 - \omega_0)$.

List of experiments performed
by students of
the CES in electronics (France)

Use of the oscilloscope; fundamental measurements.
Study of the gas-filled cold-cathode-diode and of the thyraton.
The characteristics of filters.
The semi-conductor diode; rectification.
Wiring up an R.C. coupled amplifier.
Study of a selective amplifier.
Study of a wide-band amplifier.
Negative feedback; the cathode follower.
Detection. Discrimination of A.M. and F.M. waves.
The multivibrator; harmonic analysis.
Study of piezo-electricity with a quartz crystal.
Measurement of transistor parameters.
The transistor amplifier.
The analogue computer and the D.C. amplifier.
Positive feedback; H.F. and V.H.F. oscillators.
Study of pulse techniques and delay lines.
Frequency and impedance measurements using centimetric waves.
Study of the working of a 2K 25 klystron.

Each period lasts for four hours: notes on the experiments are provided, and the work is supervised by an assistant. The apparatus is always that in current industrial use.

Each CES course, of which the syllabus is given in Appendix III C4, is complemented by an experimental course such as that just outlined.

294

University syllabus in general physics
in the U.S.S.R.

Introduction

Matter and motion. Interconnexion of natural phenomena. The laws of
nature. The subject-matter of physics. The place of physics in the natural
sciences. Methods of physical research. The role of experiment, practice
and theory in physical research. The contribution and history of physics
in the U.S.S.R.

Part I

Mechanics and acoustics

Space and time as forms of the existence of matter. Mechanical motion.
The subject-matter and purposes of mechanics. Kinematics and dynamics.

Fundamentals of kinematics and dynamics of a mass point. System of
reference. Vectors of displacement, velocity and acceleration. Tangential
and normal accelerations. Angular velocity as vector.

Mass, moment of momentum, force. Newton's laws. Motion of mass
point in the presence of constraints. Centripetal force.

Law of the conservation of momentum. Motion of a body of variable
mass. Meshchersky's work. Tsiolkovsky's ideas on reactive motion.

Gravity, elasticity, friction. The law of universal gravitation. Kepler's
laws; the concept of gravitational mass. Cavendish's experiments; the
gravitational constant. Gravitational and inertial mass. Methods of
measuring gravitational acceleration. Lomonosov's 'universal barometer'.
Elastic forces. Connexion between force and deformation. Hooke's

law. Forces of friction. Dry and wet friction. Frictional motion. The concept of rolling friction.

Work, energy, power. Work of a force. Potential and kinetic energy. Law of the conservation of energy. Energy as a measure of motion. Collision of bodies.

Motion in a non-inertial system of reference. Motion relative to a system of reference in translation. The force of inertia. A rotating system of reference. Centrifugal force. Motion in a rotating system of reference. The Coriolis force. Motion on the surface of the globe. Foucault's experiment.

Motion of a system of mass points and a solid. Centre of mass. Moment of momentum and moment of force. A solid as a system of mass points. Rotation of a body about a stationary axis. Dynamic equation for rotary motion of a solid. Moment of inertia. Law of the conservation of moment of momentum. Free axes of rotation. The gyroscope. Kinetic energy of a moving solid. Equilibrium of a solid. Equilibrium and potential energy of a system.

Elastic properties of continuous media. Types of elastic deformation. Extension, shear, torsion, bend. Elastic limit. Elastic deformation energy.
    Pressure in a fluid. Pressure equilibrium. Compressibility of liquids and gases.

Motion of liquids and gases. Stationary motion of a liquid. Bernoulli's equation. Dynamic pressure. Flow of a liquid in a tube. Viscosity of a liquid. Poiseuille's formula. Turbulent motion.
    The Reynolds number. Flow of a liquid or a gas round a body. Drag. Zhukovsky's explanation of lift. Motion of bodies travelling at supersonic velocity.

Oscillations. Harmonic oscillation. Amplitude, frequency, phase. Natural oscillations. Pendulums. Oscillatory energy. Damping of oscillations. Addition of oscillations. Beating. Forced oscillations. Resonance. Compound oscillations. Breakdown of oscillations into harmonic components and oscillation spectrum. Self-oscillatory systems.

Waves in a continuous medium. Amplitude, phase, velocity of wave propagation. Plane and spherical waves. Longitudinal and transverse waves. The wave equation. Elastic properties of the medium and propa-

296

gation velocity of a wave. Interference waves. Standing waves. Energy flow. Energy flow according to Umov.

Elements of acoustics. Nature of sound. Pitch. Speed of sound and its measurement. The Doppler effect. Intensity of sound and its measurement.

Sources of sound. Vibrations of strings and tubes. Vibrations of membranes and plates.

Loudness. Analysis of sounds and timbre. Ultrasound.

The concept of hydrolocation.

Molecular physics

Subject-matter of molecular physics. Atoms and molecules. Ideal gas. Equation of state for an ideal gas. Clapeyron, Mendeleev. Absolute temperature. Lomonosov as the founder of the kinetic theory of heat.

Basic propositions of the kinetic theory of gases. Calculation of gas pressure according to kinetic theory. The Boltzmann constant.

Manifestation of new qualities in a system consisting of a large number of molecules. Statistical regularities. Objective character of the statistical regularity.

Molecular beam. Measurement of velocities of gas molecules. Velocity distribution of molecules. Maxwell's law. Field of force of a gas. The Boltzmann principle. The barometric formula. Perrin's experiment for estimates of Avogadro's number. The concept of fluctuation. Brownian movement. Verification of the kinetic theory in experiments on Brownian movement.

Transmission. Average length of free path of molecules. Gas kinetic cross-section. Diffusion, internal friction and thermal conductivity of gases. Calculation of the coefficients of diffusion of internal friction and of thermal conductivity.

Rarefied gases. Laws of equilibrium and flow of rarefied gases. Thermal conductivity and friction in rarefied gases. Methods of producing and measuring a high vacuum.

First law of thermodynamics. The method of thermodynamics and its comparison with the kinetic theory method. Thermodynamic equilibrium. Internal energy and external work. Quantity of heat. The first law of thermodynamics. Law of the conservation and conversion of energy and its philosophical significance. Critique of 'energeticism'.

Application of the first law of thermodynamics to an ideal gas. Work of an expanding gas. Thermal capacity of a gas. Distribution of energy according to degrees of freedom. Limits of applicability of the law of equal distribution of energy. Principle of the quantum theory of thermal capacity.

Adiabatic processes. The adiabatic equation.

Second law of thermodynamics. Reversible and irreversible processes. Cycles. The Carnot cycle. Carnot's theorem. The second law of thermodynamics. The thermodynamic temperature scale.

Entropy. Statistical character of the second law of thermodynamics. Critique of the idealist inferences from the second law of thermodynamics.

Real gases and liquids. Evaporation of a liquid. Properties of vapours. Diagram of state of a biphasal vapour-liquid system. The boiling curve. Critical temperature and its discovery by Mendeleev. Critical state.

Molecular forces. Van der Waals' equation. Explanation of the mutual transformation of vapours and liquids. The Joule-Thomson effect. Liquefaction of gases. Modern methods of producing low temperatures.

Surface tension. Surface tension and surface curvature. Wetting. Capillarity. Vapour pressure above a curved surface.

Solids. Crystalline and amorphous states.

Elements of crystal symmetry. Space lattice. Crystallographic systems. Surface energy and external shape of crystals. Polymers.

Thermal capacity of solids. Thermal expansion of solids.

Phase conversions. First order and second order phase transitions. Metastable states.

Melting and crystallization. The melting curve. Super-cooling of liquids. Evaporation of solids. Diagram of state of a three-phase system. Triple point.

Polymorphism in solids. Application of the second law of thermodynamics to phase conversions. The Clausius-Clapeyron equation.

Examples of second order phase transitions. Properties of liquid helium.

Solutions. Osmotic pressure. The van 't Hoff law. Dissociation. Diagram of state of a binary system. Eutectics. Solid solutions.

Electricity and magnetism

Fundamental electrostatic effects. Coulomb's law. Quantity of electricity. the CGSE system. Fundamental particles as carriers of electric charge.

Electrostatics. Electric field. Electric field as an objective reality not reducible to mechanical effects. Field strength. The Gauss-Ostrogradsky theorem. Work in an electric field. Potential difference. Potential gradient and field strength. Conductors in an electrostatic field. Capacitance. Capacitors. Energy of an electric field.

Dielectrics. Polarization of dielectrics. Field in a dielectric. Induction vector. Permittivity. Boundary conditions. Field energy in a dielectric. Molecular explanation of the polarization of dielectrics. Polar and nonpolar dielectrics. Dependence of permittivity on temperature.

Ferroelectrics. Piezoelectricity. Electrostriction.

Direct electric current. Electric field of direct current. Ohm's law. Dependence of resistance on temperature. Metals, semiconductors, insulators. Superconductivity. Electromotive force. Ohm's law for a closed circuit. Kirchhoff's laws. Thermal effects of current. The Lenz-Joule law. Work and power of a current.

Electron theory of metals and semiconductors. Elementary electric charge and its measurement. The electron. Determining the nature of charged particles in metals. Explanation of the electrical conductivity of metals. Peculiarities of the electrical conductivity of semiconductors.

Connexion between thermal conductivity and electrical conductivity of metals. Difficulties of classical electron theory.

Contact potential difference. Thermal effects in contacts. Thermoelectric effects. Effects in contacts between metals and semiconductors.

Magnetic field of a current. The principle of magnetic interaction of currents. Magnetic field strength. Eddy character of a magnetic field. Effect of a magnetic field on a current. The CGSM system and its connexion with the electrostatic system. Practical system of units.

Effect of a magnetic field on moving charges (Lorentz force). Magnetic field of moving charges. Eichenwald's experiments with convection currents.

Electromagnetic induction. Faraday's experiments. Induced e.m.f. Lenz's law. Mutual and self-induction. Eddy currents. Work of induced e.m.f. Magnetic energy of current. Mutual energy of currents. Energy of a magnetic field.

Magnetics. Magnetic field in magnetics. Vector of magnetization. Magnetic induction. Magnetic susceptibility and permeability.

Diamagnetic and paramagnetic substances. Curie's law. Ferromagnetics. Ferrites. Magnetization curves for ferromagnetic bodies. Stoletov's work. Dependence of ferromagnetism on temperature. The Curie point. Magnetic hysteresis. Permanent magnets. Fundamentals of magnetostatics.

Explanation of magnetization in electron theory. Magnetomechanical and mechanical effects. Explanation of diamagnetism and paramagnetism. Magnetic and mechanical moments of an electron. Current ideas on the nature of ferromagnetism. Physical meaning of field strength and induction in ferromagnetics. Influence of magnetics on interaction of currents and magnets. Magnetic field energy in magnetics.

Electron emission and laws of the movement of charged particles in electric and magnetic fields. Electron emission and the laws governing it. Electronic current in a vacuum. Influence of space charge. The electron valve and its use in rectifying and amplifying electric current. Auto-electric effects.

Motion of electrons in electric and magnetic fields. Measuring the ratio of charge to mass in electrons.

Electric conductivity of gases and liquids. Ionization and recombination of gas ions. Townsend avalanche. Principal types of gas discharge (pulse, corona, glow, arc). Petrov's arc.

Electrolysis. Laws of electrolysis. Determination of elementary charge. Motion and mobility of ions.

Electrical oscillations. Quasi-stationary currents. Natural electrical oscillations in a circuit of concentrated capacitance and inductance. Damping of oscillations. Self-oscillation. Producing undamped oscillations.

Forced electrical oscillations. Alternating current. Resistance, capacitance and self-induction in an alternating-current circuit. Principle of the vector diagram and complex amplitude method. Work and power of alternating current.

Tension resonance. Branching of alternating currents. Parallel resonance. The transformer and its invention by Usagyn. Electric motors. Three-phase currents. The work of Dolivo-Dobrovolsky.

Electromagnetic fields. Non-stationary currents. Maxwell's theory. Eddy currents. Displacement current. Eichenwald's experiments verifying Maxwell's hypotheses. Maxwell's equation.

Electromagnetic waves. Propagation velocity of electromagnetic waves.

Standing electromagnetic waves and oscillations in distributed electric circuits. Waveguides. Transmission lines. Free electromagnetic waves.

300

Standing electromagnetic waves. The open vibrator and its field. Hertz's experiments. The Umov-Poynting vector of energy flow of electromagnetic waves for communications purposes. Popov's invention of the radio. Physical principles of radio transmission.

Short electromagnetic waves. The mass radiator. Lebedev's work on the production and investigation of short electromagnetic waves. Principle of modern methods of generating ultrashort radio waves. Principles of radar.

Optics

Introduction. Brief outline of the history of light. Electromagnetic nature of light. Light waves. Electromagnetic wave scale. The work of Glagoleva-Arkadeva.

Interference of light. Coherent sources. Methods of producing coherence in optics. Equal thickness and equal inclination curves. Applications of interference. Interferometers. Interference under conditions of large path-differences. Monochromatic light. Spectral line width. Standing light waves. Light vector.

Diffraction. The Huygens-Fresnel principle. Rectilinear propagation of light. Diffraction at a circular aperture, on a circular screen, at the straight edge of a screen. Diffraction from a slit. The diffraction grating. Resolving power of a diffraction grating. Multidimensional gratings. Producing X-rays. Diffraction of X-rays. The Bragg (Wulff) equation. Principal methods of structure analysis.

Spectral apparatuses. Dispersion, dispersion region and resolving power of spectral apparatuses (prism, grating, interference spectroscopes).

Geometric optics and its limitations. Refraction and reflection at a plane boundary. Conditions for regular reflection and refraction. Total reflection. Eichenwald's work. Refraction at a spherical surface. A centred optical system and its cardinal elements. Defects of optical systems. Optical instruments. The role of the diaphragm in optical instruments. Diffraction theory of the optic image. Resolving power of the telescope and microscope. Ultramicroscopy.

Fundamental photometric concepts and units.

Polarization of light. Transverse character of light waves. Polarization in reflection and refraction. Fresnel's formulas.

Birefringence. The Huygens construction in uniaxial crystals. Polarizing instruments. Dielectrical and optical properties of an anisotropic medium. Pleochroism. Polaroids.

Interference of polarized light. Production and investigation of elliptically polarized light. Uniaxial and biaxial crystals in parallel rays. Artificial anisotropy in deformations. Birefringence in an electric field.

Rotation of a polarizing plane.

Dispersion of light. Normal and anomalous dispersion and methods of observing them. The crossed prisms method. Rozdestvensky's hook method. Absorption of light. The electron theory of dispersion. Resolution of spectral lines in magnetic field. The Zeeman effect. Explanation of normal resolution, using electron theory. Magnetic rotation of a polarizing plane.

Diffusion of light. Optically homogeneous and inhomogeneous media. Critical opalescence. Molecular diffusion of light. Dependence of the intensity of diffused light on wavelength. Sky colour and the red sun. Polarization of diffused light.

Light pressure. Lebedev's work on light pressure on solids and gases. Momentum of an electromagnetic wave.

The velocity of light and methods of measuring it. Phase and group velocity. The Cherenkov effect. The Doppler effect in optics. Experiments of Belopolsky and Golitsyn. The Michelson experiment. Limitations of the notions of space and time in classical mechanics.

Constancy of the velocity of light. The special theory of relativity.

Thermal radiation. Radiating and absorbing power of bodies. Kirchhoff's law. Absolute black body. Wien's distribution law and the Stefan-Boltzmann law. Distribution of energy in a radiation spectrum. The optical pyrometer. Inadequacy of classical theory. Planck's formula. Radiation quanta. Discrete character of light flux. Vavilov's experiments.

The photoelectric effect. Stoletov's experiments. The photoelectric effect law. Photons. Einstein's equation. The elementary photo effect. Ioffe's and Dobronravov's experiments. Photocells. The internal photoelectric effect. Barrier-layer photocells.

Fluorescence and phosphorescence. Stokes' law. Vavilov's law of quantum emission. Fluorescence. The application of luminescence. Fluorescent lighting.

302

Part II

Atomic physics

Brief historical outline of modern notions of atomic structure. Nineteenth- and twentieth-century achievements in atomic science outside the Soviet Union as a new stage in understanding the objective laws of the material world.

Motion of a charged particle in an electric field. The laws of similarity. Refraction of electron paths. The principle of electron optics. The electron lens. The electron multiplier.

Motion of a charged particle in a magnetic field. Focusing in a transverse and in a longitudinal field. The electron microscope.

Some cases of the motion of particles in combined fields. Methods of determining e/m for electrons and ions. Mass spectroscopy. Separation of isotopes.

Motion of charged particles at velocities comparable with the speed of light. Ratio between energy and mass (Einstein's law).

The cyclotron. Principles of its operation and construction. The betatron. Principle of its operation and construction. Electrostatic accelerators.

Passage of electrons through a gas. Dependence of effective cross-section on energy in the case of noble gases. Impossibility of explaining diffusion processes from the classical point of view.

Experiments on the reflection of electrons from crystals. Explanation of the results of such experiments in terms of the wave properties of the electron. Wavelength of an electron and its determination by experiments on diffraction, using the Bragg (Wulff) equation. Diffraction of electrons in a polycrystalline film. De Broglie's formula. The wave function of a free electron. Physical meaning of the wave function. Principle of the wave equation.

Experimental data underlying modern atomic theory. (a) Rutherford's experiment in the scattering of alpha particles; Rutherford's formula. (b) Atomic spectra (general characteristic); the combination principle; the hydrogen spectrum; the Lyman, Balmer and other series. (c) Franck's and Hertz's experiments; determination of the excitation and ionization potentials of atoms.

The hydrogen atom according to Bohr energy levels and stability of orbit. Bohr's theory as an intermediate stage in the development of atomic ideas.

Atomic structure in terms of quantum mechanics. Stationary states of electron motion. The electron cloud. Quantum numbers and their physical meaning.

Experimental data on the properties of complex atoms. Structure of alkali metal atoms; valence electron. Spectra of alkali metal atoms. The doublet character of these spectra. Electron spin.

Vector model of the atom. Classification of the spectra of complex atoms. Selection rules in optical transitions.

The Pauli principle. Parahelium and orthohelium. Metastable states.

Atomic magnetism. Spatial quantization. Magnetic moments of atoms. Bohr's magneton. The Stern-Gerlach experiments. Modern methods of determining the magnetic moments of atoms. Gyromagnetic effects.

The Zeeman effect. Qualitative explanation of the Zeeman effect on the basis of quantum theory. The Landé splitting factor. The Paschen-Back effect.

Diamagnetism. Larmor's theorem. Diamagnetic susceptibility.

Structure of electron shells. Explanation of Mendeleev's periodic system

X-rays. Continuous and characteristic X-ray spectrum. Moseley's law. X-ray series. The doublet character of X-ray spectra.

X-ray absorption spectra. Dependence of the coefficient of absorption on atomic number and wavelength. The Compton effect.

Fine structure of the atomic spectrum of hydrogen. Experiments in investigating the expansion of energy levels of the hydrogen atom.

Nature of the molecular bond. Dipole bond. Homopolar bonds and qualitative explanation thereof.

304

Part III

Nuclear physics

Introduction. Brief historical review of the main stages in the history of nuclear physics.

Passage of fast charged particles through matter. Ionization losses. Energy losses due to bremsstrahlung (radiation losses). Penetrating power of charged particles (range-energy).

Interaction of gamma radiation with matter. Scattering on electrons. Photoelectric absorption. Pair production in the field of the atomic nucleus. Conversion of a pair into photons. Attenuation factor of a gamma-ray beam and its dependence on the gamma-photon energy and nature of the substance.

Modern methods of recording and measuring the energy of fast charged particles and gamma-quanta. Condensation chambers in a magnetic field. The use of photoemulsions and gas-discharge instruments (ionization chambers, gas-discharge counters). Luminescent methods. Magnetic spectrometers.

Radiation dosimetry. Basic information on radiation dosimetry of fast charged particles and gamma-quanta. Biological effect of radiation. Dosimetrical units. Dosimeters. Efficiency of shields made of various materials.

General properties of atomic nuclei. Short-range character of nuclear forces. Hyperfine structure of atomic spectra and their explanation. Data on nuclear moments. Proton-neutron composition of the nucleus. Methods of measuring nuclear mass. Proton and neutron mass. Binding energy of the nucleus and its dependence on mass number. Saturation property of nuclear forces. Conditions of stability in relation to different types of decay. Semi-empirical formula for nuclear mass.

Principle of modern radio frequency methods of measuring magnetic nuclear moment; application thereof (measurement and stabilization of magnetic-field strength). Magnetic moments of proton and neutron. Structure of deuterons.

Neutron-proton scattering; spin dependence of nuclear forces; exchange interaction. Data on the periodicity of nuclear properties. The nuclear shell.

Radioactive decay. The law of radioactive decay. Consecutive radioactive conversions. Radioactive series and other examples. Gamma radiation. Internal conversion. Nuclear isomerism. Beta decay and capture of atomic electrons. Laws of the conservation of energy, pulse and momentum in beta decay and electron capture. The neutrino. Mirror asymmetry in beta decay effects (asymmetry of angular distribution of electron emitted in beta decay of polarized nuclei; longitudinal polarization effect). Application of artificial radioactivity (labelled atoms, defectoscopy, etc.). Alpha radioactivity. Impossibility of classical explanation. The tunnel effect and its use in explaining the process of alpha decay; dependence of the alpha decay constant on alpha-particle energy.

Nuclear reactions. Methods of accelerating charged particles (direct acceleration, resonance and induction accelerators). Modern methods of accelerating to relativistic energies. Principle of automatic phase stabilization.

General ideas on the course of nuclear reactions at various energies of the bombarding particles. The compound nucleus. Resonance reactions.

Principles of neutron physics. Neutron sources. Recording fast neutrons. Moderation and diffusion of neutrons. Nuclear reactions with slow neutrons (the $1/v$ law, resonance reactions). Recording slow neutrons. Slow-neutron diffraction and its use for structural analysis.

Splitting heavy nuclei and the nuclear chain reaction. Experimental findings on neutron-induced fission of heavy nuclei. Spontaneous fission. Physical analysis of the fission process on the basis of the liquid-drop model of the nucleus. Isotopes of uranium and transuranic elements capable of slow-neutron-induced fission. Nuclear chain reaction and the conditions for its occurrence. Nuclear reactors. Explosive nuclear chain reaction. Thermonuclear reactions and their role in the universe.

Fundamental particles and processes at high energies. List of fundamental particles and their classification. Decay of fundamental particles. Collision formation of elementary particles. Pi-mesons and their role in nuclear interactions. Simultaneous generation of K-mesons and hyperons. Particles and 'anti-particles' (pair production and annihilation). Star formation caused by high-energy particles. Cosmic radiation (composition of cosmic radiation, primary component of cosmic radiation, general picture of the passage of cosmic radiation through the atmosphere).

Achievements of modern physics, the child of dialectical materialism.

Theoretical physics syllabus in the U.S.S.R.

Part I

Mechanics

Introduction. Various types of motion of matter. Mechanical motion and its place among other forms of motion. Critique of mechanism.

Relativity of mechanical motion. System of reference. Critique of idealist interpretations in relation to mechanical motion.

Particle kinematics. Motion of a particle relative to a system of reference; velocity vector and acceleration vector. Trajectory. Analysis of velocity and acceleration vectors along the tangent and the normal to the trajectory. Projections of velocity and acceleration on the axis of a rectangular Cartesian system of co-ordinates. Curvilinear co-ordinates. Velocity components with respect to co-ordinate lines. Projections of acceleration on co-ordinate lines (Lagrange's formulas). Cylindrical and spherical co-ordinates.

Basic laws of particle dynamics. Free particles. The law of inertia. Inertial systems of reference. Galilean transformation. Transformation of velocity and acceleration. The principle of relativity. Newton's second law. Momentum and its dependence on velocity. Mass. Transmission of momentum and force. Kinetic energy and its connexion with velocity. Connexion between momentum and energy and their conversion on transition to another inertial system of reference.

Motion of a particle in one dimension. Forces depending on the position of the particle, potential energy. Integration of the equations of motion and qualitative investigation of motion. Positions of equilibrium. Small oscillations about positions of equilibrium. Forces depending on velocity (friction and resistance). Small oscillations in the presence of resistance and constraints.

Motion of a particle in a space. Moment of momentum and force. Potential fields of force. Potential energy. Equations of motion in curvilinear co-ordinates. Generalized force.

Motion under the influence of central forces. Conservation of moment of momentum and conservation of areas. Radial motion and its qualitative investigation. Keplerian motion.

General laws of dynamics of a system of particles. External and internal forces. Momentum of a system and its variation. Law of the conservation of momentum. Centre of inertia. Motion of the centre of inertia. Kinetic energy of a system. Koenig's theorem. Variation of kinetic energy and work of forces. Potential energy of internal forces. Law of the conservation of energy. Moment of momentum of a system relative to a stationary point and relative to the centre of inertia. Law of the conservation of moment of momentum. Moment of external forces.

Lagrange's equations. Conservative and non-conservative links of forces. Generalized co-ordinates and generalized velocities. Generalized forces. Derivation of Lagrange's equations. Lagrangian function and energy. Cyclical co-ordinates and integrals of motion.

Two particles. Lagrangian function for two bonded particles. Motion of the centre of mass and relative motion. Reduced mass. Collision of particles. Differential and total effective cross-section.

Kinematics of solids. Translation and rotary motion. D'Alembert's theorem. Pseudo-vector of rotation (angular velocity). Distribution of velocities in a rotating solid (Euler's formula). Plane motion.

Eulerian angles. Euler's kinetic formulas.

Principal dynamic characteristics of a solid. Elements of tensor calculation. Momentum of a solid and velocity of the centre of mass. Kinetic energy and moment of momentum and their connexion with angular velocity. The inertia tensor. Transformation of the components of the inertia tensor on transmission and rotation of a system of co-ordinates. Reduction of inertia tensor to principal axes. Principal moments of inertia.

Equation for the motion of a solid. Variation of moment of momentum of a solid. Euler's dynamic equations. Free movement of a solid. Elementary gyroscope theory.

Equilibrium of a solid. Torque. Static equivalence of forces and couples.

Small oscillations of a system of particles. Equilibrium configurations. Small motions around equilibrium configurations. Kinetic and potential energy in small motions. Equations of small motions. Normal oscillations. Finding the frequencies and amplitudes of normal oscillations. Orthogonality of amplitudes. Case of uniform frequencies. Normalization of amplitudes. Normal co-ordinates. Generalized forces for normal co-ordinates. Forced oscillations and oscillations in the presence of resistance.

Motion in non-inertial systems of reference. The equations of motion in non-inertial systems of reference. Forces of inertia. Rotating systems of reference. Centrifugal and rotary forces of inertia. Energy and momentum. Motion on the Earth.

The variation principle and canonical equations. Least-action principle for conservative systems. The integral of action. Derivation of equations of motion in generalized co-ordinates. Invariability of action with various transformations and the laws of conservation. Generalized momenta. Conversion to canonical variables. Hamilton's equations. Phase space. Invariability of phase volume on transition to other canonical variables. Liouville's theorem.

Kinematics of a moving fluid. Velocity field. Equation of continuity. Analysis of the motion of a fluid particle into translation, rotation and pure-strain motion. Vorticity.

Ideal fluids. Pressure. Euler's equation.Conservation of entropy. Boundary conditions. Equilibrium of an ideal fluid. Stationary motion. Bernoulli's equation. Conservation of circulation. Pulse flow and energy flow.

Non-vortical motion of an ideal fluid. Velocity potential. Potential flow of an incompressible ideal fluid.

Viscous fluids. Tensor of rate of shear. Tensor of viscous stresses. Connexion between tensor of viscous stresses and rate of shear. Viscous forces. Equations of motion. Pulse flow. Equation of entropy. Energy flow. Dissipation.

Poiseuille flow, flow between rotating cylinders, flow round a sphere. Boundary layer. The Reynolds number. Principle of generation of turbulence.

Sound waves. Equations of hydrodynamics for small motions. Plane sound wave. Speed of sound. Energy and pulse of a sound wave. Reflexion of sound. Absorption of sound.

Basic laws of the theory of elasticity. Strain tensor and stress tensor in elastic bodies. Hooke's law. Connexion between strain and stress tensors. Elastic moduli and coefficients. Equilibrium of elastic bodies. Equations of motion for an elastic medium. Energy. Boundary conditions. Homogeneous deformation. Sound waves in an elastic medium.

Part II

Electrodynamics

Introduction. The electromagnetic field as a form of matter.

History of the doctrine of electricity and magnetism. Maxwell's theory. Einstein's theory of relativity.

The principle of relativity. Velocity of propagation of interactions. Interval invariance. The Lorentz transformation. Proper time. Addition of velocities. Critique of the idealist interpretation of the relativity of distances and time intervals. Four-dimensional vectors and tensors. Four-dimensional velocity and acceleration.

Relativistic mechanics of a free particle. The principle of least action. Lagrangian function. Energy and pulse. Moment. Mass defect. Collision of particles. Critique of the idealistic interpretations of the connexion between energy and mass.

Small charge in an electromagnetic field. Field potentials. Equations of motion. Motion of a charge in uniform field. Field tensor, gradient invariance. Field invariants. Lorentz transformation for a field.

Maxwell's equations. Law of electromagnetic inductance. Solenoidal character of a magnetic field. Law of total current. Displacement current. Maxwell's equations. Four-dimensional vector of current density and its transformation. Four-dimensional form of Maxwell's equations. Lagrangian function for a field. Energy-pulse tensor. Law of the conservation of energy for a field and particles. Vector of energy flux.

Electrostatics and magnetostatics 'in vacuo'. Coulomb's law. Charge energy. Dipole moment. System of charges in an external field. Permanent magnetic fields. Magnetic moments. Larmor's theorem.

Electromagnetic waves. The wave equation. Plane waves. Monochromatic plane waves. The Doppler effect. Polarization. Natural oscillations of a cavity.

Field of moving charges and radiation. Vector potential. Dipole radiation. Radiation of a rapidly moving charge. Bremsstrahlung. Instability of the classical atom. Natural width. Width of radiation line due to collisions.

Equations of electrodynamics in material media. Averaging of field equations. Field and induction vectors. Polarization and magnetization. Work during the variation of a field. Law of the conservation of energy. Connexion between field and induction vectors. Boundary conditions at the interface between two media.

Electrostatics in material media. Dielectrics and conductors. Basic equations of electrostatics. Dielectric sphere in an homogeneous field. Capacitors. Field energy. Polar and non-polar dielectrics. Dielectric constant of polar dielectrics.

Direct current. Constant field in conductors. Ohm's law. Kirchhoff's rule. Joule heating. Electronic conductors. Electronic conductivity of metal. Principle of superconductivity. Ionic conductivity. Principle of semiconductors. Contact potential difference. Thermo-electricity.

Permanent magnetic field in magnetics. Basic equations. Magnetic susceptibility. Field energy. Energy of a current in a magnetic field. Coefficients of inductance. Paramagnetic susceptibility of a gas. Diamagnetic susceptibility of a gas. Phenomenological theory of ferromagnetism. Principle of gyromagnetism.

Alternating currents. Quasi-stationary conditions. Inductance and capacitance in a sinusoidal current. Resonance. Oscillations in a circuit.

Electromagnetic waves in media. Basic equations. Plane monochromatic waves in an homogeneous medium without losses. Plane waves in a medium with losses. The skin effect. Reflexion and refraction of waves at an interface. Index of refraction for a model of an oscillator. Normal and anomalous dispersions. Phase and group velocity. Principle of waves in wave guides and in resonators. Approximation of geometric optics.

Part III

Statistical physics

Introduction. Subject-matter and method of statistical physics. Connexion between statistical and phenomenological thermodynamics. History of thermodynamics and statistical physics. Elements of probability theory.

Basic propositions of statistical physics. Phase space and microscopic description of a macroscopic system. Theorem of the conservation of phase volumes. Macroscopic quantities as phase averages. Distribution function. Equilibrium. Microcanonical distribution. Quasi-independent subsystems. Gibbsian distribution. Temperature.

Ideal gas. Boltzmann distribution. Maxwellian distribution. Ideal gas in an external field. Barometrical formula.

Thermodynamic quantities and thermodynamic ratios. Thermodynamic quantities as mean values of microscopic quantities. Quasi-static processes. Internal energy of a system. Heat and work. Pressure. First law of thermodynamics. Functions of state and functions of process. Statistical weight of a state. Entropy. Adiabatic process. Thermal capacity in various processes. Thermodynamic magnitudes for states of inequilibrium.

Increase of entropy. Various formulations of the second law of thermodynamics. Critique of the contention that the 'thermal death' of the universe is inevitable.

Thermodynamic consequences of the law of increase of entropy. Condition of equilibrium of a closed system.

Thermodynamic potential and thermodynamic identity. Equations of equilibrium of open systems. Thermodynamic identities for irreversible processes. Approximation to state of equilibrium.

Calculation of derivatives from thermodynamic magnitudes. Connexion between thermal capacities. Thermodynamic temperature scale.

Thermodynamic inequalities and conditions of stability. Stable and labile states.

Calculation of thermodynamic potentials. Statistical integral. Calculation of free energy.

Thermodynamic potentials of an ideal gas. Law of equidistribution. Equation of state of ideal gases. Non-ideal gases. Van der Waals' equation. Joule-Thomson effect and the liquefaction of gases.

312

Free energy and thermal capacity of crystals at high temperatures. Crystal lattice oscillations.

Elements of statistical theory of polymers. Deformation of polymers. Properties of high-plasticity polymers.

Thermodynamics of a substance in an electromagnetic field. Principal thermodynamic ratios for a system of bodies in a field. Striction. Thermal effect of polarization. Magnetic cooling.

Systems with a variable number of particles. Dependence of thermodynamic quantities on number of particles. Chemical potential. Equilibrium of a body in an external field. Gibbsian distribution for a system with a variable number of particles.

Phase equilibrium and transitions. Condition of phase equilibrium. Heat of change. Equilibrium curves. Clausius-Clapeyron equation. Dependence of pressure of unsaturated vapours on temperature. Critical point. Principle of Landau's theories of second order phase change.

Multicomponent systems. Gibbs' rule and its consequences. Mixture of ideal gases. Weak solutions.

Condition of chemical equilibrium. Law of mass action. Temperature of reaction.

Surface effects. Surface tension. Laplace's formula. Pressure of saturated vapours above a curved surface. Adsorption. Contact angle.

Fluctuation theory. Semithermodynamic theory of fluctuation. Gaussian distribution. Fluctuation of principal thermodynamic quantities (temperature, volume, density).

Brownian movement as a fluctuation process. Mean square deviation of a Brownian particle.

Quantum statistics. Gibbsian distribution. Entropy. Nernst theorem. Bose and Fermi distribution. Thermal capacity of solids at low temperatures. Thermal radiation. Fermi's degenerate gas. Electron gas in a metal. Principle of the theory of solids.

Elements of statistical kinetics. Collision of gas particles with a wall. Collision of particles with one another. Length of free path. Probability of free path. Relaxation time.

Simplest form of kinetic equation (with relaxation term). Calculation of particle flow and energy flow. Electric and thermal conductivity of gases (elementary theory).

Boltzmann's kinetic equation. Principle of detailed balancing. Collision integral. Proof of the H theorem for an ideal gas, using the kinetic equation.

Einstein-Fokker equation.

Part IV

Quantum mechanics

Introduction. Basic experimental data leading to the invention of quantum mechanics. Origin and development of quantum mechanics.

Basic propositions of quantum mechanics. Formulation of the problems of quantum mechanics. Wave function. Principle of superposition. Eigenvalues and eigen-functions. Mean values of physical quantities. Operators and their properties. Conditions for simultaneous determinacy of physical quantities. Indeterminacy ratio. Critique of idealist interpretations of the indeterminacy ratio. Transition to classical mechanics.

Variation of state and physical quantities with time. The wave equation. Derivatives of physical quantities with respect to time. Integrals of motion. Energy. Momentum. Moment. Parity. The Schrödinger time-dependent equation. Probability density and flow.

Stationary states. The stationary state wave function. Schrödinger's equation for stationary states. Free motion of a particle. States with definite momentum. Potential wells. The tunnel effect. The linear oscillator.

Motion in a field of central symmetry. General properties of the motion of a particle in a field of central symmetry. Equation for the radial wave function. Motion in a coulomb field. The hydrogen atom. Orbital magnetic moment.

Representation theory. Various representations of state and physical magnitudes. Matrices. Pulse and energy representations. Finding the proper and mean values of physical quantities by the matrix method. Possible values of a moment. The oscillator.

Spin. Spin moment. Wave functions of particles with spin. Pauli matrices. Total spin. Total momentum.

314

Appendixes

Particles in magnetic fields. The wave equation for a particle without spin in a magnetic field. Spin magnetic moment. Pauli's equation for an electron in a magnetic field. Current density in a magnetic field. Motion of an electron in an homogeneous magnetic field.

Systems consisting of equal particles. Identity of similar particles. Symmetrical and antisymmetrical states. Bose and Fermi particles. Wave functions of equal-particle systems. The Pauli exclusion principle. The atom. Mendeleev's periodic table of elements. Exchange interaction.

Perturbation theory. Variation of stationary states under the influence of perturbation. Primary and secondary correction to energy values. Anharmonic oscillator. The Stark effect. The Zeeman effect. Fine and hyperfine structure of atomic levels. Transition between stationary states under the influence of perturbation. Probability of transition under the influence of periodic and constant perturbation. Transitions in continuous spectrum.

The diatomic molecule. Separation of nuclear from electron motion. Electronic states. Chemical forces. Oscillatory and rotary nuclear motion. Orthohydrogen and parahydrogen. Predissociation.

Collision theory. Differential scattering cross-section. The Born approximation. General theory of elastic scattering. Elastic scattering of slow particles. Inelastic scattering.

Electromagnetic field and electron radiation. Quantization of an electromagnetic field. The photon. State of a photon of definite moment and polarization. Moment of a photon. Interaction of an electron with an electromagnetic field. Dipole radiation. Conservation of moment and selection rules. Conservation of parity. Intensity of radiation.

Relativistic electron. Lorentz transformations and transformation of the wave function. Dirac matrices. The Dirac equation. Charge and current density. Spin. Free electron. Negative energy state and positrons. The hydrogen atom.

315

Specimen list of special-subject courses available at university faculties of physics in the U.S.S.R.

Theoretical physics

Special course on higher mathematics. Integral equations. Mathematical methods of theoretical physics. Solid-state theory. Nuclear and fundamental particle theory. Quantum statistics theory. Quantum electrodynamics. Gravitational field theory. Special seminar. Quantum chemistry.

Low temperature physics

Low temperature measurement techniques. Properties of matter at low temperatures. Special courses on low temperature physics. Special seminar.

Molecular physics

Kinetic principles of the condensed medium theory. Combustion and explosion physics. Gas dynamics. Molecular structure. Structure of fluids and high polymers. Quantum theory of molecular forces. Acoustic methods of investigation in molecular physics. Special seminar.

Optics and spectroscopy

Applied optics. Electromagnetic theory of light. The theory of radiation. Luminescence. Theoretical optics. Atomic spectroscopy. Molecular spectroscopy. The physics of gas discharge. Physical optics. Special seminar. Supplementary aspects of nuclear physics. Electronics. Radiospectroscopy.

X-ray physics and the physics of metals

X-ray physics. X-ray analysis. Solid-state physics. X-ray of metals. Technology of metals. Metallurgical science. Electron theory of metals. Physics of metals. Electronography. Special seminar. Physical chemistry.

Magnetism

Alternating currents. Electrical and magnetic measurements. Ferromagnetism. Physical-chemical analysis. Principles of magnetic analysis. Quantum theory of magnetism. Quantum theory of metals. Magnetic resonance and magnetic relaxation. Special seminar.

Solid-state physics

The physics of metals. The physics of semiconductors. The physics of dielectrics. Crystal physics. Crystallography. Metallography. Special seminar. Optics and spectroscopy of solids.

Physics of semiconductors

Methods of measuring the electrical, magnetic and optical properties of matter. Crystal physics. Crystal chemistry. Physics of metals. Semiconductor electronics and semiconductor instruments. Cathode physics. X-ray analysis. Principles of physical-chemical analysis. Technology of semiconductors and special alloys. Special parts of solid-state theory. Special seminar.

Electro-physics

Vacuum physics and techniques. Electron emission. Electronic semiconductors. Electron optics.

Nuclear physics

Nuclear electronics. Physics of the atomic nucleus. Experimental methods of nuclear physics. Physics of radioactive isotopes. Cosmic ray physics. Physics of fundamental particles. Neutron physics. Special seminar. Radiochemistry.

Radiophysics

Oscillation theory. VHF electrodynamics. VHF electronics. Principles of pulse technology. Special parts of electrodynamics. Special radio measurements. Radiation and propagation of radio waves. Non-linear systems. Special problems of oscillation. Special aspects of information theory. Semiconductor circuits. Special seminar.

Electronics

Oscillation theory. VHF electrodynamics. VHF electronics. Electronic and ionic instruments. Oscillatory circuits in VHF electronics. Electronic circuits. Calculation and construction of powerful electronic apparatuses. Technology of semiconductor instruments. Calculation and construction of instruments; calculation and construction of wideband VHF generators. Modern problems in electron optics. Physics of gas discharge. Electron emission and cathode physics. Formation and study of electron fluxes. Special seminar.

High-polymer physics

Selected aspects of organic chemistry. Methods of physical-chemical research. Chemical physics. Physics of high-polymer compounds. Thermodynamics of irreversible processes. Chain reaction theory. High-polymer statistical thermodynamics. Kinetics and mechanism of polymerization processes. Automation and control methods. Special seminar.

Physics of the atmosphere

Methods of investigating the atmosphere. Dynamic meteorology. Synoptic meteorology. Actinometry. Atmospheric optics. Atmospheric electricity. Physics of the upper atmosphere. Thermodynamics and dynamics of the atmosphere. Theory of turbulence. Special seminar.

Geophysics

Physics of the Earth. Geology. Applied geophysics. Terrestrial magnetism. Wave seismics. Radiometry. Seismology and seismometry. Hydromechanics. Sea temperatures. Marine optics. Marine acoustics. Marine dynamics. Special seminar.

List of laboratory exercises in practical physics at the University of Moscow

Part I

Mechanics

Study of verniers.
Study of the laws of fall on an Atwood machine.
Determining gravitational acceleration by means of a pendulum.
Precision weighing.
Determining the density of solids with a pycnometer and by hydrostatic weighing.
Determining the density of liquids with a pycnometer and by hydrostatic weighing.
Determination of elastic modulus from extension and bending.
Determining shear modulus from torsion.
Determining the moment of inertia and verifying the theorem of the translation of axes of moments of inertia by the torsional oscillation method.
Determining the coefficient of recovery and the time of impact of elastic spheres.
Study of resonance effects on a torsion pendulum.
Study of oscillations of bound systems.
Investigation of natural vibrations of a string by the resonance method.
Study of a gyroscope.
Verifying the law of conservation of momentum.
The stroboscope.
Determining the speed of sound and Young's modulus in solids.
Motion of bodies of variable mass (rocket).
Measuring the flight velocity of a bullet with a ballistic pendulum.

Studying the natural vibrations of a concentrated system.
Motion of Maxwell's pendulum.
Motion of the centre of mass.
Torsional ballistic pendulum.
Determining the speed of sound by the Kundt method.
Study of the laws of stationary flow of liquids in tubes.

Part II

Molecular physics and heat

Measuring the heat of vaporization of liquid nitrogen.
Determining the ratio of specific thermal capacities of gases.
Determining the thermal capacity of metals by the cooling method.
Determining the coefficients of thermal conductivity of metals.
Determining atmospheric humidity.
Determining the mechanical equivalent of heat.
Producing and measuring a high vacuum.
Determining the coefficient of surface tension from the height to which the liquid rises in a capillary tube.
Determining the coefficient of surface tension by means of an horizontal capillary.
Studying the dependence of the coefficient of surface tension of a solution on its concentration and temperature by the method of maximum pressure in bubbles.
Determining the coefficient of internal friction of liquids with the capillary viscosimeter.
Determining the coefficient of internal friction of liquids by the Stokes method.
Studying Brownian movement of a gas bubble.
Determining the coefficient of surface tension by the wave method.
Determining the coefficient of thermal conductivity of insulators.
Making and calibrating thermocouples.
Studying the isothermal compression and expansion of water vapours.
Determining the coefficient of internal friction of viscous media with the Volarovich rotation viscosimeter.
Determining the speed of sound in gases and the ratio of specific thermal capacities by the standing-wave method.
Determining surface tension over a large temperature range.
Determining critical temperature.
Determining the coefficient of thermal conductivity of gases.

320

Measuring the average length of free path of a metal molecule in a
vacuum.
Determining the coefficient of heat emission in natural convection.
Determining Avagadro's number.
Familiarization with statistical laws on mechanical models.

Part III

Electricity and magnetism

Studying an electrostatic field by the electrolytic-bath method.
Measuring resistances with a D.C. bridge.
Studying the dependence of resistance on temperature in metals.
Studying the dependence of resistance on temperature in an electrolyte.
Measuring e.m.f. by the compensation method.
Studying the operation of an electron valve.
Studying the operation of multi-electrode radio valves and observing
secondary emission.
Determining electrochemical equivalents and calibrating an ammeter
with the aid of a voltmeter.
Studying a galvanometer in a magneto-electrical system.
Determining the capacitance of a capacitor by means of a ballistic
galvanometer.
Investigating induction in iron by the ballistic method.
Determining the magnetic field intensity of a solenoid at its axis.
Studying the influence of the geometrical shape of the field on the mag-
netic susceptibility and hysteresis loop of a ferro-magnetic.
Studying a D.C. generator and motor.
Measuring the capacitance of a capacitor, using a bridge circuit.
Measuring capacitance by the bridge method, allowing for the influence
of leakage in the capacitor.
Measuring the coefficient of self-induction of coils with the aid of a
bridge circuit.
Determining inductance by the bridge method, using constant capaci-
tance.
Measuring the coefficient of self-induction, measuring capacitance and
verifying Ohm's law for A.C. current.
Measuring the power of A.C. current and phase shift between current
and voltage.
Studying the operation of contact rectifiers.
Studying the oscillatory discharge of a capacitor, using a ballistic gal-
vanometer and pendulum interrupter.

321

Familiarization with the operation of a very simple valve oscillator and using the approximate-resonance method to measure inductance and capacitance.

Studying voltage resonance and using it to measure the parameters of an oscillatory circuit.

Studying current resonance in an oscillatory circuit and using it to determine the Q factor.

Studying the operation of a cathode oscillograph.

Studying the characteristic of a low-frequency resistance-coupled amplifier.

Determining the charge to mass ratio of an electron by the magneton method.

Determining elementary charge by measuring the rate of displacement of charged particles in a capacitor field. Millikan's experiment.

Investigating damped oscillations generated by means of a multivibrator in a circuit containing self-capacity and resistance and studying a multivibrator.

A ferroresonance voltage stabilizer.

The magneto-electrical method of measuring the magnetization curve of an hysteresis loop and curie point.

Studying the operation of crystal diodes and triodes.

Studying a vacuum diode and determining the specific charge of an electron.

Studying the charging and discharging of a capacitor.

Studying the operation of a thyratron.

Calibrating an electrostatic voltmeter with an absolute electrometer.

Determining the ratio of thermal to electrical conductivity. The Wiedemann-Franz law.

Electromagnetic waves in two parallel wires. Lecher system.

Measuring concentration and mobility of charge carriers in semi-conductors.

Determining the work of an electron yield by compensating the filament cooling.

Harmonic analysis.

The electron microscope.

Diffraction of X-rays on mono- and polycrystals.

Part IV

Optics

Determining the luminosity and luminous efficiency of an incandescent lamp.

322

Determining the principal focal length of collecting and diffusing lenses.
Study of lens errors.
Determining the magnification of a telescope and a microscope.
Determining the refractive index, the dispersion and the resolving power of the glass prism of a spectrometer.
Determining the refractive index of liquids and solids with a refractometer.
Determining the refractive index of liquids and solids with an R-23 refractometer.
Determining the diffusion coefficient by the optical method.
Determining the length of a light wave with double lens and biprism.
Determining the radius of curvature of a lens and the length of a light wave with a Newton ring.
Study of a diffraction grating and determining the length of a light wave.
Study of radiation spectra of vapours and gases; spectral analysis and calibration of a spectroscope.
Investigating the absorption spectra of solutions with a photometer.
Measuring the absorption of light by solid and fluid filters with a spectrophotometer.
Study of the principal effects of polarization of light in parallel beams.
Study of crystal optic effects with a polarizing microscope.
Study of circular polarization.
Study of the principal laws of the external photoelectric effect.
Study of light diffraction on circular and straight apertures and discs.
Study of a telescope.
Measuring high temperatures with a disappearing-filament optical pyrometer.
Spectral photometry.
Study of the Zeeman effect.
Spectroscopic investigation of chromatic polarization effects.
Study of the spectrograph and measurement of the wave lengths of spectral lines.
Study of diffraction in parallel beams from an individual slit and on simple diffraction gratings.
Investigation of complex optical systems.
Study of diffraction effects in the formation of an optic image.
Production and investigation of polarized light.
Investigation of dispersion by the Rozhdestvensky hook method.
Photometry of a bright-line spectrum with a stylometer and its application in spectral analysis of steel.
Study of the serial patterns in the hydrogen spectrum.
Diffraction of light on ultrasonic waves.

Study of photo multipliers.

Measurement of the refractive indices of gases with an interferometer.

Interferometer study of the refractive index to pressure ratio of a gas.

Study of the principal light interference effects with a Michelson interferometer.

The zone plate.

Study of the magnetic rotation of a plane of polarization.

Measuring the refractive index of solids with a crystal refractometer.

Part V

Photography

Technique of reproducing a photograph and processing the negative.

Photographing a three-dimensional object and the technique of processing the negative.

Studying the special properties of photographic materials.

Constructing the characteristic curves of a photolayer.

Technique of microphotography in reflected light.

Technique of microphotography in direct light.

Technique of contact printing and processing the positive.

Technique of projection printing and processing the positive.

III E1   Syllabuses of the Manchester course for honours physics B.Sc.

First year

Classical mechanics (44 hours)
Vibrations and waves (25 hours)
Relativity (11 hours)
Electricity and magnetism (44 hours)
Properties of matter (40 hours)
Pure mathematics (65 hours)

Second year

Electricity and magnetism (44 hours)

Experimental basis of Maxwell's equations, expressed in vector calculus.
Electrostatics and magnetostatics: Laplace's and Poisson's equations, images.
Energy and momentum densities of static and electromagnetic fields. Poynting's vector.
Forces on charges and currents in fields.
Solutions of Maxwell's equations: plane waves in isotropic dielectrics and conductors, skin effect, relaxation time.
Reflection and refraction of plane waves: boundary conditions, dielectric boundary, total internal reflection, inhomogeneous plane waves, conductors at normal incidence.
Transmission lines: principal wave on uniform transmission line, voltage and current on line, lumped impedance treatment of lines, lossy lines, matching, circle diagram.

Wave guides: TEM, TE, TM modes, cut-off frequency, cavity resonators, microwave oscillators.

Generation of waves: vector and scalar potentials, retarded potentials, harmonic dipole, radiation resistance, half-wave dipole, arrays of aerials, illuminated aperture, polar diagrams and power gains, receiving aerials.

Black-body radiation: radiation pressure and momentum, Stefan's law, electromagnetic spectrum of white light, random e.m.f. in resistor and relation to black-body radiation.

Interaction of radiation with matter: Lorentz model of dielectric, Lorentz expression, normal and anomalous dispersion, propagation in an ionized gas, ionosphere, scattering of radiation—Rayleigh, Thomson, resonance, coherence, Cerenkov effect.

Relativity: magnetic phenomena as relativistic effects. Lorentz force as illustration (elementary treatment without use of 4-vectors).

Quantum mechanics (26 hours)

Electronics (22 hours)

Atomic physics (27 hours)

Discreteness of charge and mass

Atomicity of charge: measurement of e and e/m.

Mass spectra: atomic masses, isotopes.

Wave-particle dualism for light and matter: the relations $E = h\nu$ and $p = hk$

Photo-electric effect: to give $E = h\nu$ dependence on frequency and intensity.

Velocity of photo-electrons, etc., determination of h.

Production of X-rays (considered as inverse of photo-electric effect): determination of h from X-ray spectra.

Wave nature of light and matter; diffraction of light, electron diffraction: to give $p = hk$.

Uncertainty principle as consequence of wave nature.

Uncertainty principle illustrated for wave packets.

Relativistic connexion of E with p and of ν with k. Hence:

(a) $E = h\nu$ implies $p = hk$.

(b) uncertainty principle for (x, p) implies that for (E, t).

326

Illustration of wave-particle dualism and of interaction of radiation
with matter for:
  Compton scattering
  pair creation and annihilation
  Bremsstrahlung
  energy and Z-dependence for these processes.

Atomic structure, energy levels, spectra
  Rutherford atom: general.
    Alpha-particle scattering (classical).
  Standing waves on a string or circle, implying 'quantization'.
  H-atom, stationary states:
    quantum numbers j, l, m: allowed values.
    energy levels, degeneracy, removal of degeneracy.
  Interpretation of quantum numbers:
    n: size of 'orbit'
    l: angular momentum $hk(l + 1)^{\frac{1}{2}}$
    m: z-component of A.M.

Spectral lines $E_n - E_m = h\nu$ and selection rules (mention simplicity
due to $kR \ll 1$):
$\Delta l = \pm 1 \quad \Delta m = 0, \pm 1$
Spectral series in hydrogen.

Spin: postulate A.M. $h/2$ and magnetic moment.
Zeeman effect: orbital, spin.
Classical discussion (including polarization).

Other evidence for electron spin: Na D-lines.
  Mention spin-orbit coupling ($=$ fine structure effects): get order of
  magnitude of splitting classically.

Many-electron atoms
  Pauli principle.
  Periodic table. Effect of screening and of centrifugal barrier on
  order of levels; closed shells (zero A.M. and M.M.); valency electrons (alkali series, etc.).

Measurements of atomic and nuclear magnetic moments: microwave
  method; atomic beam method.

Line width: various effects.

Optics (30 hours)

Waves in optical systems. Huyghens' principle. Accuracy of optical surfaces. Superposition of harmonic disturbances. Conditions for observing interference. Division of amplitude and of wavefront.

Michelson and Fizeau interferometers. Fringe geometry. Fringe profile with two-beam and multiple beam interference.

Fraunhofer diffraction, single, double, and multiple slits. General aperture function and Fraunhofer pattern as its Fourier transform.

Two dimensional screens—circular aperture. Regular and random multiple apertures. The microscopic image. Phase contrast.

Fresnel diffraction and Cornu spiral.

Coherence considerations in two-beam interferometers, source homogeneity and finite size of source.

Interference in spectroscopy, the diffraction grating. The Fabry Perot interferometer as a scanning and photographic instrument.

Interference in metrology, application of the Fabry Perot principle to wavelength determination and surface topography.

Special applications of the Michelson interferometers.

Film optics, dielectric layers, reflecting and antireflecting films; interference filters.

Polarization of light by scattering and reflection. Polarized light in simple crystals.

Thermodynamics (20 hours)

Thermodynamics concerned with relations between macroscopic quantities. Thermodynamic equilibrium. Zeroth law. Empirical temperature. Perfect gas temperature. Joule's experiments. Heat as form of energy. First law. Calculation of work terms (including magnetic energies). Reversible and irreversible processes. Transformation of heat into work. Carnot cycle. Second Law (Kelvin and Clausius formulations). Introduction of entropy. Thermodynamic temperature. $dU = TdS - pdV$. Perfect differentials. Temperature as integrating factor for heat. $dS \geqq 0$ for isolated system. Entropy and disorder. $d(U - T_0 S) = p_0 V) \geqq 0$ for any system. Helmholtz and Gibbs free energies. Maxwell's relations. Manipulation of partial differentials.

Relations between specific heats. Adiabatic equation. Real gases. Joule and Joule-Thomson effects. Inversion. Enthalpy and Bernoulli's theorem. Liquefiers. Experimental facts of radiation and thermodynamic properties. Stefan and Wien displacement laws. Gibbs-Helmholtz equation (reversible cell, surface tension, etc.). Phase equilibrium. Clausius-Clapeyron equation. Second order and other phase changes.

Pure mathematics (48 hours)

Vector spaces

Idea of a vector space. Examples: sets of numbers, functions. Linear combinations. Linear independence. Dimension: Linear basis, representation of arbitrary vector in n-dimensional space in component form. Scalar product: Schwarz inequality. Orthogonality and normalization. Schmidt orthogonalization process. Normal orthogonal basis; coefficients as scalar products. Completeness.

Matrix theory

Change of basis: corresponding linear transformation in the component representation. Matrix of coefficients of transformation. Multiplication of matrices and vectors and of matrices and matrices.

Unit matrix, reciprocal matrix.

Linear transformation as a mapping.

Similarity transformations.

Transformation from one normal orthogonal basis to another. Matrix elements as scalar products. Unitary property. Real orthogonal transformations as special case of unitary transformations. Adjoint operator and its matrix. Self-adjoint operator.

Linear equations and eigen-value problem

For n linear equations in n unknowns, solution exists and is unique for any right-hand side if columns are linearly independent.

Systematic elimination technique.

Determinants: cofactors. Cramer's rule.

Determinantal condition for homogeneous system to have non-initial solution.

Eigen-value problem. Secular equation. Reality of eigen-functions of self-adjoint operator.

Diagonal form by unitary transformation.

Expansion theorem.

Partial differential equations and Fourier analysis

A descriptive account of the main types of partial differential equation arising in physics: Laplace's equation, wave equation, diffusion equation.

Types of boundary condition needed for unique solution in the different cases. (No proofs to be attempted.)

Method of solution by separation of variables. Fourier series solutions.

Fourier series from the function-space point of view: expansion of a function in terms of a complete set.
Limiting case as period tends to infinity.
Fourier integral, Fourier transforms.

Ordinary differential equation with non-constant coefficients
How they arise from separation of variables in partial differential equations. Series solution in second-order case. Examples.

Spherical harmonics
Legendre polynomials and associated Legendre polynomials and their applications to Laplace's equation and the wave equation.

Cylindrical harmonics
Bessel functions of order n and $n + \frac{1}{2}$ and of first, second and third kinds, and their applications to Laplace's equation and the wave equation. Asymptotic results must be taught, if necessary without proof.

Third year

Quantum mechanics (35 hours)

Orthogonality and completeness of energy eigenfunctions, expansion theorem; degeneracy. Harmonic oscillator. H-atom: separation into radial and angle parts. Solution of radial equation. Solution of angular equation. One-dimensional potential barrier. One- and three-dimensional square-wells of finite depth.

Interpretation of quantum mechanics: (a) One observable: eigenstates and eigenvalues, dispersion. (b) commuting observables: compatibility, etc., illustrations. (c) Non-commuting observables: uncertainty principle and complementarity: illustrations. Matrix form of Q.M.—as particular representation of Schrödinger theory. Angular momentum. Spin. Addition of angular momentum. Many-particle systems: A.M., exclusion principle. Stationary perturbation theory: 1st order (including degeneracy), 2nd order; applications. Variational methods. Time-dependent perturbation theory: transition probabilities (also for radiation). Symmetry, constants of motion, selection rules (illustrate from atomic and for nuclear spectroscopy and reactions). Scattering theory. Cross-section. Born approximation (time-dependent treatment): Coulomb scattering. Phase-shift analysis (time permitting). Examples (e.g. hard sphere).

Nuclear physics (35 hours)

Masses and binding energies. Scattering and size. Orders of magnitude. Radioactivity. Stopping power. Shape of β-spectrum. Nuclear reactions (qualitative). Electrostatic generators, cyclotrons. Detectors. Stable mass valley, mass formula, liquid drop. Irregularities—symmetries, pairing, magic numbers. Spontaneous fission. Measurement of angular momentum, magnetic moment, quadruple moment. Systematics of spin and magnetic moment. Nature of models. Shell model as antithesis of liquid drop model. Mass irregularities, abundances, etc. Schmidt model (parity). Quadruple moment systematics. Rainwater model. Rotational spectra. Spectra near closed shells. Nilsson model. Reactions giving neutrons. Induced fission. Reactors (qualitative). Slow neutron reactions and methods of measuring neutron energies. Compound nucleus. Fast neutron reactions—radii. Charged particle reactions—Coulomb barrier. α-decay. Breit-Wigner formula (qualitative). Direct reactions—stripping. β and γ selection rules. Range and magnitude of nuclear forces. B.E. of D, H^3, He^3, He^4 (v.qual.). Saturation. Two-body scattering and the forces. Charge symmetry and charge independence. Isotopic spin formalism. Coulomb energies. Yukawa theory—pions. Pion-nucleon scattering.

Solid-state physics (42 hours)

Study of structure of solid state. Point lattice. Atomic scattering factor. Geometric structure factor. X-rays. Electrons. Neutrons.

Imperfections in solids: liquids. Dislocations. Crystal growth. Yield strength. F-centres. Photographic process. Liquids.

Vibration spectra: thermal conduction. Vibration spectra. Significance of Debye 0. Anharmonicity. Umklapp process.

Magnetic and dielectric materials. Paramagnetic resonance and relaxation. Theory of para, ferro-, and antiferromagnetism. Domains. Spin waves. Dielectric properties.

Electrons in solids. Passage of waves through periodic structures. Properties of Fermi gas. Energy bands in crystals. Elementary band theory of metals, semi-conductors and insulators. Applications of semi-conductors including transistors.

Experimental methods (36 hours)

Principles of experiment. Systematic errors and their detection. Drift and noise. Elementary ideas of information theory.

Electronics. Feedback circuits including (mathematically) complex feedback paths—Miller integrator, etc. Response of circuits to pulses and steps. Shaping circuits. Two state circuits—multivibrator and derived circuits. Transistors. Millimicrosecond methods.

Electrical measurements, galvanometers, electrometers, D.C. amplifiers.

Optical instruments, intensity and resolution. Photographic and photoelectric photometry.

Radiation detection and their limitations.

Systems for measuring nuclear rays.

Statistical mechanics (24 hours)

Purpose of statistical mechanics and relation to thermodynamics. Meaning of words system, assembly, ensemble. Based on quantum mechanics (discrete energy levels). Principle of equal *a priori* probability. Microcanonical assembly. Method of maximum probability. Sharpness of maximum. Distribution function for distinguishable (localized) systems. Identification of temperature and entropy. Nernst's heat theorem. Assembly of localized oscillators. Partition function. Magnetic dipoles in S state. Canonical ensemble. More general identification of temperature and entropy. Equivalence to micro-canonical assembly. Deviations from most probable distribution. Classical statistical mechanics. Phase space. Freely falling particles. Liouville's theorem. Ergodic hypothesis phase space for simple harmonic oscillator. Size of cells in phase space. Equivalence in limit to equal *a priori* probability. Waves in a box approach equivalent to cells in phase space. The 'classical' perfect gas. Identification of Boltzmann's constant. Equipartition of energy. Gibbs' paradox. Symmetry of wave functions. Exclusion principle. Indistinguishability considered properly. Bose-Einstein and Fermi-Dirac statistics. The classical limit. Application to electrons in metals. Vibration and rotation of gas molecules. Ortho- and para-hydrogen. Radiation (vacuum oscillators, Einstein's A and B coefficients, photons). Lattice specific heat of solids (Einstein theory, normal co-ordinates, Debye theory). Schottky anomalies. Co-operative effects. Bragg-Williams theory of order-disorder transitions. The classical imperfect gas. Virial expansion. Fluctuations. Einstein approach. Availability. Fluctuations of radiation. Irreversible processes. Onsager reciprocal relations. Thermoelectricity.

332

Third-year syllabuses in physics
for the Manchester ordinary degree
with physics as one subject

Nuclear Physics

(26 hours)

Properties of stable nuclei

Rutherford's experiment for existence of nucleus. Constituents of nuclei, discovery of neutron. Isotopes, isobars, isotones. Curve of stable nuclei, abundances, masses of nuclei and nucleons, binding energy, mass defect, binding energy per nucleon. Radii and density of nuclei. Nuclear forces, saturation, exchange, range, spin, hyperfine structure, magnetic moments, gyromagnetic ratios, nuclear magnetic resonance.

Nuclear reaction

Cross-section. Energetics, Q-values. Centre-of-mass calculations. Excited states and unstable nuclei. Compound nucleus, resonances, coulomb barrier. Types of reactions.

Nuclear models

Liquid drop model, semi-empirical binding energy formula. Shell model, magic numbers. Collective model, α-particle model.

Radioactivity

Disintegration constant. Curie. α-decay, natural series, Geiger-Nuttall Law, barrier penetrability. β-decay, general criteria for β–β^+ and K-capture. Neutrino postulate, C^{14} dating. Industrial, medical and chemical uses.

Interaction with matter

Range-energy relations for charged particles. Interaction of gamma-rays; photo-electric effect, Compton scattering, pair production.

Detectors

Photographic emulsions. Cloud chambers. Gas chambers. Scintillation counters. Semiconductor counters. Neutron detection.

Fission and fusion

Fission. Elementary theory of thermal reactors. Moderators. Criticality. Delayed neutrons. Production of radioactive isotopes. Breeder reactors. Fusion. Stars, thermonuclear bombs, thermonuclear reactors.

Particle accelerators

Ion sources. Direct voltage machines; Cockcroft-Walton and Van de Graaff. Cyclic machines; cyclotron, synchrocyclotron, synchrotron, betatron, electron synchrotron. Phase stability. Linear accelerators. Production of neutrons.

Cosmic rays

Telescopes, cloud chambers, photographic emulsions. Latitude and longitude effects. Production of mesons. Time variations.

Atomic physics

(26 hours)

Introduction. Avogadro's number.

Conduction of electricity in solids, liquids and gases. Faraday's constant. Measurement of ionic mobility and atomic excitation potentials. Gas discharges.

Deflection of charged particles in E and H e/m for particles. Charge on electron. Mass spectrographs.

Quantization of energy. Cavity radiation. Specific heats of solids.

Quanta. Photo-electric effect. Compton effect.

Nuclear atom. Scattering.

Atomic emission spectra. Stationary levels in atom. Bohr model of stationary levels in H-like atom. Correspondence principle.

Wave mechanical classification of H-like atomic stationary levels. Fine structure and electron spin. Magnetic moments and magnetic interactions. Anomalous and normal Zeeman effects. Landé g factor. Energy levels of more than one electron atom. $L - S$ and $j - j$ coupling.

334

Molecular spectra.
X-rays. Origin and properties. Absorption and emission spectra.
Diffraction of X-rays by crystals. Measurement of X-ray wavelengths.
X-ray detectors.
Diffraction of electrons by crystals. Matter as waves.

Solid state physics

(26 hours)

The elements of crystallography: symmetry; Millerian indices.
The study of crystalline material: diffraction of X-rays, electrons and
neutrons by single crystals and crystalline powders.
Crystal structures: metals, alloys, elements, inorganic compounds.
Free electron theory of metals: electron statistics, thermionic and photo-
electric emission.
Band theory of solids: metals, insulators, intrinsic semiconductors, im-
purities.
Application: semiconductors and transistors.
Perfect crystals: dielectric properties, magnetic properties.
Imperfect crystals: lattice vibrations, defects, luminescence, dislocations,
mechanical properties.
Summary and review of solid state physics.

Electromagnetism

(26 hours)

Introduction of vector notation. Electromagnetic induction. Maxwell's
equations—experimental basis.
Reflection and refraction of plane waves in isotropic media. Skin effect.
Electromagnetic machinery. A.C. and D.C. generator, induction motor
and transformer.
Transmission lines. Voltage and current on line. Lumped impedance,
lossy lines, and matching.
Waveguides. TEM, TE and TM modes, cut-off frequency, cavity reso-
nators. Generation of waves. Dipoles, aerials, radiation resistance,
polar diagrams.
Interaction of radiation and matter. Propagation in an ionized medium.
Ionosphere.

Experimental methods

(26 hours)

Mechanical design of apparatus. Vacuum technique. Electrical and magnetic measurements. Optical technique. Spectrometry of light and microwaves, X-rays, β-rays, masses. Nuclear counting. Electronics: amplifier D.C., A.C., pulse and wideband; feedback and filters; servo systems; power supplies and stabilization; counting circuits; electronic measuring instruments; transistors and circuits.

Physical optics and spectroscopy

(26 hours)

Entrance and exit pupils, photometry of optical instruments.
Theory of Fraunhofer diffraction, revision and extension.
Detectors of radiation: photocell, photomultiplier, solid state photocells, thermocouples and bolometers, the photoplate, the eye.
Sources of radiation and the width of spectral lines.
Theory and practice of prism and grating spectroscopes for visible, infra red, ultra-violet, resolution and luminosity.
Interferometers, the Fabry Perot as a high resolution instrument and as a scanning instrument. Interference filters. Examination of surfaces by interferometry.
The Michelson and Twyman Green interferometers.
Determination of wavelengths and metrological applications of interferometers.

Elementary quantum mechanics

(26 hours)

Wave equation in one dimension, vibrations of strings. Fourier series. Three dimensions. Separability. Initial and boundary problems. Eigenfunctions and Eigenvalues. Infinite medium. Fourier integral wave packet.
Quantum mechanics of free particle. De Broglie relations. Superposition. Schrödinger equation with and without time. Gaussian wave packet. Uncertainty principle with examples. Quantum mechanical state of a particle.
Quantum mechanics of particle in one-dimensional box. Stationary states

and energy eigenvalues. Superposition of states. Three-dimensional box.

Schrödinger equation with more general potential. One-dimensional harmonic oscillator. Wave functions. Eigenvalues and expectation values.

Two dimensional rotator with one degree of freedom. Qualitative treatment of atomic wave functions.

Tunnelling α decay.

Symmetries and conservation laws.

Translational and rotational invariants (in classical and quantum mechanics). Linear and angular momentum.

Centre-of-mass and relative variables. Simple deuteron problem.

Identical particles: symmetric and antisymmetric wave functions; qualitative treatment of a spin; exclusion principle; Bosons and Fermions.

Minimal course requirements in physics, mathematics, and chemistry at four institutions for a bachelor's degree with a physics major in the U.S.A.

University of California at Berkeley

Course	Subject	Credit in semester hours	1961/62 enrolment
First two years			
Physics 4A	General: mechanics, properties of matter, wave motion, sound (incl. lab.)	4	608
Physics 4B	General: electricity and magnetism (incl. lab.)	4	190
Physics 4C	General: heat, light, modern physics (incl. lab.)	4	413
Chemistry 1A, 1B	General chemistry (incl. lab.)	10	
Mathematics 1A, 1B[1]	Calculus and analytical geometry I	8	
Mathematics 2A, 2B[1]	Calculus II	8	
Last two years			
Physics 105A, 105B	Analytical mechanics	5	82, 102
Physics 108B	Physical optics	3	112
Physics 110A, 110B	Electricity and magnetism	6	81, 72
Physics 110C, 110D[2]	Advanced electrical and modern physics laboratory	4	12, 33
Physics 112[2]	Thermodynamics and kinetic theory	3	48

1. Students with superior high school preparation take mathematics 3A, 3B, 4A, 4B, which are more advanced courses.
2. Recommended and usually elected, but not required.

Course	Subject	Credit in semester hours	1961/62 enrolment
Physics 115	Introduction to quantum mechanics	3	96
Physics 121	Introduction to atomic physics	3	223
Mathematics 119[1]	Differential equations	3	
Mathematics 185[1]	Introduction to functions of a complex variable	3	
Physics H 197	Course in theoretical physics, required only of honours students	2	11

1. Recommended and usually elected, but not required.

Columbia University

Course	Subject	Credit in semester hours	1961/62 enrolment
First two years			
Physics C 1006	General: mechanics and heat	4	220
Physics C 1007	General: electricity and magnetism	3	255
Physics C 1008	General: light and atomic physics	3	227
Physics C 1009	General physics laboratory	1.5	235
Physics C 1010	General physics laboratory	1.5	190
Mathematics C 1105	Vectors and co-ordinate geometry	3	
Mathematics C 1106[1]	Calculus I	3	
Mathematics C 1205[1]	Calculus II	3	
Mathematics C 1206[1]	Calculus III	3	
Chemistry	6 semester hours	6	
Last two years			
Physics G 4003, 4004	Mechanics	6	72, 64
Physics G 4007, 4008	Electricity and magnetism	6	96, 74
Physics G 4009	Geometrical and physical optics	3	23
Physics G 4013	Thermodynamics	3	38
Physics W 3081, 3082	Intermediate laboratory work	4	16, 43
Physics G 4015	Atomic physics	3	64

1. Exceptionally well-qualified students take mathematics C 1108, 1207 1208, which are more advanced courses.

Course	Subject	Credit in semester hours	1961/62 enrolment
Physics G 4016	Elementary quantum mechanics	3	56
Physics C 3072	Seminar in current research problems	2	23
Mathematics W 3027	Differential equations	3	

Plus one additional course in mathematics for a total of 18 semester hours in mathematics. Usually the additional course is one in advanced calculus for science students.

Massachusetts Institute of Technology

Course	Subject	Credit in semester hours	1961/62 enrolment
First two years			
Physics 8.01	Physics (mechanics) (incl. lab.)	5	912
Physics 8.02	Physics (mechanics: heat and kinetic theory, waves) (incl. lab.)	5	837
Physics 8.031[1]	Physics (electromagnetism) (incl. lab.)	5	600
Physics 8.041[1]	Physics (electromagnetism, theory of light and physical optics) (incl. lab.)	5	508
Mathematics 18.01	Calculus	3	
Mathematics 18.02	Calculus	3	
Mathematics 18.03	Calculus	3	
Mathematics 18.04	Differential equations	3	
Chemistry 5.01, 5.02	General chemistry (incl. lab.)	10	
Last two years			
Physics 8.05, 8.06	Physics of atoms and molecules	8	219, 196
Physics 8.09T, 8.10T	Experimental atomic physics	5	152, 135
Physics 8.08	Electronics	4	152
Physics 8.711	Mechanics	4	166
Physics 8.11	Experimental physics and thesis	7	98

1. Physics 8.031 and 8.041 (to be followed by 8.05) are prescribed, but physics 8.03 (electricity and magnetism) and 8.04 (optics and atomic physics) are acceptable for students transferring into physics from another major.

Course	Subject	Credit in semester hours	1961/62 enrolment
Physics 8.72	Electromagnetic radiation	4	131
Physics 8.07	Statistical mechanics and thermodynamics	4	158
Electrical engineering 6.14	Electronic networks and devices	4	
Mathematics 18.05	Advanced calculus for engineers	3	
Plus one additional subject in mathematics		3	
Plus one additional subject in chemistry, chosen from organic, physical, and structural chemistry		3	
Other electronics		6	

Swarthmore College

Course	Subject	Credit in semester hours	1961/62 enrolment
First two years			
Physics 1	General: mechanics, kinetic theory, heat (incl. lab.)	4	100
Physics 2	General: electricity and magnetism, optics, introduction to quantum physics (incl. lab.)	4	100
Physics 11, 12	Mechanics and wave motion (incl. lab.)	8	22
Mathematics 3, 4[1]	First year mathematics (calculus and analytical geometry)	8	
Mathematics 11, 12	Calculus	8	
Chemistry 1, 2	General chemistry (incl. lab.)	8	
Last two years[2]			
Physics 102	Electricity and magnetism (incl. lab.)	4	18
Physics 112	Radiation and statistical physics (incl. lab.)	4	12
Physics 113	Quantum and nuclear physics (incl. lab.)	4	18
Mathematics 101, 102	Advanced calculus	8	

1. Students with superior preparation take mathematics 5, 6—an advanced course.
2. These courses are taken by *honours majors*. Course majors take, in place of these, physics 51 (atomic and nuclear physics), physics 52 (special topics), electrical engineering 53 (circuit theory), electrical engineering 56 (electromagnetic field theory), chemistry 61, 62 (physical chemistry), and mathematics 51, 52 (advanced analysis).

Example of schedule for one semester
for students in physics
(Columbia University)

Each student is informed of the textbook to be used by the instructor,
and receives a detailed schedule of the subjects to be studied (see following example).

Date	Section I[1]	Section II[1]	Subject	Reading[2]	Problems in chapters cited in previous column
September					
29	L	L	Charge and matter	26	4, 6, 10, 11, 12, 15
October					
2	L	L	Electric field	27	5, 6, 7, 8, 9, 11, 21, 22
4	L	L	Electric field		
6	R	L	—		
9	L	R	Gauss's law	28	1, 4, 5, 7, 8, 9, 16, 21
11	L	L	Gauss's law		
13	R	L	—		
16	L	R	Potential	29	5, 8, 10, 17, 23, 26
18	L	L	Potential		
20	R	L	—		
23	L	R	Capacitors	30	1, 3, 8, 9, 10, 12, 13
25	Question day on above subjects				
27	R	L	—		
30	L	R	Dielectrics		
31	L	R	—		
November					
1	L	L	Ohm's law	31	1, 4, 14, 15
3	R	L	—		

1. L = lecture; R = recitation.
2. Figures represent the chapter numbers in *Physics for Students of Science and Engineering*,
   Part II by D. Halliday and R. Resnick, published by John Wiley and Sons, New York, 1960.

Date	Section I	Section II	Subject	Reading	Numbers in chapters cited in previous column
November					
6	L	R	Circuits	32	1, 6, 7, 9, 11, 20, 22
8	L	L	Circuits		
10	R	L	—		
13	L	R	Magnetic field	33	1, 4, 8, 10, 13, 24
15	Question day on above subjects		Midterm		
17	R	L	—		
20	L	R	Magnetic field		
22	L	L	Ampère's law	34	1, 2, 4, 5, 6, 13
24	No classes. Thanksgiving holiday				
27	L	R	Ampère's law		22, 23 8, 9, 11, 13
29	L	L	Faraday's law	35	
December					
1	R	L	—		
4	L	R	Faraday's law		
6	L	L	Inductance, transients	36	2, 4, 6, 14, 15
8	R	L	—		
11	L	R	Ferromagnetism	37	3, 4
13	Question day on above subjects				
15	R	L	—		
18	L	R	Oscillations	38	1, 4, 11, 16
20	L	L	Resonance		
22	R	L	—		
January					
8	L	R	Maxwell's equations	39	7, 10, 12, 17
10	L	L	Electromagnetic waves		
12	R	L	—		
15	L	R	Wave motion		
17	L	L	Doppler effect		
19	R	L	—		

Laboratory experiments in general
physics at four institutions in the U.S.A.

Experiment	California	Columbia	Massachusetts Institute of Technology	Swarthmore
Mechanics				
Errors in measurement	×	×	×	×
Surface tension	×	—	—	×
Young's modulus	×	×	—	—
The principle of moments: statics	×	—	—	×
Centre of gravity and principle of moments	×	—	—	—
Newton's second law by Atwood machine	×	—	—	—
Centripetal force	×	—	—	—
Force of impact of a moving stream	×	—	—	—
Moment of inertia	×	×	—	—
Longitudinal waves in gases and solids	×	—	—	×
Standing waves in strings	×	×	—	×
Physical pendulum	×	—	—	—
Impact: colliding spheres on bifilar suspensions	—	×	—	—
Acceleration due to gravity	—	×	—	—
Conservation of momentum: colliding air pucks	—	—	×	—
Scattering of steel shot	—	—	×	—

344

Experiment	California	Columbia	Massachusetts Institute of Technology	Swarthmore
Damped forced harmonic motion	—	—	×	—
Comparison of masses by inertial cars	—	—	×	—
Torque and angular momentum	—	—	×	—
Centripetal force by air puck	—	—	×	—
Precession of motor-driven gyroscope	—	—	×	—
Characteristics of sound waves	—	—	×	—
Motion in a straight line	—	—	—	×
Equilibrium when forces are concurrent and coplanar	—	—	—	×
Newton's second law: accelerating cart on a track	—	—	—	×
Uniform motion on a rough inclined plane	—	—	—	×
Simple harmonic motion	—	—	—	×

Heat

Specific heat	×	—	—	—
Heat of fusion	×	—	—	—
Ideal gas laws	×	×	—	×
Mechanical equivalent of heat	×	—	—	—
Gamma of a gas	—	×	×	—
Effusion of gases	—	—	×	—

Electricity and magnetism

Equipotential lines and electric fields	×	×	—	—
Electrostatic force between parallel charged plates	×	—	×	—
The potentiometer	×	×	—	×
Resistance measurements; Wheatstone bridge	×	×	—	×
Moving coil galvanometer	×	×	×	—
Ballistic galvanometer	×	—	—	—
Construction of ammeter, voltmeter, and ohmmeter	—	×	—	—
Force on current in magnetic field	—	×	—	×

Experiment	California	Columbia	Massachusetts Institute of Technology	Swarthmore
Electrical transients. The oscilloscope	—	×	×	—
Magnetic field measurements by Gauss A and B experiments	×	—	—	—
Vacuum diode	×	—	—	—
Capacity bridge	×	—	—	—
L, C, and R in A.C. circuits	×	×	×	—
Vacuum triode; amplifier	×	×	—	×
Magnetization and hysteresis in iron	×	—	—	—
Resonance in A.C. circuits; transformer and wave filter	—	×	×	—
Wiring session and the use of meters	—	—	×	—
Determination of μ_0 and ε_0 in Maxwell's equations	—	—	×	—
Electrostatic deflection of electron beam	—	—	—	×
Magnetic deflection of electron beam	—	—	—	×

Electromagnetic radiation

Experiment	California	Columbia	Massachusetts Institute of Technology	Swarthmore
Interference and diffraction of light	—	—	—	×
Velocity of light by Foucault's rotating mirror	—	—	×	—
Interference, diffraction and grating spectrometer	—	—	×	—
Fresnel zones; prism spectrometer	—	—	×	—
Microwave optics: reflection, refraction, interference, polarization	—	×	×	—
Polarized light	×	—	×	—
Index of refraction	×	—	—	—
Lenses and lens combinations	×	×	—	×
Telescopes	×	—	—	×
Interference by Newton's rings	×	—	—	—
Spectra	×	×	—	—

Experiment	California	Columbia	Massachusetts Institute of Technology	Swarthmore
Atomic and nuclear physics				
h/e by photo-electric effect	×	×	×	—
Balmer series of hydrogen	×	—	—	×
e/m for the electron	—	×	×	—
Visual techniques in nuclear physics: cloud-chamber, bubble-chamber photographs	—	×	—	—
Absorption of beta and gamma rays	—	×	—	—
Rutherford scattering of alpha particles	—	—	×	—
Faraday's law of electrolysis and the mass of atoms	—	—	—	×
Millikan's oil droplet experiment	—	—	—	×

Example of examination in general
physics in the U.S.A. Massachusetts
Institute of Technology

1. A plano-convex lens of index of refraction n_2 and radius of curvature
R is immersed below a water (index of refraction n_1) surface to a
depth d as shown in the figure. A scratch on the flat surface of the
lens is located at point 0.
   (a) Derive an expression for the apparent depth of the scratch below
   the water surface as seen by an observer in air above the surface.
   (b) What is the apparent depth below the water surface when $n_1 = n_2$?

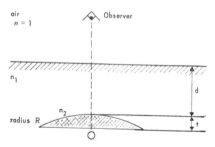

Figure 14

2. Consider a plane wave of velocity v travelling in the x-direction. The
plane $x = o$ is covered by an opaque screen with two circular holes of
radius R, one centred at $x = y = z = o$, and the other centred at

$$z = \sqrt{x_0 v t_1}, \qquad x = y = o.$$

Calculate the disturbance at $x = x_0$, $y = z = o$ for the following two
cases. Specify all relevant times and amplitudes. Either graphical or
analytical solutions are acceptable. Assume $R \ll v t_1$ and $x_0 \gg v t_1$.

348

(a) The incident wave is a pulse which makes a disturbance on the $x = o$ plane given by

$$E(t, o) = o \qquad\qquad\qquad\qquad\quad t < o$$
$$E(t, o) = A[1 - \cos(2\pi t/t_1)] \quad o \leq t \leq t_1$$
$$E(t, o) = o \qquad\qquad\qquad\qquad\quad t > t_1$$

(b) The incident wave is an infinite sinusoidal wave train of amplitude A and period t_1.

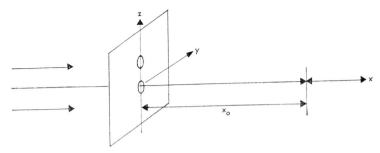

Figure 15

3. An opaque screen has seven open slits arranged as shown schematically in the figure. The central slit has a width w, and the other slits are progressively narrower, as indicated. The separations between the centres of adjacent slits are all equal to d. A plane monochromatic wave is incident upon this screen. Behind the screen is a converging lens of focal length f, the axis of the lens being perpendicular to the plane of the screen (fig. 16).

Assume $w \ll d$, and assume normal incidence for the monochromatic wave having wavelength λ.

What are the positions of the first four maxima and their amplitudes relative to the amplitude of the central maximum?

What are the positions of the first four minima?

Note

$$e^{ix} = \cos x + i \sin x$$
$$\cos 2x = 2 \cos^2 x - 1$$
$$\cos 3x = 4 \cos^3 x - 3 \cos x$$

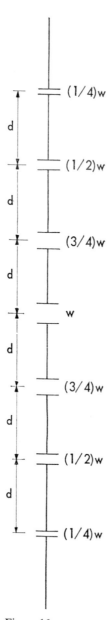

Figure 16

4. A beam of right-handed circularly polarized light of intensity I_0 is reflected at essentially *normal incidence* from the front surface of a crystal plate. The plate is cut from a uniaxial crystal so that the front face is parallel to the optic axis. The principal indices of refraction are n_y and n_z.

The reflected beam then passes through a quarter wave plate whose fast axis (smaller index of refraction) is parallel to the y-axis. Finally, the beam passes through a polarization filter whose transmission axis makes an angle θ with respect to the y-axis.

(a) What is the state of polarization of the beam in region II just after reflection (i.e., is it unpolarized, plane polarized, right- or left-handed circularly or elliptically polarized)?

(b) What is the state of polarization in region III?

(c) Write an expression for the intensity of the beam in region IV in terms of I_0, θ, n_y, and n_z.

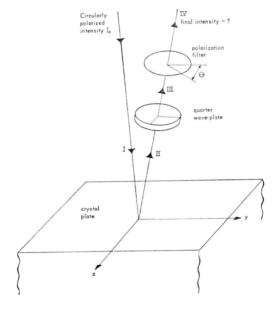

Figure 17

5. (a) Consider a *free* electron in interplanetary space scattering sunlight. Calculate the average outward force exerted by sunlight on the free electron, and express your answer in terms of

P = total power radiated by sun
r_e = classical radius of electron
c = speed of light
R = distance from the sun.

(b) What is the *numerical value* of the ratio between the outward force of sunlight and the inward force of the sun's gravity on the free electron?

Assume the following numerical quantities:

s = solar constant = 10^3 joules m^{-2}sec^{-1}
(flux of solar radiation energy at earth's orbit)
R = radius of earth's orbit = 1.5×10^{11} m
r_e = 3×10^{-15} m
c = 3×10^8 m sec^{-1}
G = 7×10^{-11} Newton's m^2 kg^{-2} (gravitational constant)
m = mass of electron = 9×10^{-31} kg
M = mass of sun = 2×10^{30} kg.

6. A plane sinusoidal wave train with wavelength λ is incident upon a semi-infinite opaque screen. Demonstrate that the intensity at point **P** inside the region of the geometrical shadow approaches zero in the limit $\lambda \rightarrow o$.

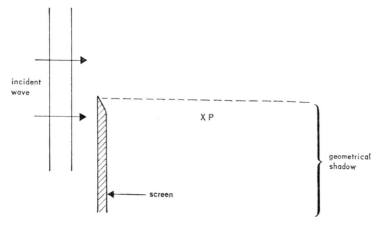

Figure 18

III F5   Experiments in upper-division laboratories at four institutions in the U.S.A.

Experiment	California	Columbia[1]	Massachusetts Institute of Technology	Swarthmore
Mechanics				
Orbit of projectile by photographic method	—	—	—	×
Velocity of a rifle bullet by ballistic pendulum	—	—	—	×
Comparison of kinetic energy and momentum	—	—	—	×
Forced damped simple harmonic motion	—	—	—	×
Elastic collision of two spheres	—	—	—	×
Gravitational torsion balance	—	—	—	×
Physical pendulum and Kater's pendulum	—	—	—	×
Gyroscopic precession	—	—	—	×
Ellipsoid of inertia	—	—	—	×
Shearing force and bending moment in simple beam	—	—	—	×
Deflection of a simple beam	—	—	—	×
Waves on stretched wire	—	—	—	×
Acoustical cavity resonator	—	—	—	×
Acoustical interference between sinusoidal waves	—	—	—	×

1. Only the basic experiments performed in the Adams Laboratory at Columbia are listed here.

Experiment	California	Columbia	Massachusetts Institute of Technology	Swarthmore
Vibrations of bars	—	—	—	×
Viscosity of a gas	—	—	—	×
Velocity of sound in gases by standing wave pattern in tube	—	—	—	×

Heat and thermodynamics

Statistical fluctuations near critical point of a fluid	—	—	×	—
Stefan Boltzmann law	—	—	—	×

Electromagnetism and electronics

L — R — C series circuits, sine-wave, square-wave excitation	×	—	—	—
Inductively coupled resonant circuits	×	—	—	—
Characteristics of vacuum tubes and thyratrons	×	×	—	—
Resistance coupled amplifier	×	×	—	×
R — C coupled amplifier	×	×	—	×
Small-time-interval measurement	×	—	—	—
Frequency measurements	×	—	—	—
Thermionic emission: Richardson's and 3/2 power laws	×	×	—	×
Electrical properties of p-type germanium	×	—	—	—
1000-cycle A.C. bridge	—	×	—	×
Characteristics and uses of cathode ray oscillographs	—	×	—	—
Free-running multivibrators	—	×	—	—
Tuned-plate and resistance-capacitance oscillators	—	×	—	—
Resonance, series and parallel	—	×	—	—
Secondary electron emission and photomultipliers	—	×	—	—
Contact potential difference	—	×	—	—
Electronic charge by Millikan's oil droplet method	—	×	×	×
Measurement of e/m by magnetron method	—	×	—	×

Experiment	California	Columbia	Massachusetts Institute of Technology	Swarthmore
Photocells, barrier layer and surface	—	×	—	—
Hall effect	—	—	×	—
Thermionic emission including construction of vacuum tube	—	—	×	—
Electrical discharges in gases	—	—	×	—
Relativistic e/m for electron	—	—	×	—
Omegatron	—	—	—	×
Laplace's equation and the electrolytic tray	—	—	—	×
Constant gradient magnetic field	—	—	—	×
Precision D.C. bridges	—	—	—	×
High-sensitivity galvanometer	—	—	—	×
Current balance	—	—	—	×
Magnetic field calibration	—	—	—	×
Fourier analysis and electrical transients	—	—	—	×
Filters	—	—	—	×
Optics and electromagnetic waves				
Standing wave measurements at microwave frequencies	×	—	×	—
Polarized light	×	×	—	×
Fraunhofer diffraction	×	×	—	×
Fresnel diffraction	×	×	—	×
Optical interference	×	×	—	—
Michelson interferometer	×	×	×	—
Polarimeter	—	×	—	—
Spectroscopy	×	×	—	—
Polarized light and the Faraday effect	—	—	×	—
Sodium resonance absorption	—	—	×	—
Critical slit width in spectroscopy	—	—	×	—
Laue pattern for cubic crystals	—	—	—	×
X-ray powder diffraction pattern	—	—	—	×
Atomic and nuclear physics				
Coincidence circuit with short resolving time	×	—	—	—

Experiment	California	Columbia	Massachusetts Institute of Technology	Swarthmore
Characteristic X-ray spectra	×	—	—	—
Excitation and ionization potentials of gases	×	—	×	×
Balmer series of hydrogen	×	—	—	—
180° beta-ray spectrometer	×	—	—	—
Beta- and gamma-ray spectrometer	×	—	—	—
Mass spectrometer	×	—	—	×
Nuclear magnetic resonance	×	—	×	—
Analysis of a K^+ Meson decay in nuclear emulsion	×	—	—	—
Gamma-ray scintillation spectrometer	×	—	×	—
Zeeman effect	×	—	×	—
Beta-ray electroscope	—	×	—	—
Mössbauer scattering	—	—	×	—
Construction and testing of a simple D.C. ionization chamber	—	—	×	—
Optical pumping	—	—	×	—
Random distribution of events in time: Poisson distribution	—	—	—	×
Half-life of Thoron by D.C. ionization chamber	—	—	—	×

Sample examination in upper-division physics undergraduate courses in the U.S.A. in 1962 (University of California, Berkeley)

Answer eight of the nine questions. Be sure to indicate on the front of the blue book which question you are *not* answering. All questions have equal weight. In your solutions, make free use of the formulae appearing after question 9.

1. Consider a particle moving in the (x, y) *plane* under the influence of a central force potential, $V(r)$.
   (a) Set up the Schrödinger equation in polar co-ordinates, r and φ. (You can get the correct expression in these co-ordinates for $\nabla^2 = \partial^2/\partial x^2 + \partial^2/\partial y^2$ from the expression for ∇^2 in cylindrical co-ordinates given below.)
   (b) Treat the equation by the method of separation of variables. Solve the φ equation and find the orthogonal, normalized functions which express the dependence of the stationary states on φ.
   (c) In what way, if any, does the angular momentum appear in the radial equation?

2. A particle moving in a spherically symmetrical potential (in three dimensions) is in such a state that a measurement of L^2 gives $2h^2$ with certainty, while a measurement of L_z gives h with a probability of $1/2$ and $-h$ with a probability of $1/3$. The radial part of the wave function is $R(r)$ where

$$\int_0^\infty R^2 r^2 \, dr = 1.$$

Write the complete, explicit wave function for the particle.

3. The density of states for a free particle in a box of volume V is

$$N(E)\, dE = 2\pi \left(\frac{2m}{h^2}\right)^{3/2} \cdot V \cdot \sqrt{E}\, dE \cdot$$

Derive this expression.

4. Interpret the expression

$$\psi(r \xrightarrow{} \infty)e^{ikz} + f(\theta)\frac{e^{ikr}}{r}$$

justifying your statements about probability current. Find the relationship between $f(\theta)$ and the differential cross-section, $\sigma(\theta)d\Omega$, for scattering into solid angle $d\Omega$.

5. Considering a particle moving in a spherically symmetrical potential, derive the radial equation for $l = 0$. Sketch the character of the solution to this equation (a) when there is no scattering potential, (b) when the scattering potential corresponds to an inpenetrable sphere of radius r_0. Comparing these, use the method of phase shifts to calculate the differential and total scattering cross-sections—in the low energy limit—for such an inpenetrable sphere.

6. Describe the procedure for obtaining the 1st order energy and the 0th order wave functions for a group of states having the same energy before a perturbing potential, V, is applied. You need not derive equations, but explain exactly how one proceeds.

7. Use the result of question No. 3 and Fermi's 'Golden Rule No. 2' to derive an expression, in Born approximation, for the differential cross-section for elastic scattering by a scattering potential $V(\vec{r})$.

8. An electron, which can move only in the x direction, is bound in an harmonic oscillator potential. Calculate the mean life of the state $n = 1$.

9. Find the eigenvalues and normalized eigenfunctions of the matrix

$$\begin{pmatrix} 0 & \sqrt{2}/2 & 0 \\ \sqrt{2}/2 & 0 & \sqrt{2}/2 \\ 0 & \sqrt{2}/2 & 0 \end{pmatrix}$$

358

Formulae

$$\vec{S} = \frac{\hbar}{m} Im\, (\psi^* \vec{\nabla} \psi)$$

$$Y_l^m(\theta, \varphi) = \sqrt{\frac{2l+1}{4\pi} \frac{(l-\mid m \mid)!}{(l+\mid m \mid)!}}\; e^{im\varphi}\, P_l^{\mid m \mid}\, (\cos \theta)$$

$$P_l^{\mid m \mid}\, (\cos \theta) = (\sin \theta)^{\mid m \mid} \cdot \frac{d^{\mid m \mid}}{d \cos \theta^{\mid m \mid}}\, P_l\, (\cos \theta)$$

$$P_l(\mu) = \frac{1}{2^l l!} \frac{d^l}{d\mu^l}\, (\mu^2 - 1)^l$$

$$\psi_n(x) = (2^n n!\, \sqrt{\pi})^{-\frac{1}{2}} \left(\frac{m\omega}{\hbar}\right)^{1/4} \times$$

$$\times\, H_n\left(\sqrt{\frac{\omega m}{\hbar}} \cdot x\right) \exp\left(-\frac{m\omega}{\hbar} \frac{x^2}{2}\right)$$

$$2n\, H_{n-1} - 2x\, H_n + H_{n+1} = 0$$

$$H = \frac{-\hbar^2}{2m} \frac{1}{r^2} \frac{\partial}{\partial r}\left(r^2 \frac{\partial}{\partial r}\right) + \frac{L^2}{2mr^2} + V(r)$$

In cylindrical co-ordinates

$$\nabla^2 = \frac{1}{r} \frac{\partial}{\partial r}\left(r \frac{\partial \psi}{\partial r}\right) + \frac{1}{r^2} \frac{\partial^2 \psi}{\partial \varphi^2} + \frac{\partial^2 \psi}{\partial z^2}$$

IV A1 Curricula[1] of the teaching combination mathematics-physics in Czechoslovakia

Subject	Semester					
	Fifth	Sixth	Seventh	Eighth	Ninth	Tenth
Selected parts of experimental physics	4/0 ex	3/0	—	—	—	—
Theoretical physics	6/2 ex	4/2 ex	5/2 ex	—	—	—
Physical electronics	—	3/0 ex	—	—	—	—
Solid state physics	—	—	—	2/0 ex	—	—
Astronomy	—	—	—	2/0	2/0 ex	—
Nuclear physics	—	—	—	—	2/0	—
Geophysics and meteorology	—	—	—	—	2/0 ex	—
Mathematical analysis	3/1 ex	—	—	—	—	—
Elementary arithmetic and algebra	3/0	2/1	—	—	—	—
Elementary geometry	3/0 ex	2/1	2/1 ex	—	—	—
Differential geometry	—	2/0	2/0 ex	—	—	—
Elementary theory of numbers	—	—	—	3/0 ex	—	—
Probability and statistics	—	—	—	—	3/0 ex	3/0
Mathematical machines	—	—	—	—	2/0	2/0
School demonstration experiments	—	—	0/2 mv	0/2 mv	0/2 mv	—
Topography practice	—	—	—	0/1	—	—
Psychology	2/0	2/0 ex	—	—	—	—
Pedagogics	2/0	2/0	2/0	2/0 ex	—	—
Methods of teaching physics	—	—	2/0	2/0	—	—
Seminar in methods of teaching physics	—	—	0/1 mv	0/1 mv	0/1 mv	—
Methods of teaching mathematics	—	2/0	2/1	2/0	2/0	—
General education	6	5 ex	6	6 ex	—	—
Optional lectures	—	—	2/0	2/0	—	—
School practice	—	—	0/1	0/2	—	—
Professional practice	—	—	—	4 weeks	4 weeks	—
Diploma project	—	—	—	—	5	20
Excursions	—	2 days	2 days	2 days	—	—
Total number of weekly hours	32	31	31	27	22	25
Total number of examinations	4	4	3	4	3	—

1. In reproducing the curricula, the following abbreviations are used:
   4/2 = four weekly periods of lectures and two periods of connected exercises.
   ex = examination.
   mv = marked validation, used for evaluation of the result of the students' laboratory work and given immediately upon completion of the exercise.

Physics syllabus for chemists
and biologists in France

A basic course for non-physicists is provided in all faculties of science.
Instruction is spread over forty hours, with about ten demonstration
sessions. The students are assumed to have covered the baccalaureat
syllabus.[1]

Programme for the first year[1] (*propédeutique*)

Units, systems of units. Physical measurement error. Measurements of
length, angles and time.
Force, the couple; work and power. Studies of a few problems of solid
statics. Acceleration, force, potential and kinetic energy. Studies of a
few examples of motion.
Pressure of a gas, law of perfect gases. Kinetic theory. Pressure in a
liquid in equilibrium; surface tension. Concept of flow of a fluid;
viscosity.
Temperature; classical thermometers. Quantity of heat; specific heat,
calorimeters. Heat transfer; conduction, convection, radiation. Principle of the conservation of energy; Carnot's theorem. Brief study of
diluted solutions (ebullioscopy, cryoscopy, dialysis) and of concentrated solutions (solubility). Colloids.
Sinusoidal vibrations; composition of vibrations. Free and forced oscillations; resonance; progagation of a vibration by waves.
Recapitulation of work done on lenses and mirrors. The magnifying

1. Reference to Lliboutry, *Physique de base pour les biologistes* (Masson), will give a general idea
   of the usual scope of the course. Guy's *Mathématiques pour biologistes* (SEDES, 5 place de
   la Sorbonne, Paris-5e) will give the reader an idea of the mathematics which chemistry and
   biology students are required to know before starting the above course in physics.

glass, microscope; spectacles. Photometry. Natural and polarized light; the polarimeter. Prism spectrographs. Spectroscopes. Ultra-violet and infra-red radiations.

Current—potential—resistance (Ohm's law). Calorific action of a current; thermo-electric effect. Electrolysis, contact potential difference; pH. value. Batteries and accumulators. Capacitors; force between the armatures; electric field; inductance; magnetic field. Discharge of a capacitor into an inductance; electrical oscillations. Galvanometers, ammeters and voltmeters. Measurement of resistances and potential differences.

Structure of the atom; the nucleus and electrons; general explanation of the process of ray emission; X-ray spectrum. Thermo-electric and photo-electric effects; applications. Cathode ray oscilloscopes and electron microscopes. The nucleus: natural and artificial radioactivity.

Programme for the second year[1]

Electricity

Electrostatics. Fields and potentials. Capacity. Dielectrics. Active field. Polarizability and polarity of molecules. The Clausius-Mosotti relationships. Debye's theory.

Electromagnetism. Magnetic field. Ampère's theorem. Electromagnetic induction. Electromotive field. Mutual inductance and self-inductance. The laws of electromagnetism stated as differential equations: Maxwell's equations.

Magnetism. Magnetic properties of materials: dia-, para- and ferro-magnetism (basic phenomena, elementary interpretation). Electro-magnets.

The dynamics of the movements of charges. (a) Electron sources: thermionic and photo-electric effects. The motions of free electrons and electron optics. The electron microscope. Valves (diode, triode). X-ray tubes. Photo-electric cells. (b) Discharges in gases. (c) Charges in solids. Conductivity. Simple interpretation of certain electromotive effects (Peltier, Thomson, Volta). Semiconductors.

Alternating currents. Single- and multi-phase currents. Impedance. Rectification and detection. Transformers.

Optics

The wave equation. Electromagnetic waves, their identity with light waves.

1. See J. P. Mathieu, *Physique expérimentale*, Masson.

Two-wave and multiple wave interference (only one type of interferometer is studied).

Diffraction (at infinity), in the vicinity of an image. Gratings. Resolving power of spectroscopes using gratings and using prisms. Diffusion of light. Refraction and dispersion. Absorption. Polarization of light. Natural and artificial birefringence. Rotating power.

Thermodynamics

Elementary statistical thermodynamics. Interpretation of specific heats. Black body radiation. Elementary heat transfer.

Proposed syllabuses for physics
in Part I of the natural sciences
tripos of Cambridge

First year

Forces and particles

Mass and force. Equations of motion of a particle in vector form.
Conservative forces, potential energy, conservation of energy, non-conservative forces, especially frictional forces.
Conservation of momentum
Galilean transformation. Centre of mass co-ordinates, collisions.
Fictitious forces, d'Alembert's principle, centrifugal force, rotating co-ordinates, Coriolis force.
Gravitational and electric forces, charge and mass as intrinsic properties of particles, superposition of forces, spherical charge and mass distributions, identity of gravitational and inertial mass.
Central inverse square orbits, Kepler's laws, elliptical orbits, Rutherford scattering.
Gravitational fields and potentials, centrifugal potential, tides.

Forces between charges in vacuum, electrostatic units, Gauss's theorem, lines of force, potential, fields of charge, dipole and quadripole.
Conductors, boundary conditions, Cavendish's experiment, self-capacity and mutual capacity, forces on conductors, work needed to establish field, conservation of energy, induced currents caused by charge movement, change of capacity due to polarizable material.
Current and continuity equation, forces between currents, electromagnetic units, lines of force and potential, Ampère's theorem, shells, fields in coils and solenoids, forces between coils.
Motion of charges in electric and magnetic fields, cathode-ray tube, Larmor's theorem.

Electromagnetic induction, moving fields and conductors, conservation of energy, work needed to establish field, self-inductance and mutual inductance, vector potential, formulae for M and L, $M_{12} = M_{21}$, $M^2 = L_1 L_2$, change of inductance due to polarizable material.

Units, esu and MKS, dimensions of mechanical and electrical quantities, dimensional analysis, number of basic units.

Measurement of esu/emu, displacement current, electromagnetic waves.

Structure of matter

Atoms and molecules, their size and mass.

Gas of non-interacting molecules, pressure impacts, equation of state, temperature.

Boltzmann distribution stated, Maxwell distribution, experimental verification, equipartition.

Forces between molecules, origin of van der Waals' forces, strength of forces, chemical bonds, temperature variation of rate of reaction.

Imperfect gases, van der Waals' and Dieterici's equations, virial coefficients, law of corresponding states, critical point.

Solids, types of structure, ionic solids, binding energy, compressibility, shearing, elastic moduli, specific heat, thermal expansion, ultimate strength, dislocations, melting.

Liquids, structure very qualitatively discussed.

Electric and magnetic properties of matter, origin and magnitude of ε and μ, modification of forces between charges, poles and currents, velocity of light in matter, origin of double refraction, etc., ferromagnetism.

Transport phenomena, mean free path in gases, flow of open gases, diffusion, etc., in gases and solids, viscosity in gases and liquids, thermal conduction in gases and solids, including electron and lattice conduction, electrical conductivity of metals.

Origin of surface tension.

Waves and particles in modern physics

A short descriptive course which might with advantage include a brief account of wave-motion, group velocity, etc.

Second year (Course 1)[1]

Continuous media

Rigid body dynamics, derivation of laws for two-dimensional lamina, simple problems, elementary examples of three-dimensional dynamics, simple theory of gyroscopes.

Elasticity, relation between elastic constants, bending of beams, waves, Euler instability, whirling shafts.

Hydrodynamics, Archimedes, Bernoulli, Poiseuille, Stokes, Reynolds, Mach, dimensional analysis.

Surface tension, form of meniscus, dimensional analysis of drop-weight.

Heat conduction, differential equation and simple solutions, dimensional analysis of convection.

Field theory of dielectrics, Poisson and Laplace, rod disc and spherical cavities, depolarizing factor, microscopic and macroscopic fields, forces on conductors and dielectrics.

Field theory of magnetism, electromagnets, permanent magnets.

Thermodynamics (18 hours)

Free energy, etc., to be discussed, and energy of electric and magnetic fields, electrostriction, etc.

Relativity (6 hours)

Instruments and physical measurements (12 hours)

Second year (Course 2)

Oscillations and waves

Complex algebra, D.C. and A.C. circuit theory, L and C under aperiodic and periodic conditions.

RC circuits as model of relaxation phenomena, with examples from elasticity, polyatomic gases, dielectrics, etc.

LRC circuits as model of resonance phenomena, with examples such as galvanometer, anomalous dispersion, etc.

Coupled resonant circuits.

Non-linear oscillations, hysteresis.

Valves, rectifiers, amplifiers.

1. Students may choose between Course 1 and Course 2.

Waves, types and equations including dispersive equations and linear chain, boundary conditions, reflexion, refraction, wave impedance, inhomogeneous media, resonance and normal modes, enumeration of modes.

Fourier integral, group velocity, group paths in anisotropic medium, rays, geometrical optics, Fermat's principle, pulse dispersion, energy spectrum of aperiodic disturbance.

Momentum and wave-pressure for strings, sound waves and electromagnetic waves.

Optics (16 hours)

Diffraction, including Fourier theory (especially Fourier series) and mention of X-ray diffraction, Kirchhoff's theory.

Interference and interferometers.

Polarization and anisotropic media, molecular theory of optical properties.

Quantum mechanics (20 hours)

A typical programme of post-graduate
studies: the advanced electronics
course at the University of Paris

Compulsory for all students (75 hours)

Basic theory of electromagnetics; the restricted Theory of Relativity
and its applications. Electromagnetic radiation by accelerated particles.
Propagation of electromagnetic waves; guides, lines and cavities. Propa-
gation in gyromagnetic media.
Theory of random phenomena; background noise. Oscillator theory.
Fluctuations of amplitude and frequency.
V.H.F. measurements; generators, receivers, general measuring equip-
ment.

In addition, every student must take an optional course covering seventy-
five hours of tuition and classes (including practical). The following is a
list of optional courses.
1. *Particle accelerators.* Relevance of relativistic mechanics; theory of
   circular and linear accelerators. Electron optics.
2. *Quantum electronics.* Quantum mechanics; microwave spectroscopy.
   Theory of masers and lasers.
3. *Nuclear electronics.* Various types of radiation detectors; fast pulse
   circuits; data processing.
4. *Servomechanisms and information theory.* Theory of servomechanisms
   and optimization of control; binary circuits and their applications.
5. *Semiconductors and micro-electronics.* The physics of semiconductor
   materials and devices. Basic circuits and their embodiment in integral
   circuits.
6. *Plasma physics.* Plasma diagnostic methods; production of plasma by
   gaseous discharge. Interaction of waves and plasma.

The above introductory course is compulsory for all graduates wishing to undertake research in electronics. The course (150 hours for a year) is taken at the beginning of the research period.

The diploma for advanced studies
in physics at Manchester University

Diploma candidates are required to attend at least three approved post-graduate courses in each of the first and second terms, and to sit written examinations on these; to undertake an experimental or theoretical project of a research nature under supervision, and to submit a written report on it; and to sit an oral examination on the courses attended, and on the project and related topics. A very wide choice of courses and lectures is available. The list of two or three term courses in the session (1963/64) includes:

Quantum mechanics. Statistical mechanics. Theoretical nuclear physics. Mathematical methods of physics. Selected topics in experimental nuclear physics. Instruments of nuclear physics. Physics of organic molecules. Biophysics. Low temperature techniques. Plasma physics. Scattering theory. Electrodynamics and relativity. The Mossbauer effect. Electronics.

In addition one-term courses are being given on:

Physics of organic crystals. Statistical mechanics. Solid-state theory. Chemical physics. Field theory.

The range of courses reflects the variety of research interests of the department, and it is usually possible to select a combination of courses to suit the particular needs of any individual student.

In addition to these formal lecture courses, various post-graduate seminars and colloquia in nuclear physics, theoretical physics, molecular physics, solid-state and low temperature physics and optics are held throughout the session, and diploma students are encouraged to attend any of these which are of interest to them.

Each student is allocated to a supervisor, who is responsible for the

370

direction of his experimental or theoretical project work. In the case of a potential Ph.D. student the project is normally undertaken in one of the specialist research groups and corresponds to the initial stages of his ultimate research studies. A potential M.Sc. student may also undertake his project work with a research group, to enable his particular interests to be met. The majority of advanced course students and those who do not wish to proceed beyond the diploma undertake their experimental project work in the advanced laboratory, where they can receive more detailed supervision and training in experimental techniques. All students of experimental physics are also allocated to a tutor, who advises them on any special problems encountered in their studies in theoretical or mathematical physics. Some typical projects undertaken for the diploma are as follows:

Measurement of neutron energies and angular distribution in (d, n) reactions.

The scintillation process in a binary liquid solution.

A helical-focusing lens beta-spectrometer.

The development of a spark chamber and associated pulsing system.

The semiconductor radiation detector.

The 2.9 MeV excited state of the Be^8 nucleus.

The design of an instrument for the study of organic fluorescence decay.

A review of current theories of ferroelectricity and antiferroelectricity and their possible occurrence in DNA.

The design of a focusing system for secondary particles for subsequent acceleration.

The range of N^{15} ions in nickel.

An investigation of a gas scintillation counter with applied electric field.

The measurement of the temperature dependence of fluorescence.

The propagation of second sound in rotating liquid helium.

Solid-solid boundary resistance at low temperature.

The ground-state of a many-boson system.

Single pion production in pion-nucleon scattering.

The project report, which corresponds to a minor thesis, is prepared and submitted for examination during the third term. The oral examination, which is held towards the end of June, is of about one hour's duration and is conducted by a panel of three examiners. Some candidates may also be required to attend a further oral examination, conducted by the external examiner.

The diploma may be awarded with distinction. Candidates who wish to proceed to a research degree are required to have shown satisfactory evidence of research ability in their project work. Those wishing to enter

371

the M.Sc. course (one year) are required to satisfy fully the requirements for the award of the diploma. Those wishing to enter the Ph.D. course (two years) are required to have reached a high standard in the diploma examination as a whole.

Some graduate courses in physics either required or frequently recommended to students at three institutions in the U.S.A.

Course	Subject	Credit in semester hours	1961/62 enrolment
University of California at Berkeley (Requirements)			
Physics			
205 A	Advanced dynamics	3	44
210 A, B	Theory of electricity and magnetism	3, 3	47
219	Thermodynamics and statistical mechanics	3	57
221 A, B	Quantum mechanics	3, 3	55
Columbia University (Knowledge of subject matter of these is required)			
Physics			
G4040	Nuclear physics	3	48
G6019, 6020	Mathematical methods in physics	4.5, 4.5	74
G6051, 6052	Advanced laboratory work	1 to 6	22
G6092, 6093	Electromagnetic theory I, II	4.5, 4.5	57
G6102, 6103	Analytical dynamics I, II	3, 3	32
G8036	Statistical mechanics	4.5	38
G8037, 8038	Quantum mechanics	4.5, 4.5	43
G8057, 8058	Advanced nuclear physics	4.5, 4.5	19

Course	Subject	Credit in semester	1961/62 enrolment
Massachusetts Institute of Technology			
(Suggestions to first-year graduate students)			
Physics			
8.21	Physical electronics	3	11
8.231	Electrical discharges in gases	3	15
8.27	X-rays and crystal physics (incl. lab.)	4	28
8.361	Quantum theory of matter I	3	108
8.44	Introduction to solid-state physics	3	18
8.511	Nuclear physics I	3	47
8.541	Introduction to fundamental particle physics	3	16
8.721	Electromagnetic theory I	4	81
8.731	Introduction to quantum theory I	3	92
8.791	Methods of theoretical physics I	4	45

Size of physics departments of British universities

University	Full professors	Total academic staff	Annual intake honours physics students
England			
Birmingham	5	36	About 80
Bristol	3	21	About 70
Cambridge	4	43	About 100
Durham			
Durham Colleges	2	12	40–60
King's College, Newcastle upon Tyne	3	20	About 50
Exeter	1	10	About 40
Hull	2	13	45
Keele	1	7	About 40
Leeds	2	20	About 65
Leicester	1	10	20–30
Liverpool	3	29	About 35
London			
Bedford College	1	8	25
Imperial College of Science and Technology	8	45	About 100
King's College	4	21	30–35
Queen Mary College	2	16	About 50
Royal Holloway College	1	6	About 10
University College	3	25	About 45
Manchester	6	43	About 100
College of Science and Technology	1	16	About 35

University	Full professors	Total academic staff	Anual intake honours physics students
Nottingham	2	15	About 50
Oxford	2	39	About 150
Reading	2	14	15
Sheffield	2	15	About 50
Southampton	2	11	About 36
Sussex	2	11	55
Scotland			
Aberdeen	1	19	15
Edinburgh	2	32	85
Glasgow	2	28	
St. Andrews			
St. Salvator's College, St. Andrews	2	10	About 18–20
Queen's College, Dundee	1	11	About 8
Northern Ireland			
Belfast			
Queen's University	1	10	50–60
Wales			
Aberystwyth			
University College of Wales	1	9	About 20
Bangor			
University College of North Wales	1	10	About 25
Cardiff			
University College of South Wales and Monmouthshire	1	11	About 10
Swansea			
University College	1	10	40

Workshop equipment of institutes
of physics at a university with
approximately 300 students of physics
in the Federal Republic of Germany

It is assumed that in the case of 300 students approximately 100 experimental tasks are executed by *Dozenten*, Assistants, *Doktoranden* and
Diplomanden. The following personnel and equipment of workshops is
required. The workshop may be universally used by all institutes or it
may be divided into separate workshops for the individual institutes.
Large machines must be used by all institutes.

Mechanical workshop

One workshop with approximately twenty precision mechanics (foreman
and mechanics), five apprentices, one welder, joiner, locksmith, electrician.

Precision mechanics

Size of workshop: 350 square metres. One foreman's office with a drawing table; twenty work places for fine mechanics each with 2 m work-
bench; two tool cabinets; vice and hand tools; two SS- and SC-lathes
with 300 mm centre height, 1.5–2 m turning length; three SS- and SC-
lathes with 150 mm centre height, 1–1.5 m turning length; six mechanical
lathes of various sizes; universal tool milling machine; universal milling
machine (table size approximately 250 × 1,000 mm); three column-type
drilling machines; shaping machine; two watchmaker's lathes; fine boring
machine; tapping machine; surface grinder; metal circular saw; recessing
grinder; hacksaw machine; tool sharpening machine (lathe); tool grinding machine; engraving machine; spark erosion machine; various small
machines (portable drilling machines, grinding machines, etc.); various
measuring tools; various cutting tools; hydraulic press; glowing and
tempering furnace with temperature regulator 1,400 °C; protective gas

hard-soldering furnace with up to 1,200 °C; compressed air installation up to 10 atm., with twenty connecting points at work places and machines respectively; metal-band saw-filing machine; test stand for high vacuum parts; fine spotwelding machine; wall chests and other equipment; electric crane carriage.

Material store

Size approximately 80–100 square metres for bars, pipes, sheet, iron, synthetic plates and small parts. Hacksaw machine; metal circular saw. Furthermore a big store of materials.

Welding shop

Size 60 square metres. Autogenous welding apparatus; electric welding apparatus for D.C. and A.C. with protective gas equipment; welding table with two work places and suction fan; pair of plate shears with power drive, 2 m cutting length, 3 mm sheet-iron thickness; folding and rounding machine, 2 m working width, 2 to 3 mm sheet iron thickness; levelling plate, 1,000 × 2,000 mm; spot welding machine, approximately 2 × 2 mm sheet-iron thickness; sandblast blower; column-type drilling machine; hacksaw machine (forge with anvil, etc.); work-bench, 5 m long, with two vices and four tool chests, including tools; grinding machine; small folding bench up to 1.5 mm sheet-iron thickness; various small machines (portable drilling machines, portable grinders, portable electric shears).

Galvanizing plant

Size 50 square metres. Generating plant for baths; nickel bath up to 500 litres capacity; copper bath up to 500 litres capacity; degreasing bath, 500 litres capacity; silver bath, 50 litres capacity; sulphuric acid bath, 500 litres capacity; pickling bath for light metal, 200 litres capacity; pre-pickling and pickling bath for nonferrous metal, 100 litres capacity; baths for electrolytic polishing of superior alloy steel and nonferrous metal; drum galvanizing apparatus, 30 litres capacity; two polishing machines in separated room with suction equipment; suction equipment for the entire room (price depends on building conditions and facilities); bath-cleaning plant; ultrasonic cleaning plant; various small items of equipment (bath heater, etc.); depot table.

Lacquering shop

Size 30 square metres. Spraying cabin with spray gun; dashboard with spray gun; shelf drier; depot tables and shelves.

Plastics workshop

Size 30 square metres. Hot-air blast, 2 m working width; folding bench for plastics with heatable jaws, 2 m working length; circular saw for plastic substances; column-type drilling machine; welding apparatus for plastics.

Joiners' workshop

Size 50 square metres. Carpenter's bench; combination circular saw; planing and thicknessing machine; band saw; grinding machine (for planing knives, etc.); various tools for woodwork; various small machines; toolchests, shelves, etc.

Electricians' workshop

Size 30 square metres. Workbench with built-in drawer-chests and vice, approximately 4 m long; test field for electric machines, etc.; drilling machine; mechanical lathe; grinding machine; various tools and small machines; chests and shelves.

Electronics workshop

One workshop with three electronic mechanicians. Size 50 square metres. Three work places (each 3 m work bench with built-in tool and spare chests, including the necessary tools); column-type drilling machine; mechanical lathe; grinding machine; coil winding machine; electric hand drilling machine; ohmmeter; two oscillographs; valve-testing outfit; transistor-testing outfit; induction- and farad-meter; two valve voltmeters; calibrating-transmitter test oscillator from 100 kc up to 50 mc and one from 50 mc to 500 mc; impulse generator; three multiple-measuring devices; various tables and chests.

Glass-blowing plant

One plant with two glass-blowers. Size 50 square metres. Work table with three work places (6 m work bench with built-in drawer-chests);

tempering furnace; grinding machine (for polishing); glass-cutting machine; glass-drilling machine; glass-blower lathe; vacuum pump stand; various tools (blowlamps, etc.); ventilation system (price depends on building conditions and facilities).

All workshops are connected to compressed-air line. Installation of ventilation to be provided as required.

Some typical books for students in universities of the Federal Republic of Germany

Lectures on experimental physics for beginners

W. H. Westphal. *Physik*. Springer.
Grimsehl. *Lehrbuch der Physik*. B. G. Teubner.
L. Bergmann; Cl. Schaefer. *Lehrbuch der Experimentalphysik*. Walter de Gruyter.
R. W. Pohl. *Einführung in die Physik*. Springer.
Chr. Gerthsen. *Physik*. Springer.

Practical physics for beginners

Chr. Gerthsen; M. Pollermann. *Einführung in das physikalische Anfängerpraktikum*. Springer.
Cl. Schaefer; L. Bergmann; Kliefoth. *Grundaufgaben des Physikalischen Praktikums*. B. G. Teubner.
W. H. Westphal. *Physikalisches Praktikum*. Springer.
F. Kohlrausch. *Praktische Physik*. B. G. Teubner.
W. Riezler, K. Kopitzki. *Kernphysikalisches Praktikum*. B. G. Teubner.

Lectures on theoretical physics

G. Joos. *Lehrbuch der theoretischen Physik*. Akademische Verlagsgesellschaft.
F. Hund. *Theoretische Physik*. B. G. Teubner.
W. Weizel. *Lehrbuch der theoretischen Physik*. Springer.
R. Becker; F. Sauter. *Theorie der Elektrizität*. B. G. Teubner.
S. Flügge. *Lehrbuch der theoretischen Physik*. Springer, 1963.

A. Sommerfeld. *Vorlesungen über theoretische Physik*. Akademische Verlagsgesellschaft.

L. D. Landau; E. M. Lifshitz. *Course of theoretical physics*. Pergamon Press.

W. Döring. *Einführung in die Quantenmechanik*. Vandenhoeck und Ruprecht.

L. I. Schiff. *Quantum mechanics*. McGraw-Hill Book Company.

Lectures on experimental physics for advanced students

W. Finkelnburg. *Einführung in die Atomphysik*. Springer.

E. W. Schpolski. *Atomphysik*. Deutscher Verlag der Wissenschaften.

P. Marmier. *Kernphysik*. Verlag des Vereins der Mathematiker und Physiker an der ETH Zürich.

G. Hertz. *Lehrbuch der Kernphysik*. B. G. Teubner.

W. Riezler. *Einführung in die Kernphysik*. R. Oldenbourg.

R. Kollath. *Teilchenbeschleuniger*. Friedrich Vieweg und Sohn.

H. Kopfermann. *Kernmomente*. Akademische Verlagsges.

A. Lösche. *Kerninduktion*. Deutscher Verlag der Wissenschaften.

K. Wirtz; K. H. Beckurts. *Elementare Neutronenphysik*. Springer.

W. Riezler; W. Walcher. *Kerntechnik*. Teubner.

S. Glasstone; M. C. Edlund. *Kernreaktortheorie*. Springer.

H. Ewald; H. Hintenberger. *Methoden und Anwendungen der Massenspektroskopie*. Verlag Chemie.

E. Fünfer; H. Neuert. *Zählrohre und Szintillationszähler*. G. Braun.

E. Broda; Th. Schönfeld. *Die technische Anwendung der Radioaktivität*. Verlag Technik.

C. Kittel. *Introduction to solid state physics*. New York, Wiley, 1958.

F. Seitz. *The modern theory of solids*. New York, McGraw-Hill, 1960.

E. Spenke. *Elektronische Halbleiter*. Springer, 1956.

K. Küpfmüller. *Einführung in die Theoretische Elektrotechnik*. Springer, 1959.

W. Gruhle. *Elektronische Hilfsmittel des Physikers*. Springer, 1960.

W. W. Gärtner. *Einführung in die Physik des Transistors*. Springer, 1963.

H. Salow; H. Beneking; H. Krömer; W. v. Münch. *Der Transistor*. Springer.

P. Pringsheim. *Fluorescence and phosphorescence*. Interscience Publishers.

M. Pollermann. *Bauelemente der physikalischen Technik*. Springer.

General

S. Flügge. *Handbuch der Physik*. Springer.

Selection of French works
for the teaching of physics[1]

Works intended for the teaching of
non-physicists

All candidates for the *baccalauréat* (the certificate to which the second-ary course leads in France) receive some instruction in physics. Amongst the numerous works designed for pupils in the last two years of the secondary course, all of which cover the same syllabus, the following might be mentioned:

J. Cessac; P. Treherne. *Physique*. (3 vols.). Nathan.
M. Eurin; P. Guimiot. *Physique*. (3 vols.). Hachette.

Under the same heading may be included works dealing with physics in general and designed for prospective chemists, biologists and physicians.

J. P. Mathieu. *Physique expérimentale*. SEDES.
P. Lliboutry. *Physique de base pour biologistes*. Masson.
M. Françon. *Expériences de physique*. Revue d'optique.

Works designed for training physicists
and engineers

To begin with there are complete collections which constitute treatises of physics. Amongst these the following might be mentioned:

J. Rossel. *Traité de physique générale*. Dunod.
P. Fleury; J. P. Mathieu. *Traité de physique générale* (8 vols.). Eyrolles.
G. Bruhat. *Traité de physique générale* (5 vols.). Nouvelle édition revue par A. Foch, E. Goudet, A. Kastler et J. Roig. Masson.

---

1. List prepared by the Société Française de Physique.

There are also many textbooks covering one part of physics in detail. The following might be mentioned:

J. Brochard. *Thermodynamique*. Masson.

J. P. Perez. *Mécanique physique*. Masson.

Y. Rocard. *Dynamique générale des vibrations*. Masson.

Y. Rocard. *Thermodynamique*. Masson.

J. Simon; J. Poux. *Chaleur*. Baillière.

J. Poux; J. Simon. *Optique géométrique*. Baillière.

J. Cabannes. *Optique ondulatoire*. SEDES.

A. Blanc-Lapierre; G. Goudet; P. Lapostolle. *Electronique générale* Eyrolles.

R. Guillien. *Electronique*. Presses Universitaires de France.

G. Goudet. *Electronique industrielle*. Eyrolles.

M. Rouault. *Electricité*. Masson.

Y. Rocard. *Electricité*. Masson.

M. Y. Bernard. *Initiation à la mécanique quantique*. Hachette.

L. de Broglie. *Eléments de théorie des quantas et de mécanique ondulatoire*. Gauthier-Villars.

G. Guinier. *Eléments de physique théorique moderne*. Bordas.

M. Rouault. *Physique atomique*. Armand Colin.

Advanced works designed for the training of specialists

In conclusion, a few French works designed for the training of physicists are listed. These works are intended for students at *licence* level. The list is restricted to basic works and does not include over-specialized technical works. The works are listed in alphabetical order of authors' names.

A. Abragam. *Magnétisme nucléaire*. Presses Universitaires de France.

J. Barriol. *Mécanique quantique*. Presses Universitaires de France.

E. Bauer. *Champ de vecteurs et de tenseurs*. Masson.

E. Bauer. *La théorie des groupes*. Masson.

L. Brillouin. *Les tenseurs en mécanique et en élasticité*. Masson.

L. Brillouin; M. Parodi. *Propagation des ondes dans les milieux périodiques*. Masson.

J. L. Delcroix. *Physique des plasmas* (2 vols.). Dunod.

E. Durand. *Electrostatique et magnétostatique*. Masson.

A. Guinier. *Radiocristallographie*. Dunod.

H. Haag. *Mouvements vibratoires* (2 vols.). Presses Universitaires de France.

A. Marechal; M. Françon. *Traité d'optique* (2 vols.). Revue d'optique.
A. Messiah. *Mécanique quantique* (2 vols.). Dunod.
P. Nozieres. *Le problème des N corps.* Dunod.
F. Perrin. *Mécanique statistique.* Gauthier-Villars.

IX D1 A list of physics books used in the general physics course and the theoretical physics course in universities of the U.S.S.R.

General physics

Part I

Basic

S. P. Strelkov. *Mechanics*. Moscow, GTTI, 1956.
S. G. Kalashnikov. *Electricity*. Moscow, GTTI, 1956.
S. E. Frish; A. V. Timoreva. *A general physics course*, vols. I and II. Moscow-Leningrad, Gostekhizdat, 1956.
G. S. Landsberg. *Optics*. Gostekhizdat, 1958. (Instruction manual.)

Supplementary

E. A. Shtrauf. *Molecular Physics*. 1949.
E. A. Shtrauf. *Electricity and Magnetism*. 1950.
V. L. Kirpichev. *Talks on Mechanics*. Gostekhizdat, 1954.
A. B. Mlodzeevsky. *Molecular Physics*. OGIZ, 1941.
A. I. Tudorovsky. *Electricity*, vols. I and II. GTTI, 1933.
N. D. Papaleksi. *A physics course*, vol. I. Moscow-Leningrad, Gostekhizdat, 1948.
A. B. Mlodzeevsky (ed.). *Lecture demonstrations in physics*. Moscow-Leningrad, Gostekhizdat.
Symposium: 'Russian Men of Science', Gostekhizdat, 1948.

Part II
Basic

E. V. Shpolsky. *Atomic physics*, vols. I and II. 1951.

386

Supplementary

N. A. Kaptsov. *Electronics.* 1954.

Harnwell; Livingood. *Experimental atomic physics.* 1956. (Russian Edition.)

Semat. *Introduction to atomic physics.* 1949.

G. Herzberg. *Atomic spectra and structure of the atom,* vol. I. 1949.

N. A. Kondratev. *Structure of atoms and molecules.* 1959.

Part III

Basic

E. V. Shpolsky. *Atomic physics,* vol. II. Gostekhizdat, 1951.

E. Fermi. *Lectures on atomic physics.* IL, 1952.

S. V. Skachkov, *et al. Symposium on nuclear physics.* Gostekhizdat, 1958.

Supplementary

L. D. Landau; Y. A. Smorodinsky. *Lectures on nuclear theory.* Gostekhizdat, 1956.

E. Segre. *Experimental nuclear physics,* vols. I and II. IL, 1955.

E. Andrew. *Nuclear magnetic resonance.* IL, 1957.

R. Stefanson. *Introduction to nuclear engineering.* Gostekhizdat, 1956.

R. Murray. *Introduction to nuclear engineering.* IL, 1955.

N. A. Dobrotin. *Cosmic rays.* Gostekhizdat, 1955.

Theoretical physics

Part I

L. Landau; E. Lifshits. *Mechanics.*

N. Buchholtz. *A basic course in theoretical mechanics.*

L. Landau; E. Lifshits. *Mechanics of continuous media.*

A. Sommerfeld. *Mechanics.*

G. Goldstein. *Classical mechanics.*

Part II

I. Tamm. *Theory of electricity.*

L. Landau; E. Lifshits. *Field theory.*

R. Bekker. *Electron theory.*

L. Landau; E. Lifshits. *Electrodynamics of continuous media.*

A. Vlasov. *Macroscopic electrodynamics.*

Part III

L. Landau; E. Lifshits. *Statistical physics.*
M. Leontovich. *Introduction to thermodynamics.*
V. Levich. *Introduction to static physics.*
K. Shefer. *Theory of heat.*
L. Landau; E. Lifshits. *Electrodynamics of continuous media.*

Part IV

D. Blokhintsev. *Fundamentals of quantum mechanics.*
L. Landau; E. Lifshits. *Quantum mechanics.*
L. Schiff. *Quantum mechanics.*

Practical physics

V. I. Iveronovaya (ed.). Fizmatgiz. *Manual of practical physics.*

Recommended textbooks for honours physics students at the Imperial College, London

First year

Classical mechanics

Symon. *Mechanics.*
Slater; Franck. *Mechanics.*
Synge; Griffiths. *Principles of mechanics.*
Goldstein. *Classical mechanics.*
Whittaker. *Analytical dynamics.*
Lamb. *Statics.*
Lamb. *Dynamics.*
Ramsey. *Dynamics*, vols. I and II.
Pars. *Introduction to dynamics.*
Humphrey. *Intermediate mechanics*, vols. I and II.
Milne. *Vectorial mechanics.*
Weatherburn. *Elementary vector analysis.*
Weatherburn. *Advanced vector analysis.*
Green. *Dynamics.*
Smart. *Advanced dynamics.*
Short. *Dynamics.*
D. E. Rutherford. *Fluid mechanics.*

General physics

Starling. *Properties of matter.*

Vibrations and waves

Stephens; Bate. *Wave motion and sound.*
Bickley; Talbot. *Introduction to the theory of vibrating systems.*
Feather. *Introduction to the physics of vibrations and waves.*
Kinsler; Frey. *Acoustics.*
Jenkins; White. *Fundamentals of physical optics.*

Electricity and magnetism

Starling; Woodall. *Electricity and magnetism for degree students.*
Yarwood; Fewkes. *Electricity and magnetism.*
Page; Adams. *Principles of electricity.*
Sears. *Electricity and magnetism.*
Scott. *Physics of electricity and magnetism.*
Harnwell. *Principles of electricity and electromagnetism.*

Heat and thermodynamics

R. A. Smith. *Physical principles of thermodynamics.*
A. B. Pippard. *The elements of classical thermodynamics.*
M. W. Zemansky. *Heat and thermodynamics.*

Atomic and nuclear physics

Yarwood. *Electricity and magnetism*, Vols. I and II.
Kaplan. *Nuclear physics.*
Newman; Searle. *General properties of matter.*

Second year

Geometrical and physical optics

R. W. Ditchburn. *Light.*
R. S. Longhurst. *Geometrical and physical optics.*
Jenkins; White. *Fundamentals of optics.*
W. E. Williams. *Applications of interferometry.*

Electromagnetic theory

L. Page; N. I. Adams. *Principles of electricity.*
J. C. Slater; N. H. Frank. (a) *Introduction to theoretical physics.* (b) *Electromagnetism.*

M. Abraham; R. Becker. *Classical theory of electricity and magnetism.*
Bleaney; Bleaney. *Electricity and magnetism.*

Electronics

Aldous; Appleton. *Thermionic vacuum tubes.*
Parker. *Electronics.*
Farley. *Elements of pulse circuits.*
Braddick. *The physics of experimental method.*
Evans. *Fundamental principles of transistors.*
Amos. *Principles of transistor circuits.*
DeWitt; Rossoff. *Transistor electronics.*

Magnetic and dielectric properties of matter

N. Cusack. *The electrical and magnetic properties of solids.*

Thermodynamics and statistical mechanics

G. Joos. *Theoretical physics* (relevant section).
R. A. Smith. *The physical principles of thermodynamics.*
M. W. Zemansky. *Heat and thermodynamics.*

Kinetic theory

Present. *Kinetic theory of gases.*
Kittel. *Elementary statistical physics.*
Jeans. *Dynamical theory of gases.*
Kennard. *Kinetic theory of gases.*

Spectroscopy

Herzberg. *Atomic spectra and atomic structure.*
White. *Introduction to atomic spectra.*
Kuhn. *Atomic spectra.*

Discharge physics

Arnot. *Collision processes in gases.*
von Engel. *Ionization in gases.*
Massey; Burhop. *Electronic and ionic impact phenomena.*

Electron physics

O. Klemperer. *Electron physics.*
F. K. Richtmeyer; E. H. Kennard; T. Lauritson. *Introduction to modern physics.*

Nuclear physics

Kaplan. *Nuclear physics.*

Special relativity and quantum mechanics

H. Rojanksy. *Quantum mechanics.*
L. I. Schiff. *Quantum mechanics.*
L. D. Landau; E. M. Lipshitz. *Quantum mechanics.*
P. Bergman. *Relativity.*
W. K. H. Panofsky; M. Phillips. *Classical electricity and magnetism* (Chapters 15–18).

Third year

Crystal lattice theory

C. Kittel. *Introduction to solid state physics.*

Electronic structure of metals

Hume-Rothery. *Atomic theory for students of metallurgy.*
Dekker. *Solid state physics.*
J. M. Ziman. *Electrons and metals.*

Electron conduction and emission

C. Kittel. *Introduction to solid state physics.*
Cusack. *Electrical and magnetic properties of solids.*

Transport and mechanical properties of solids

A. J. Dekker. *Solid state physics.*
C Kittel. *Introduction to solid state physics.*

Nuclear physics

Kaplan. *Nuclear physics.* (Elementary.)
Landau; Smorodinsky. *Lectures on nuclear theory.* (Principal recommendation.)
Evans. *The atomic nucleus.*
Preston. *Physics of the nucleus.*

Quantum mechanics

L. I. Schiff. *Quantum mechanics.*
L. D. Landau; E. M. Lipshitz. *Quantum mechanics.*
Mandl. *Quantum mechanics.*
Dirac. *Quantum mechanics.*

Electromagnetic theory

J. R. Reitz; F. J. Milford. *Foundations of electromagnetic theory.*
W. K. H. Panofsky; M. Phillips. *Classical electricity and magnetism.*
J. A. Stratton. *Electromagnetic theory.*

Mathematics applied to physics

G. Joos. *Theoretical physics* (1951).
Fourier's series and spherical cylindrical and ellipsoidal harmonics (1893). (For reference only.)

Typical textbooks used in physics courses at the University of California at Berkeley, 1961/62

Physics 2A, 2B (General physics: premedicine, architecture)
Harvey E. White. *Modern college physics*. New York, D. Van Nostrand Company.
Physics 3A, 3B (General physics laboratory)
Ralph S. Minor. *Selected experiments in physical measurements*. University of California Bookstore.
Physics 4A (General physics: science majors, engineers)
D. Halliday and R. Resnick. *Physics for students of science and engineering*. New York, John Wiley and Sons.
Ralph S. Minor. *Physical measurements*. University of California Bookstore.
Physics 4B (General physics: science majors, engineers)
Arthur F. Kip. *Fundamentals of electricity and magnetism*. New York, McGraw-Hill.
Laboratory notes for physics 4B. University of California Bookstore.
Physics 4C (General physics: science majors, engineers)
Francis Sears. *Mechanics, wave motion, and heat*. Reading, Addison-Wesley Company.
Francis Bitter. *Currents, fields, and particles*. Reading, Addison-Wesley Company.
Experiments for Physics 4C. University of California Bookstore.
Physics 10 (Descriptive introduction to physics)
Arthur Beiser. *Basic concepts of physics*. Reading, Addison-Wesley Company.
Physics 11A, B (Foundations of physical science)
Jay Orear. *Fundamental physics*. New York, John Wiley and Sons.
T. Bonner; M. Phillips. *Principles of physical science*. Reading, Addison-Wesley Company.

394

Physics 104 (Mathematical methods in physics)
Harry Lass. *Vector and tensor analysis.* New York, McGraw-Hill.
Physics 105A, B (Analytic mechanics)
K. Symon. *Mechanics.* Reading, Addison-Wesley Company.
Physics 108A, B (Optics)
F. Jenkins; H. White. *Fundamentals of optics.* New York, McGraw-Hill.
Physics 110A, B (Electricity and magnetism)
Reitz; Milford. *Foundations of electromagnetic theory.* Reading, Addison-Wesley Company.
Bleaney; Bleaney. *Electricity and magnetism.* Oxford, Oxford University Press.
Physics 110 C, D (Advanced electrical and modern physics laboratory)
E. B. Wilson. *An introduction to scientific research.* New York, McGraw-Hill.
Physics 112 (Thermodynamics and kinetic theory)
Francis Sears. *Thermodynamics, kinetic theory of gases, and statistical mechanics.* Reading, Addison-Wesley Company.
Physics 115 (Introduction to quantum mechanics)
Powell and Crasemann. *Quantum mechanics.* Reading, Addison-Wesley Company.
Physics 121 (Introduction to atomic physics)
H. Semat. *Introduction to atomic and nuclear physics.* New York, Rinehart and Company.
M. Born. *Atomic physics.* New York, Hafner.
Physics 124 (Introductory nuclear physics)
D. Halliday. *Introduction to nuclear physics.* New York, John Wiley and Sons.
Physics 129A, B (Nuclear physics)
L. R. B. Elton. *Introductory nuclear theory.* New York, Interscience.
H. Bethe; P. Morrison. *Elementary nuclear theory.* New York, John Wiley and Sons.
Physics 132 (Modern physics)
Weidner; Sells. *Elementary modern physics.* Boston, Allyn and Bacon.
Physics 140 (Introduction to solid state physics)
C. Kittel. *Introduction to solid state physics.* New York, John Wiley and Sons.
Physics 205A, B (Advanced dynamics)
H. Goldstein. *Classical mechanics.* Reading, Addison-Wesley Company.
A. Sommerfeld. *Mechanics of deformable bodies.* New York, Academic Press.

Physics 208 (Interactions of light with matter). Recommended:
  Born; Wolf. *Principles of optics*. London, Pergamon Press.
  A. Sommerfeld. *Principles of optics*. New York, Academic Press.
Physics 210A, B (Theory of electricity and magnetism)
  Landau; Lifschitz. *Electrodynamics of continuous media*. Reading, Addison-Wesley Company.
  Abraham; Becker. *Classical electricity and magnetism*, vol. I. New York, Hafner.
  Becker; Sauter. *Theorie der Elektrizität*, vol. I. Stuttgart, Teubner.
Physics 219 (Thermodynamics and statistical mechanics)
  C. Kittel. *Elementary statistical physics*. New York, John Wiley and Sons.
Physics 221A, B (Quantum mechanics)
  E. Merzbacher. *Quantum mechanics*. New York, John Wiley and Sons.
Physics 223A, B (Advanced quantum mechanics of atoms, molecules and solids)
  M. Tinkham. *Syllabus*. University of California Bookstore.
  Recommended: Heine. *Group theory and quantum mechanics*. London, Pergamon Press.
Physics 227 (Nuclear and electron resonance)
  A. Abragam. *Cours sur les phénomènes de résonance magnétique*, vols. I and II. Paris, Librairie Atomes.
Physics 230A, B (Quantum theory of fields)
  S. S. Schweber. *Introduction to relativistic quantum field theory*. Evanston, Row, Peterson and Company.
Physics 232A, B (Techniques of modern physical measurements)
  W. B. Fretter. *Introduction to experimental physics*. New York, Prentice-Hall.
Physics 240A, B (Solid state physics)
  C. Kittel. *Introduction to solid state physics*. New York, John Wiley and Sons.
  Recommended: A. Abragam. *Nuclear magnetism*. Oxford, Clarendon Press.
  H. Jones. *Theory of Brillouin zones and electronic states in crystals*. Amsterdam, North-Holland.